# Part 1

# Motor Vehicle Craft Studies

SECOND EDITION

Editor R Brooks
Authors J Hirst
J Whipp

Macmillan Motor Vehicle Craft Studies Series

# Part 1

# Motor Vehicle Craft Studies

SECOND EDITION

Editor R Brooks
Senior Lecturer in Motor Vehicle Subjects
Bolton Institute of Higher Education

Authors J Hirst
Lecturer in Motor Vehicle Subjects
Burnley College of Arts and Technology

J Whipp
Senior Lecturer in Motor Vehicle Subjects
Moston College of Further Education

M

First edition 1971
Reprinted 1972, 1973, 1974, 1975, 1977, 1979
Second edition 1981
Reprinted 1983

Published by
THE MACMILLAN PRESS LTD
London and Basingstoke
Companies and representatives throughout the world

ISBN 0 333 32383 1

Printed in Hong Kong

# PREFACE

This book is presented in a very similar style to the previously highly successful books in the Macmillan Vehicle Engineering Series. Its specific aim is to make easier and more rewarding the task of students, and teachers, working through the City and Guilds 381, Part 1, Motor Vehicle Craft Studies Course and comparable courses.

The form of presentation relieves both teacher and student of much of the chore of preparation and note taking. As such it enables much more of that most valuable ingredient — time — to be devoted to 'real' teaching and learning. Marking and checking is simple, and numerous sections could easily replace the traditional old-style homework.

Great care has been taken with the blank spaces that need to be filled in, and the drawings requiring completion, to allow users of the book as much freedom as possible, within the confines of the syllabus. However, for anyone requiring precise guidance as to how the spaces may be completed an 'Answer Book' is published as a companion to this volume. This can, of course, be a most valuable aid to teachers in respect of both lesson preparation and presentation.

Anyone completing this book conscientiously should be thoroughly equipped to succeed in their end-of-course examinations.

All the objectives set out in Part 1 of the City and Guilds 381 Course are carefully interpreted and properly covered, without any attempt to 'overteach'. In a very few instances the editorial team considered that a small amount of back-up learning would be helpful, and this has been included as an aid to student progress.

The work is presented in strict syllabus order and with appropriate references. It is realised that this is very unlikely to be the teaching order, but it does maintain an internationally recognisable uniformity.

The editor and authors wish success to everyone who uses this book. If you have any constructive suggestions that you would care to make about it we should be most pleased to hear from you via The Macmillan Press Ltd., Basingstoke.

R. Brooks
*Editor*

# ACKNOWLEDGEMENTS

The editor and authors wish to thank the very many organisations and individuals who have assisted with information and illustrations for this book. In some instances the results may not be easily recognisable, for example where simplified to suit teaching requirements. None the less, their help is greatly appreciated, in particular the following:

BL Cars Ltd.
Ford Motor Company Ltd.
Talbot Motor Company Ltd.
Vauxhall Motors Ltd.
SU-Butec
The Zenith Carburettor Company Ltd.
AC-Delco
Lucas Industries Ltd.
Champion Sparking Plug Company Ltd.
Automobile Association
VAG (United Kingdom) Ltd.
Motor Vehicle Staff of Burnley and Mostan Colleges

# Contents

# HEALTH AND SAFETY

# HEALTH AND SAFETY AT WORK ACT

The Health and Safety at Work Act 1974 provides one comprehensive system of law, dealing with the health and safety of working people and the public as affected by working activities. The Act has imposed responsibilities on every person to be aware of health and safety hazards in their working environment.

**General duties of employers to their employees**

To safeguard health, safety and welfare. This relates to:

(a) the condition of plant and equipment and the systems of work adopted.

(b) the use, handling, storage and transport of articles and substances.

(c) the place of work (premises).

(d) facilities and arrangements for welfare.

State three other general duties of employers

1. ......................................................................

......................................................................

......................................................................

2. ......................................................................

......................................................................

......................................................................

3. ......................................................................

......................................................................

......................................................................

State three duties of employees with regard to health and safety at work.

1. ......................................................................

......................................................................

......................................................................

2. ......................................................................

......................................................................

......................................................................

3. ......................................................................

......................................................................

**Enforcement**

A body called The Health and Safety Executive Inspectorate enforces the Act. Its inspectors have various powers and penalties at their disposal.

What procedures can be adopted by the inspectorate?

......................................................................

......................................................................

......................................................................

......................................................................

......................................................................

......................................................................

......................................................................

Give an example of a situation where an employee could be prosecuted under the terms of the Act.

......................................................................

......................................................................

......................................................................

# BASIC PRINCIPLES OF ACCIDENT PREVENTION

An accident is an unexpected, unplanned occurrence which can involve injury. The effects of an accident are not necessarily confined to the person or persons directly involved; other people may be affected in different ways. A minor accident may have trivial effects but a serious accident could affect one's whole life socially, domestically and economically. Accident prevention should therefore be a major concern at all times.

What are the basic requirements for successful accident prevention?

..........................................................................................................

..........................................................................................................

..........................................................................................................

..........................................................................................................

..........................................................................................................

..........................................................................................................

..........................................................................................................

..........................................................................................................

..........................................................................................................

Indicate in the table below, how an accident, where, for example, a man loses a limb, could affect the persons listed.

| People affected | Possible effects |
|---|---|
| Person injured | ............................................................................ |
| Service manager | ............................................................................ |
| Foreman | ............................................................................ |
| Workmates | ............................................................................ |
| Parents or family | ............................................................................ |

List ten general hazard or risk areas which are associated with the repair of motor vehicles.

..........................................................................................................

..........................................................................................................

..........................................................................................................

..........................................................................................................

..........................................................................................................

..........................................................................................................

..........................................................................................................

..........................................................................................................

..........................................................................................................

..........................................................................................................

..........................................................................................................

..........................................................................................................

..........................................................................................................

..........................................................................................................

..........................................................................................................

..........................................................................................................

**Causes of accidents**

Generally speaking accidents are caused by:

1. Ignorance of the dangers involved.
2. Failure to take adequate precautions.
3. Tiredness causing lack of concentration.
4. Fooling about.
5. Lack of skill through inadequate training.

**Personal protection**

A large proportion of accidents are due to the negligence of the person or persons involved. One very important factor with regard to accident prevention is the degree of 'personal protection' in relation to the particular hazards involved.

Personal protection can range from the use of adequate working clothes to the use of specialised protective equipment. The following headings all relate to personal protection. Describe the protective measures to be adopted, under each of the headings, for garage workers.

Ordinary working clothes (that is protective clothing)

....................................................................................................

....................................................................................................

....................................................................................................

....................................................................................................

....................................................................................................

....................................................................................................

....................................................................................................

....................................................................................................

Eye protection

....................................................................................................

....................................................................................................

....................................................................................................

....................................................................................................

....................................................................................................

....................................................................................................

....................................................................................................

....................................................................................................

Skin Protection

....................................................................................................

....................................................................................................

....................................................................................................

....................................................................................................

....................................................................................................

....................................................................................................

....................................................................................................

....................................................................................................

....................................................................................................

....................................................................................................

....................................................................................................

Tidiness

....................................................................................................

....................................................................................................

....................................................................................................

....................................................................................................

....................................................................................................

Which of the four sketches below shows the correct way to lift a heavy load?

A B C D

.....................................is correct

# FLAMMABLE LIQUIDS AND GASES

Many flammable substances are used in garages, for example

(a) Petrol (c) .......................... (e) ......................

(b) .......................... (d) .......................... (f) ......................

Some liquids are *volatile*. What is meant by this and what particular hazards can this present during the normal course of repair work?

..........................................................................................................

..........................................................................................................

..........................................................................................................

..........................................................................................................

..........................................................................................................

..........................................................................................................

..........................................................................................................

..........................................................................................................

What procedure should be adopted in the event of a spillage of flammable liquid such as petrol?

..........................................................................................................

..........................................................................................................

..........................................................................................................

..........................................................................................................

..........................................................................................................

..........................................................................................................

..........................................................................................................

..........................................................................................................

..........................................................................................................

Some accidents related to flammable liquids or gases are shown in the table below. Complete the table by stating the possible causes of the accident.

| Accident | Possible cause |
| --- | --- |
| Petrol tank explosion | .......................................................... .......................................................... |
| Battery explosion | .......................................................... .......................................................... |
| Fire in the pit | .......................................................... .......................................................... |
| Fire under a bonnet | .......................................................... .......................................................... |
| Fire at or near welding bench | .......................................................... .......................................................... |

What special precautions should be taken with regard to the storage of flammable substances? ..........................................................

..........................................................................................................

..........................................................................................................

..........................................................................................................

..........................................................................................................

..........................................................................................................

..........................................................................................................

..........................................................................................................

Which substance is the more dangerous with regard to storage, a substance with a high flash point or a substance with a low flash point?

..........................................................................................................

## ELECTRICAL SAFETY

Two dangers arising as a result of using electricity in a workshop are; *fire* caused by say overheating of an electrical circuit or a bursting bulb igniting fuel, and electric shock as a result of someone coming into contact with a live circuit.

For safety reasons hand-held electrically operated equipment, for example portable drills should be .................. volts and handlamps should be .................. volts.

What could cause a circuit to overheat?

..........................................................................................................

..........................................................................................................

..........................................................................................................

Indicate, by labelling the plug shown, the colours of the wires for a correct connection.

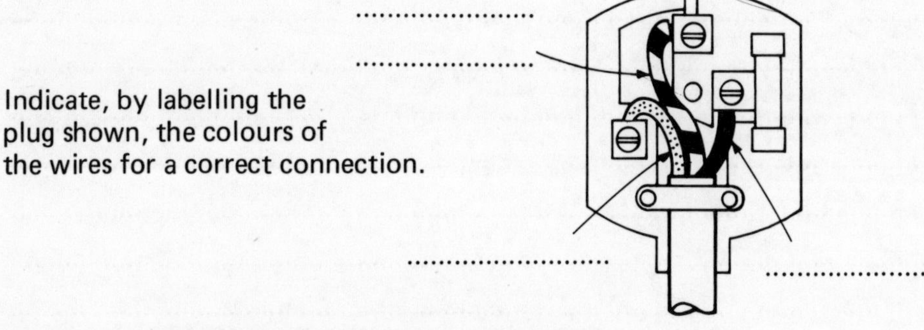

## THE SAFE USE OF HAND TOOLS

Accidents can happen when using hand tools, if the tools are not correctly cared for, or incorrectly used.

Certain tools can create hazards because of their hardness. Examples of these are:

(a) ............................................ (c) ............................................

(b) ............................................ (d) ............................................

Indicate below the possible injuries that could result from the situations listed.

| Situation | Possible consequences |
|---|---|
| Poor spanner fit on nut | ............................................ ............................................ |
| Undue effort needed owing to the use of short spanner | ............................................ ............................................ |
| Using a file without a handle | ............................................ ............................................ |
| Using a blunt screwdriver | ............................................ ............................................ |
| Using a 'mushroomed' headed chisel | ............................................ ............................................ |
| Banging two hammer faces together | ............................................ ............................................ |
| Using a file as a punch | ............................................ ............................................ |

# SAFE USE OF MACHINERY AND EQUIPMENT

Many accidents in garages are caused either by the worker not taking adequate precautions, or by faulty equipment.

State the precautions necessary when working on a vehicle raised by a jack.

........................................................................................................................

........................................................................................................................

........................................................................................................................

........................................................................................................................

........................................................................................................................

What precautions should be taken when using the following items of equipment?

Compressed-air equipment

........................................................................................................................

........................................................................................................................

........................................................................................................................

........................................................................................................................

........................................................................................................................

........................................................................................................................

Chain lifting blocks

........................................................................................................................

........................................................................................................................

........................................................................................................................

........................................................................................................................

........................................................................................................................

........................................................................................................................

Vehicle hoist

........................................................................................................................

........................................................................................................................

........................................................................................................................

........................................................................................................................

Bench drills

........................................................................................................................

........................................................................................................................

........................................................................................................................

........................................................................................................................

Grinding wheels

........................................................................................................................

........................................................................................................................

........................................................................................................................

........................................................................................................................

Which is the correct way to lift an engine using a chain sling as shown below?

(    )

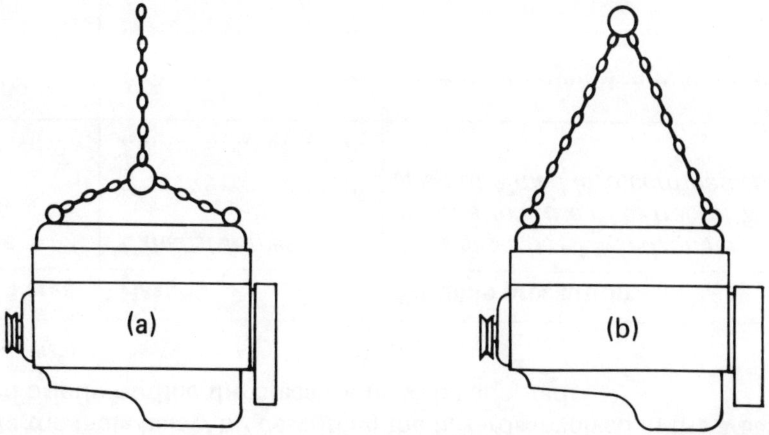

(a)

(b)

# HARMFUL SUBSTANCES

Certain areas in a motor-vehicle repair premises present particular health hazards. The hazards may for example, be due to breathing in polluted air or coming into contact with harmful substances.

What is meant by the term *toxic* when used to describe a substance or gas?

....................................................................................................

....................................................................................................

....................................................................................................

....................................................................................................

....................................................................................................

List some of the toxic gases or substances likely to be present in a motor-vehicle repair workshop.

....................................................................................................

....................................................................................................

....................................................................................................

....................................................................................................

....................................................................................................

....................................................................................................

....................................................................................................

Asbestos dust is encountered when cleaning brake assemblies. What particular hazard is associated with asbestos dust and what precautions must be taken?

....................................................................................................

....................................................................................................

....................................................................................................

....................................................................................................

....................................................................................................

Complete the table below by describing the hazards involved in the areas listed and briefly outline the precautions to be adopted.

| Hazard area | Hazard | Suitable precautions |
|---|---|---|
| Engine tuning | *Exhaust fumes*<br>..............................<br>.............................. | *Pipe gases outside, adequate ventilation, use of extractor fans, gas not aimed into confined space* |
| Welding bench | ..............................<br>..............................<br>.............................. | ..............................................<br>..............................................<br>.............................................. |
| Degreasing plant | ..............................<br>..............................<br>.............................. | ..............................................<br>..............................................<br>.............................................. |
| Body shop | ..............................<br>..............................<br>.............................. | ..............................................<br>..............................................<br>.............................................. |
| Paint shop | ..............................<br>..............................<br>.............................. | ..............................................<br>..............................................<br>.............................................. |
| Battery charging | ..............................<br>.............................. | ..............................................<br>.............................................. |

# FIRE PREVENTION AND CONTROL

Protection against fire is normally organised in accordance with the requirements of the Factory Acts and in co-operation with the local Fire Prevention Officer. Fire fighting equipment must be readily available and kept properly maintained. Doors and passages must be kept clear and a positive routine established, to be followed in the event of a fire.

Briefly describe the procedure to be followed in the event of a fire in the workshop.

..........................................................................................................

..........................................................................................................

..........................................................................................................

..........................................................................................................

..........................................................................................................

..........................................................................................................

..........................................................................................................

..........................................................................................................

**Investigation**

What are the visible signs of fire prevention in your workshop?

..........................................................................................................

..........................................................................................................

..........................................................................................................

..........................................................................................................

Different types of fire extinguishers are intended for use on different classes of fire. What are the three main classes of fire?

..........................................................................................................

..........................................................................................................

..........................................................................................................

Name three popular types of fire extinguisher and describe the circumstances in which they might be used.

Class 1 ..........................................................................................

*Uses* ..........................................................................................

..........................................................................................

Class 2 ..........................................................................................

*Uses* ..........................................................................................

..........................................................................................

Class 3 ..........................................................................................

*Uses* ..........................................................................................

..........................................................................................

Water from a hose, bucket or extinguisher is used on solid fuel fires. What effect has the use of water on burning flammable liquids.

..........................................................................................................

..........................................................................................................

List the types of extinguisher available in the college workshop.

..........................................................................................................

..........................................................................................................

**Accident reporting**

Accidents of any kind should be reported to the employer. Describe the normal procedure for reporting and recording accidents.

..........................................................................................................

..........................................................................................................

..........................................................................................................

..........................................................................................................

**Investigation**

Make a thorough inspection of the workshop at your college and make brief notes under the headings on this page to describe any potential safety hazards or lack of warning or guidance notices.

Fire risk/fire precautions

..................................................

..................................................

..................................................

..................................................

Machinery (drills, grindstones etc.)

..................................................

..................................................

..................................................

..................................................

Vehicle lifts and jacks

..................................................

..................................................

..................................................

..................................................

..................................................

Electrical (hand drills, hand lamps etc.)

..................................................

..................................................

..................................................

..................................................

..................................................

Lifting equipment

..................................................

..................................................

..................................................

..................................................

Welding area

..................................................

..................................................

..................................................

..................................................

Battery charging

..................................................

..................................................

..................................................

..................................................

Compressed-air equipment

..................................................

..................................................

..................................................

..................................................

General tidiness (floor condition etc.)

..................................................

..................................................

..................................................

..................................................

# FIRST AID

Personnel should be familiar with the location and contents of first-aid boxes. Cuts, abrasions and burns etc., however minor should be cleaned and treated promptly owing to the dirty nature of motor-vehicle repair work.

Certain personnel trained in basic first aid should be available to provide treatment and advice during working hours; the staff should know how and where to contact these people promptly in the event of an accident.

**Basic first aid**

By reference to the British Red Cross Society First Aid Chart, briefly describe the procedure to be followed when dealing with the following accidents:

Bleeding

Fractures

Burns and scalds

Unconsciousness

Breathing stopped

# SECTION A

# Vehicle Technology — Engines

A1.

# Spark-Ignition Engines: Principles and Construction

# ENGINE TYPES

Engines used in motor vehicles may be referred to as FOUR-STROKE or TWO-STROKE engines.

The term stroke refers to ..........................................................................................

..........................................................................................................................

A four-stroke engine is one in which ........................................................................

..........................................................................................................................

A two-stroke engine is one in which ..........................................................................

..........................................................................................................................

The number of revolutions completed during a working cycle on a four-stroke engine is..........................

The number of revolutions completed during a working cycle on a two-stroke engine is ..........................

These engines may use different types of fuel.

If the engine is identified as ...................... it will use ........................ fuel.

If the engine is identified as ...................... it will use ........................ fuel.

**Investigation**

Complete the tables below to identify different types of engines used in motor vehicles.

Four-stroke engines

| Vehicle | No. of cylinders | Type of fuel | Engine capacity |
|---|---|---|---|
| | | | |
| | | | |
| | | | |
| | | | |

Two-stroke engines

| Vehicle | No. of cylinders | Type of fuel | Engine capacity |
|---|---|---|---|
| | | | |
| | | | |
| | | | |
| | | | |

Identify the engines shown in terms of two and four stroke.

State two reasons why each engine can be so identified.

Name the arrowed parts.

Type..............................................

Reasons for identification

(a) ..............................................

..............................................

..............................................

(b) ..............................................

..............................................

..............................................

Type..............................................

Reasons for identification

(a) ..............................................

..............................................

..............................................

(b) ..............................................

..............................................

..............................................

# THE OTTO (OR FOUR-STROKE) CYCLE

The four-stroke cycle is completed in four movements of the piston during which the crankshaft rotates twice.

Complete the line diagrams to show the positions of the valves and piston crown at the commencement of each stroke. Indicate the direction in which the piston is moving in each case.

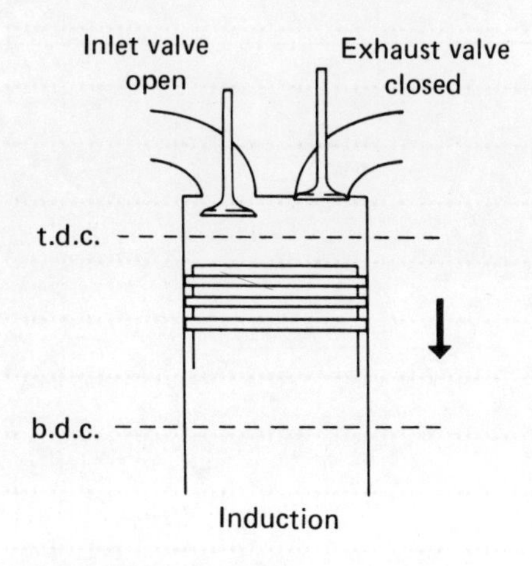

Induction

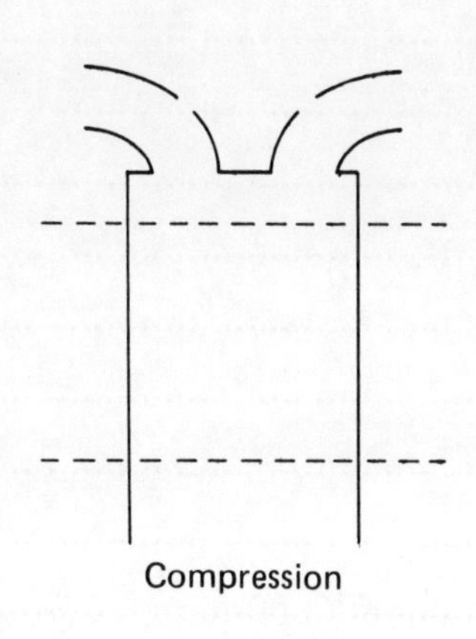
Compression

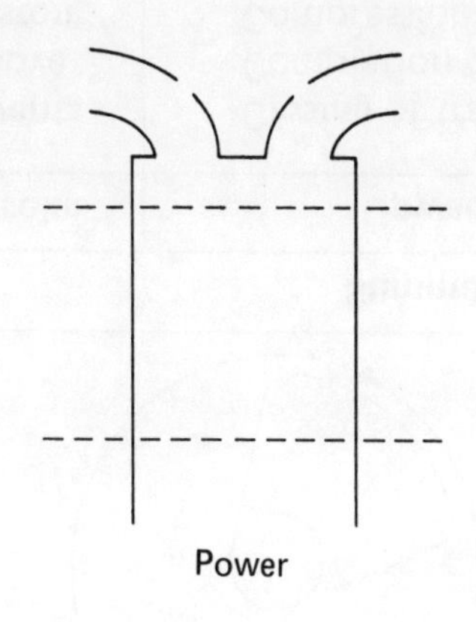
Power

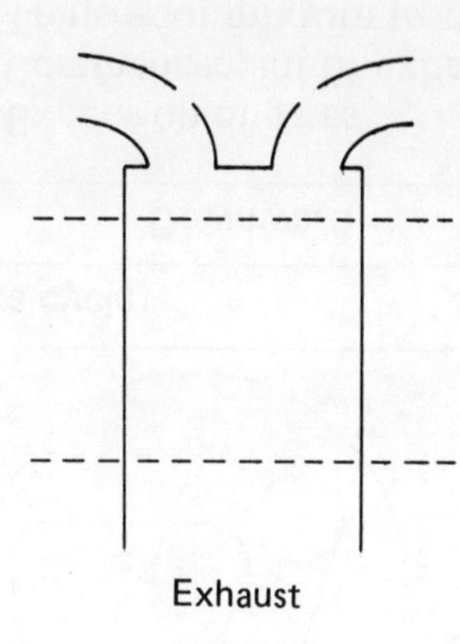
Exhaust

**Investigation**

By use of a sectioned four-stroke spark-ignition engine, note the sequence of operations of the piston, valves and spark when the engine is rotated, and describe what happens on each stroke when the engine is running.

| **Induction** | **Compression** | **Power** | **Exhaust** |
|---|---|---|---|
| ........................................ | ........................................ | ........................................ | ........................................ |
| ........................................ | ........................................ | ........................................ | ........................................ |
| ........................................ | ........................................ | ........................................ | ........................................ |
| ........................................ | ........................................ | ........................................ | ........................................ |
| ........................................ | ........................................ | ........................................ | ........................................ |
| ........................................ | ........................................ | ........................................ | ........................................ |
| ........................................ | ........................................ | ........................................ | ........................................ |
| ........................................ | ........................................ | ........................................ | ........................................ |
| ........................................ | ........................................ | ........................................ | ........................................ |

# TWO-STROKE CYCLE

## (Crank-case compression type)

By making use of both sides of the piston, the four phases, induction, compression, power, exhaust, are completed in two strokes of the piston or one crankshaft revolution.

No valves are used, the piston itself acts as a valve covering and uncovering ports in the cylinder wall.

........................................................................................................

........................................................................................................

........................................................................................................

........................................................................................................

........................................................................................................

........................................................................................................

........................................................................................................

........................................................................................................

........................................................................................................

........................................................................................................

........................................................................................................

........................................................................................................

........................................................................................................

........................................................................................................

........................................................................................................

........................................................................................................

........................................................................................................

........................................................................................................

Complete the drawings to show the position of the ports and the shape of the piston. Name the main parts and show the direction of crankshaft rotation.

(a) Show fuel entering crankcase.

(b) Show fuel transferring to cylinder and exhausting.

| Summary of two-stroke cycle | | |
|---|---|---|
| **Stroke** | **Upward** | **Downward** |
| **Events above piston** | Closing of transfer port<br>Completion of exhaust<br>Compression | Expansion of gases<br>Commencement of exhaust<br>Transfer of mixture from below piston |
| **Events below piston** | Induction of new mixture into crankcase | Partial compression of new mixture in crankcase |

# OPERATION OF THE TWO-STROKE CYCLE

**Investigation**

Answer the following questions as you dismantle a small single-cylinder two-stroke engine (removal of cylinder head and barrel only is required).

Engine Make.............................................. Model .................................

Engine capacity ......................................................................................

State type of cooling ................................................................................

*Remove the carburettor*

Look into the intake port in the cylinder and rotate the crankshaft.

Into which part of the engine does the air first go after leaving the carburettor? ..........................................................................................

How can this be determined? .....................................................................

..................................................................................................................

*Remove the cylinder head*

Hold the plug lead end about 5 mm away from the cylinder barrel and rotate the flywheel to produce a spark.

What is the position of the piston relative to top dead centre when the spark occurs? ....................................................................................................

The angle turned by the crankshaft to complete the two-stroke cycle is .........

What shape is the piston crown? ................................................................

How many transfer ports are there? ...........................................................

Using a rule placed inside the cylinder measure as accurately as possible:

(a) the diameter of bore...............................................................................

(b) the length of the stroke...........................................................................

(c) the distance from t.d.c. when:

1. the exhaust port opens.........................................................................
2. the transfer port opens.........................................................................

As the piston is descending which port:

(a) opens first ..............................................................................................

(b) closes last ..............................................................................................

*Remove the cylinder block and examine the position of the portings*

How on your engine is air swirl created? ....................................................

..................................................................................................................

How are piston rings prevented from turning on the piston? ..........................

..................................................................................................................

What is the reason for preventing them turning? ..........................................

..................................................................................................................

Show on the plan view below using dotted lines the position of the transfer port or ports.

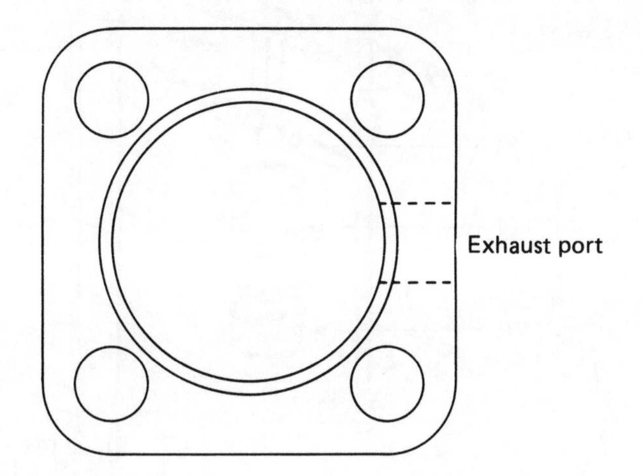


State two principal advantages of a two-stroke engine when compared with a four-stroke engine.

1. ..............................................................................................................
2. ..............................................................................................................

# ENGINE PARTS

Name the main parts of the engine.

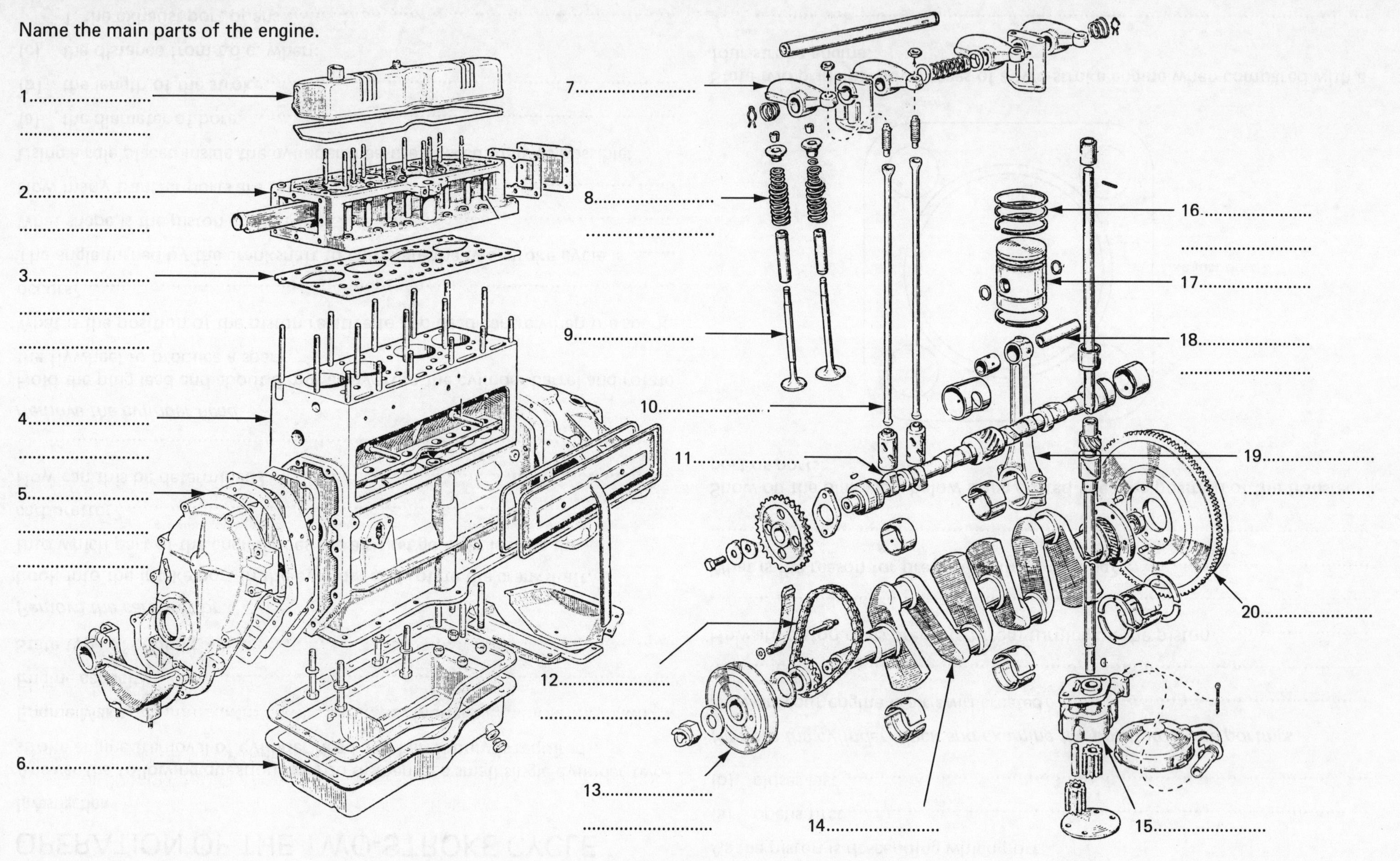

# MAIN ENGINE COMPONENTS

Examine the pistons, connecting rods, crankshaft and cylinder head of a four-cylinder spark-ignition engine and complete the following drawings. State the function of each component.

Using the faintly-dotted outline below, sketch two views of a piston, include the piston rings and label its important parts.

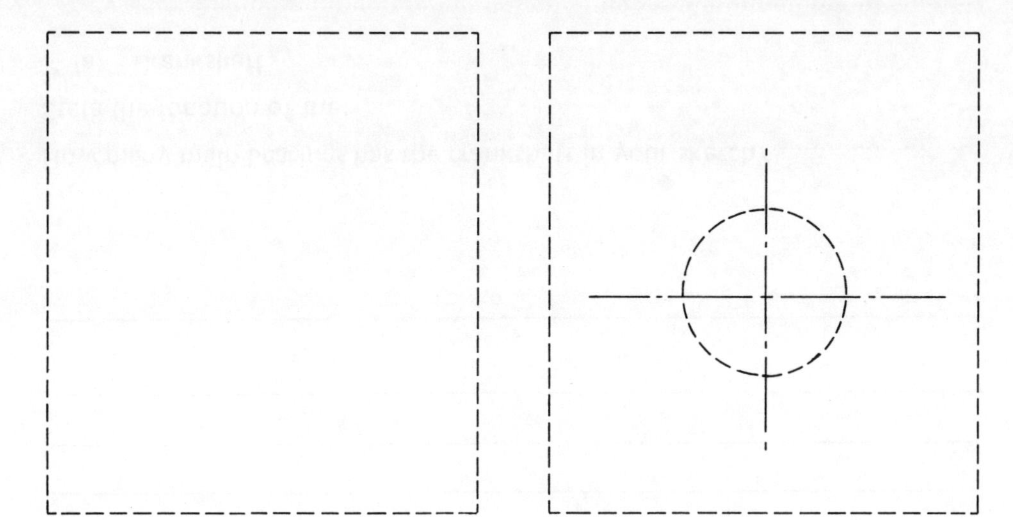

State the function of the:

(a) Piston ..................................................................................................

..................................................................................................

(b) Piston rings ..................................................................................................

..................................................................................................

..................................................................................................

..................................................................................................

Sketch a connecting rod using the centre lines shown as a guide.

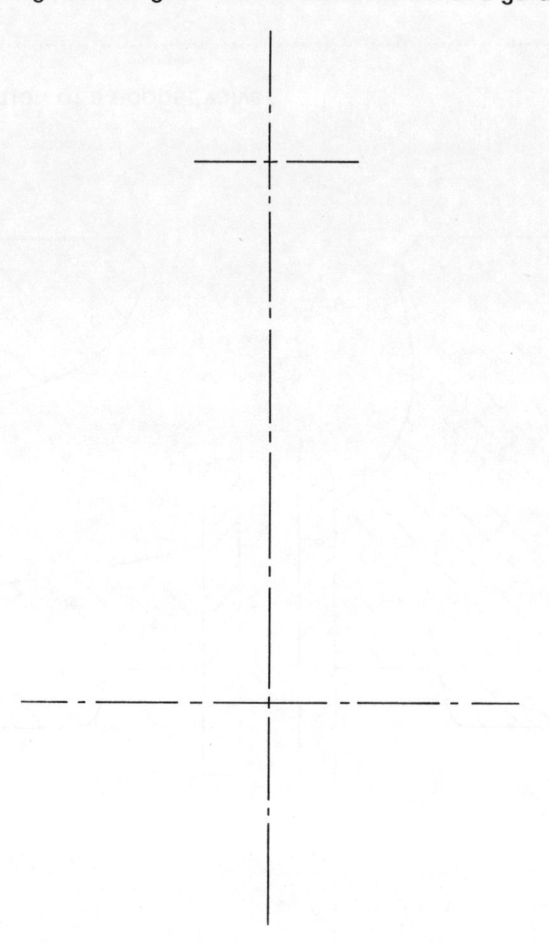

State the function of the:

(a) Connecting rod..................................................................................................

..................................................................................................

(b) Gudgeon pin..................................................................................................

..................................................................................................

Sketch a four-cylinder crankshaft. Use the guide lines to position the main and big-end bearings. Show where flywheel and fan pulley are mounted.

Name the important parts.

How many main bearings has the crankshaft in your sketch? ........................

State the function of the:

(a) Crankshaft

..........................................................................................

..........................................................................................

(b) Flywheel

..........................................................................................

..........................................................................................

..........................................................................................

..........................................................................................

Show the valve and spring assembly. Clearly indicate the method by which the spring is secured to the valve.

Name the important parts.

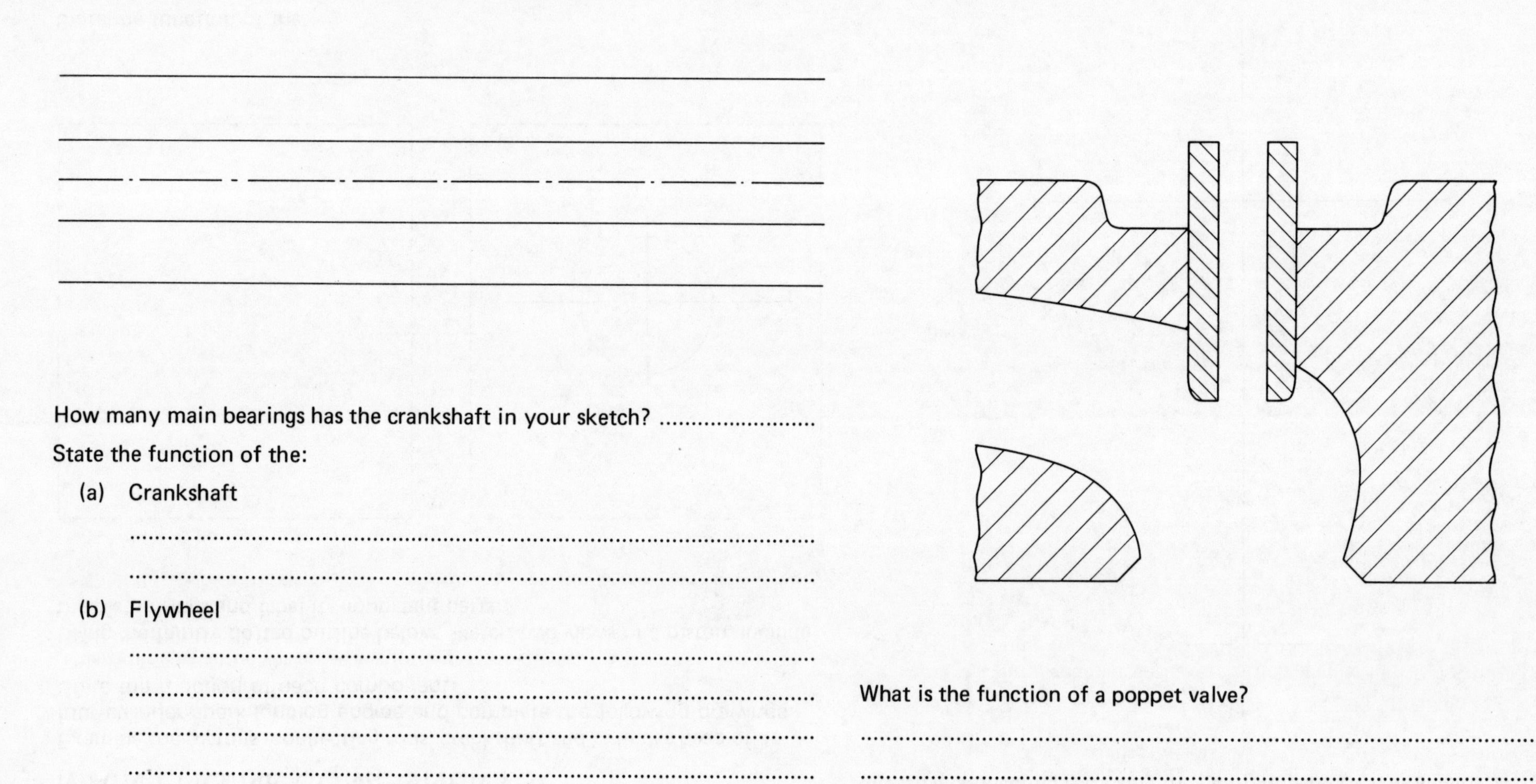

What is the function of a poppet valve?

..........................................................................................

..........................................................................................

# IGNITION TIMING

As described in the four-stroke operating cycle ignition takes place as the ascending piston nears t.d.c. on the compression stroke.

This timing must be set most accurately if the optimum power and economy of the engine is to be obtained.

Most engines have their static or slow running ignition timing set between

..............................................................................................................

If the timing was set to......... before t.d.c. it would be too far ......................

If the timing was set to......... after t.d.c. it would be too far ........................

An advanced ignition timing means that the spark occurs ...............................

..............................................................................................................

A retarded ignition timing means that the spark occurs ...............................

..............................................................................................................

Two ways in which ignition timing is altered in service are by:

1. ..........................................................................................................
2. ..........................................................................................................

Three effects of the ignition timing being too far advanced are:

1. ..........................................................................................................
2. ..........................................................................................................
3. ..........................................................................................................

Three effects of the ignition timing being too far retarded are:

1. ..........................................................................................................
2. ..........................................................................................................
3. ..........................................................................................................

**Investigation**

Examine technical data for three vehicles that are available for inspection and note their correct ignition timing.

Examine the three vehicles and sketch their engine ignition timing marks (as in (a)) showing the pulley (or flywheel) in its correctly timed position.

Use a timing light (static or strobe) to determine the point at which each engine's timing is now set.

(a)

9° t.d.c.

Vauxhall Viva
Chevette o.h.v.

Correct timing 9° b.t.d.c.

(b)

Vehicle ........................................

Correct timing ..............................

Actual timing ...............................

(c)

Vehicle ........................................

Correct timing ..............................

Actual timing ...............................

(d)

Vehicle ........................................

Correct timing ..............................

Actual timing ...............................

# VALVE TIMING

The inlet valve as well as being open on the induction stroke is also partly open on two other strokes.

The inlet valve opens on the ..........................................................

and closes on the ..........................................................

The exhaust valve opens on the ..........................................................

and closes on the ..........................................................

The reasons for these early openings and late closings are ..............................

..........................................................

..........................................................

..........................................................

The valve-open period can be represented on a valve timing diagram. This shows the number of crankshaft degrees during which the valves are open.

The diagram opposite shows a valve timing diagram and indicates the open and close points.

Measure and state the angles before and after t.d.c.

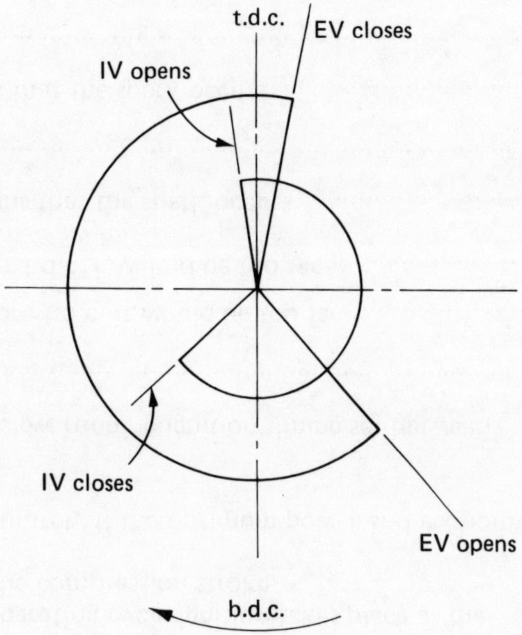

t.d.c.
EV closes
IV opens
IV closes
EV opens
b.d.c.

**Investigation**

Examine the valve timing data of two engines and construct their valve timing diagrams on the centre lines below.

ENGINE ..............................  ENGINE ..............................

Indicate on the diagrams valve lead, lag and overlap.

Valve lead is ..........................................................

..........................................................

..........................................................

Valve lag is ..........................................................

..........................................................

..........................................................

Valve overlap is ..........................................................

..........................................................

..........................................................

Valves are designed to have a greater open period when ..............................

..........................................................

# VALVE OPERATION

The most common valve arrangement is the (o.h.v.) overhead valve, with side camshaft.

Complete the drawing below and name the main parts which operate the valve.

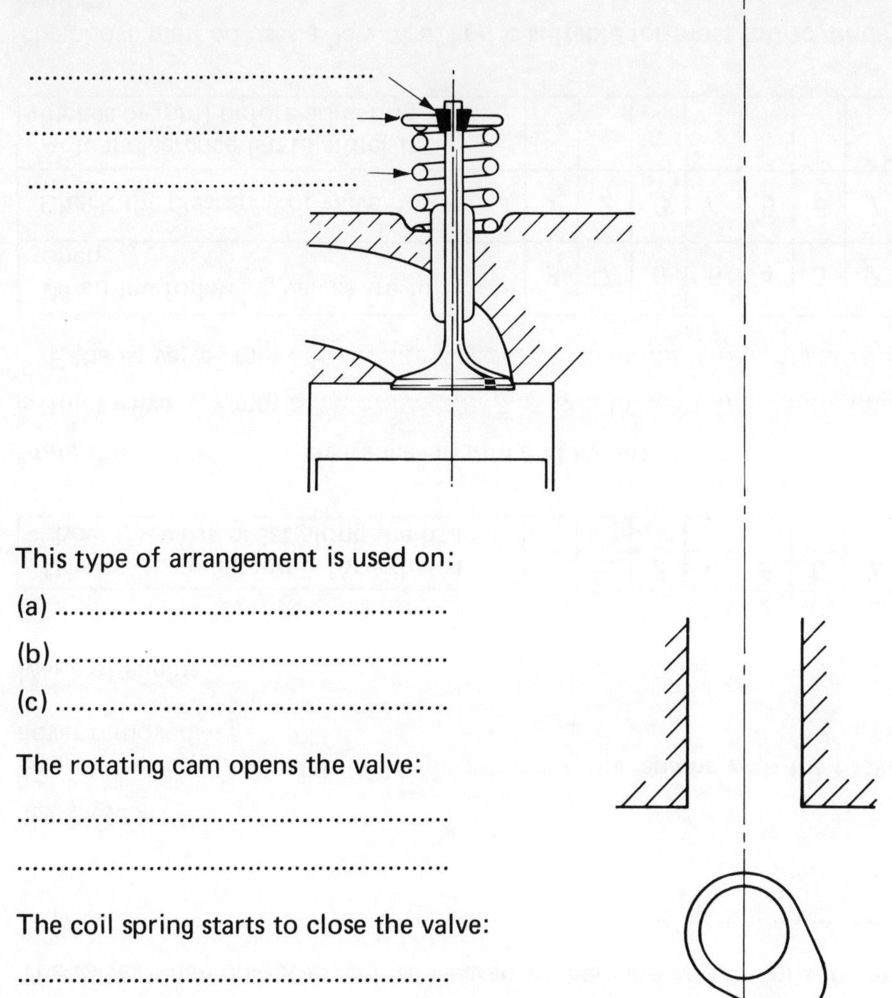

..........................................

..........................................

..........................................

This type of arrangement is used on:

(a) ..............................................

(b) ..............................................

(c) ..............................................

The rotating cam opens the valve:

..............................................

..............................................

The coil spring starts to close the valve:

..............................................

..............................................

Other valve arrangements are used on (o.h.c.) overhead camshaft engines.

Complete the sketches below showing three different types of o.h.c. valve layouts.

(a) (b) (c)

Type
(a) ............................ (b) ............................ (c) ............................

Opposite is shown a valve mechanism that was once popular.

This type was used on ......................

..............................................

Why is this arrangement not used on modern vehicles?

..............................................

..............................................

..............................................

..............................................

..............................................

Valves in line

Type: ..............................................

# VALVE CLEARANCE

The valves when operated require clearance, there are two reasons for this:

(a) ..............................................................................................

(b) ..............................................................................................

**Investigation**

Examine a conventional in-line four-cylinder o.h.v. engine with the rocker cover removed.

Make of engine ..............................................................................................

| Using I for inlet and E for exhaust show the valve order along the head. | 1 | 2 | 3 | 4 | 5 | 6 | 7 | 8 |
|---|---|---|---|---|---|---|---|---|
| | | | | | | | | |

State the engine's valve clearances in mm and inches.

Inlet valve mm .................................... in ....................................

Exhaust valve mm .................................... in ....................................

| When the following valves are fully open | 8 | 7 | 6 | 5 | 4 | 3 | 2 | 1 |
|---|---|---|---|---|---|---|---|---|
| Check the clearance of valve nos. | 1 | 2 | 3 | 4 | 5 | 6 | 7 | 8 |
| Actual clearance (state either in inches or mm) before adjusting | | | | | | | | |

The above method uses a 'law of 9' and is suitable for most four-cylinder engines.

..............................................................................................

..............................................................................................

..............................................................................................

..............................................................................................

**Methods of valve adjustment**

In each case show the position of the feeler gauge and explain how adjustment is made.

(a)

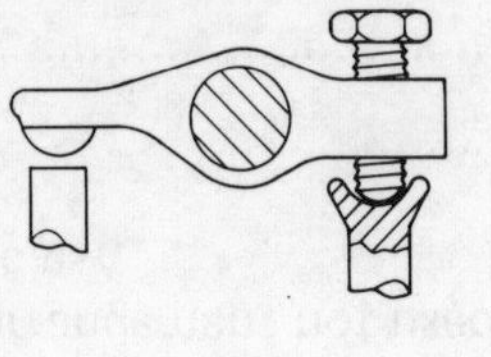

..............................................................................................

..............................................................................................

..............................................................................................

..............................................................................................

..............................................................................................

(b)

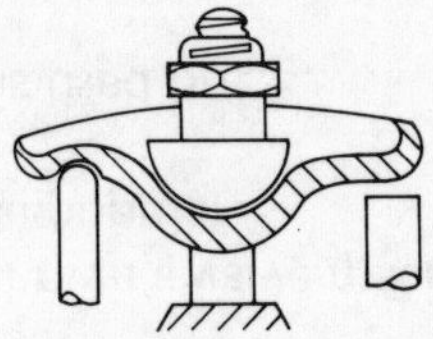

..............................................................................................

..............................................................................................

..............................................................................................

..............................................................................................

..............................................................................................

(c)

..............................................................................................

..............................................................................................

..............................................................................................

..............................................................................................

..............................................................................................

(d)

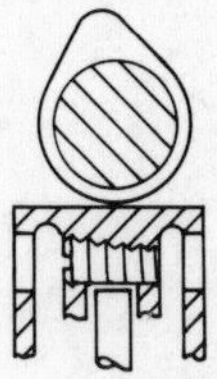

..............................................................................................

..............................................................................................

..............................................................................................

..............................................................................................

..............................................................................................

(e)

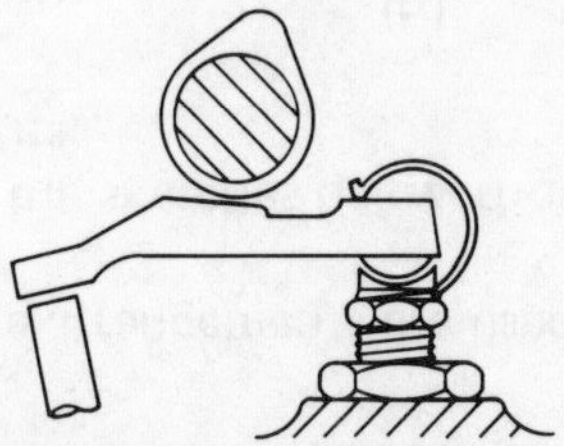

..............................................................................................

..............................................................................................

..............................................................................................

..............................................................................................

..............................................................................................

# CAMSHAFT DRIVE ARRANGEMENTS

Camshafts may be driven by gears, chains or belts.

Engines having camshafts positioned in the crankcase may be driven by

..............................................................................................................

The rotational speed of the crankshaft is .............. that of the camshaft.

The speed ratio of crankshaft to camshaft is ..............................................

How does this ratio affect the size of the gears?

..............................................................................................................

..............................................................................................................

Show in correct size relationship a camshaft gear driven from the crankshaft shown.

The camshaft gear may be made of ..............................................

..............................................................................................................

The reason for this is .................

..............................................................................................................

Camshaft rotation when gear driven is ....................................

When chain driven the camshaft rotation is ..................................

..............................................................................................................

as the crankshaft.

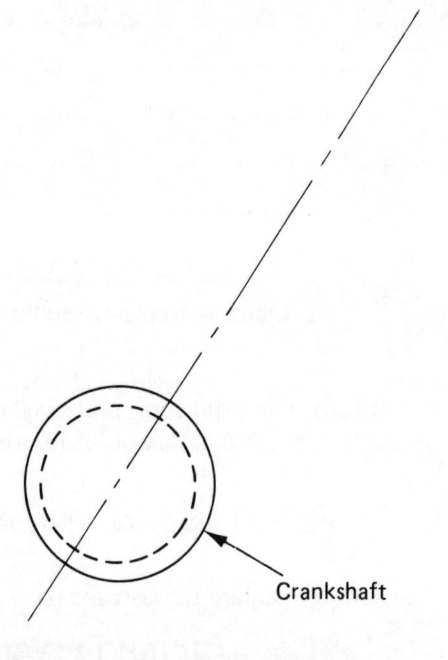


## Chain drives

Add the chains to each sketch.
Name the arrowed parts and show direction of rotation.

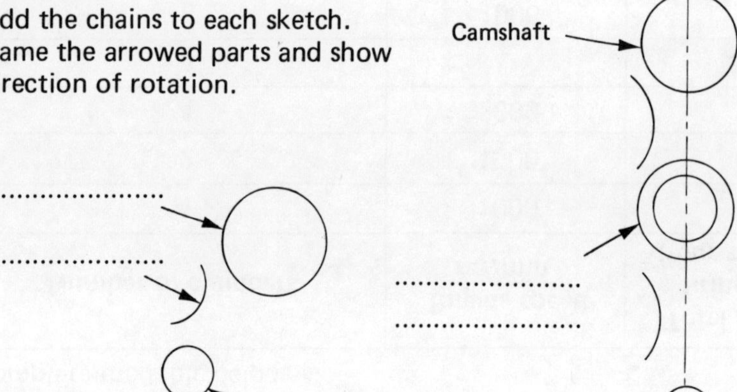


TYPE (a) .................................... (b) ....................................................

## Belt drives

Add the belts to each sketch

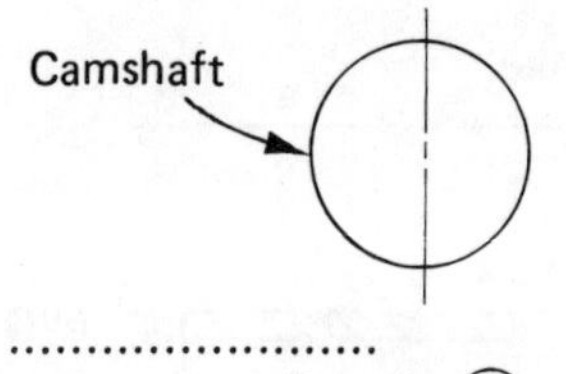


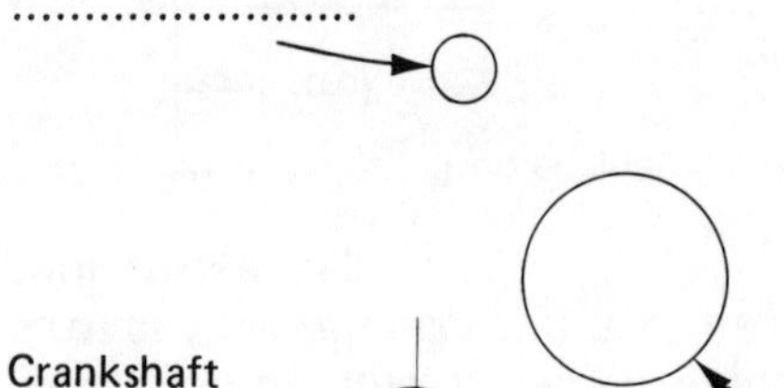


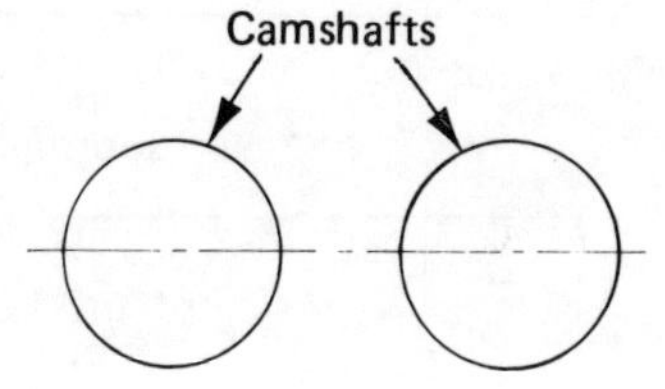


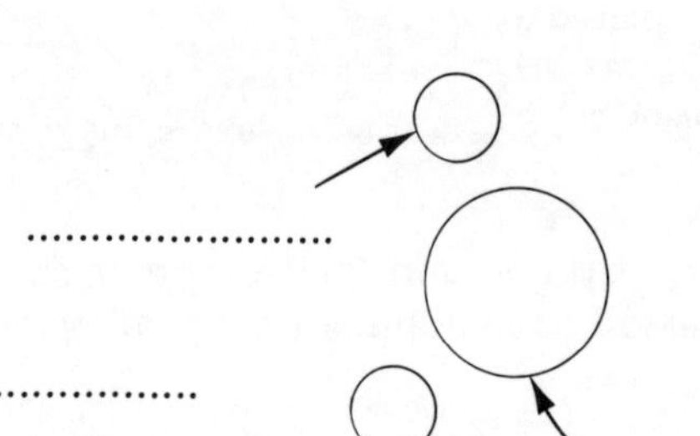

TYPE (a) .................................... (b) ....................................................

# USE OF MORE THAN ONE CYLINDER

Two of the main reasons why a conventional car uses an engine with more than one cylinder are:

1. A multi-cylinder engine has a higher power-to-weight ratio than a single-cylinder engine.
2. With multi-cylinder engines there are more power strokes for the same number of engine revolutions. This gives less fluctuations in torque and smoother power output.

State three other possible reasons for using multi-cylinder engines.

..............................................................................................

..............................................................................................

..............................................................................................

..............................................................................................

..............................................................................................

..............................................................................................

..............................................................................................

..............................................................................................

..............................................................................................

..............................................................................................

..............................................................................................

What is meant by the 'power-to-weight ratio of an engine'?

..............................................................................................

..............................................................................................

..............................................................................................

..............................................................................................

..............................................................................................

The diagram below shows the total number of power strokes occurring during two engine revolutions for a single- and six-cylinder four-stroke engine. The power strokes are indicated by blocks which each represent one stroke.

Sketch on the lines provided similar blocks to show the number of power strokes that will occur in two revolutions on a two- and four-cylinder four-stroke engine.

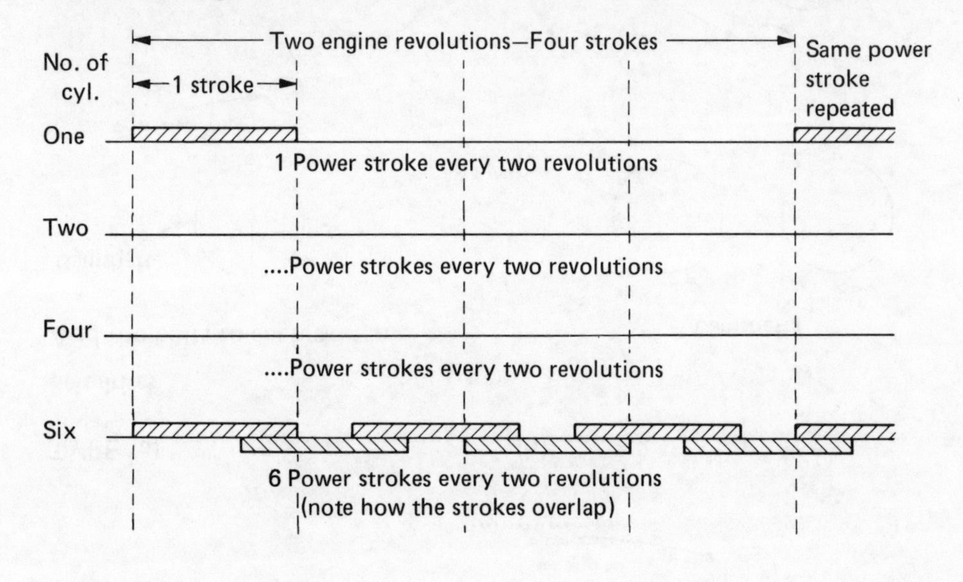


Complete the table below

| Number of cylinders | Engine speed rev/min | Total number of firing strokes (four-stroke cycle) |
|---|---|---|
| 1 | 1000 | |
| 2 | 1500 | |
| 4 | 2000 | |
| 4 | | 3000 |
| 6 | 1000 | |

# CYLINDER ARRANGEMENTS — FIRING ORDERS

The most common way of arranging the position of cylinders for multi-cylinder engines is in-line.

Name vehicles which use in-line engines.

| Vehicle | No. of cylinders | Engine capacity | Firing order |
|---|---|---|---|
| | 2 | | |
| | 4 | | |
| | 4 | | |
| | 6 | | |

*Twin-cylinder*

The cranks may be arranged in two ways.

(a) Parallel cranks (b) Cranks 180° apart

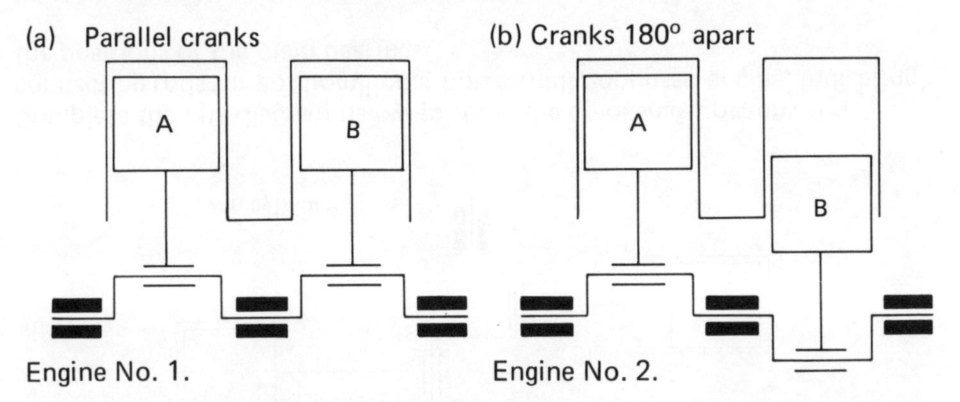


Engine No. 1. Engine No. 2.

| Referring to the above engines | Eng. 1 | Eng. 2 |
|---|---|---|
| What stroke will piston B be on when A is on the power stroke? | | |
| How many crankshaft degrees will the intervals be between the power impulses? | | |

*Four-cylinder*

Complete the line diagram to show a four-cylinder in-line engine.

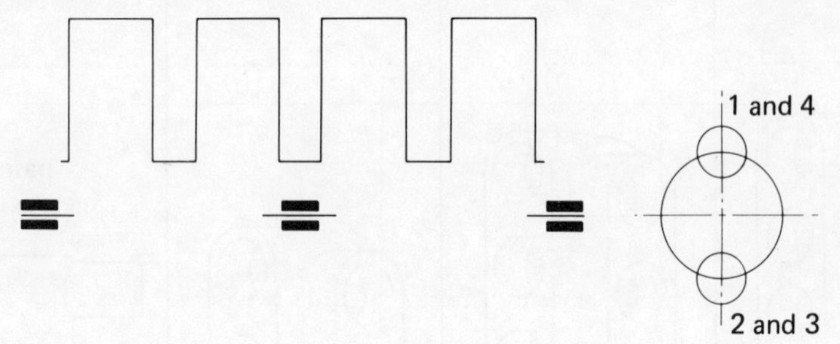


Considering a four-cylinder four-stroke in-line engine. If the firing order is 1 3 4 2 what stroke would the following be on?

(a) When no. 2 cyl. is on the power stroke no. 4 cyl. is on...................

(b) When no. 4 cyl. is on the exhaust stroke no. 1 cyl. is on ................

*Six-cylinder*

Complete the line diagram to show a six-cylinder in-line engine.

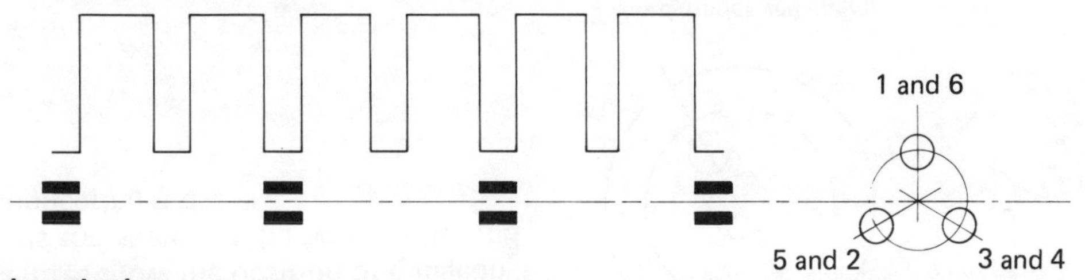


**Investigation**

Determination of firing orders on a four- and six-cylinder engine when the distributor is removed.

Remove the valve-rocker covers and chalk all the inlet valves. Turn the engine in the correct direction of rotation. The sequence in which the inlet valves open is the same as the engine firing order.

Vehicle checked ........................................ Firing order ...........................

Vehicle checked ........................................ Firing order ...........................

Alternative arrangements to the in-line engine are horizontally opposed or vee engines.

**Horizontally opposed engines**

Twin cylinder

Complete the line diagram below to show the crankshaft, pistons and connecting rods for a four-cylinder horizontally-opposed engine, indicating the positions of the main bearings.

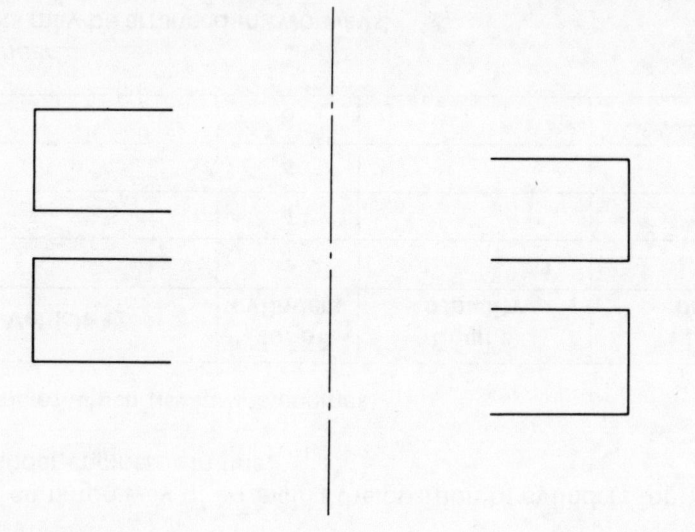

**Vee engines**

The cylinder build-up can be 2, 4, 6, 8 or 12 cylinders in two separate banks.

Both connecting rods are fitted to the same crank. If the connecting rods for the drawing are 30 mm long between centres show the position of gudgeon pins and sketch in the two pistons and connecting rods.

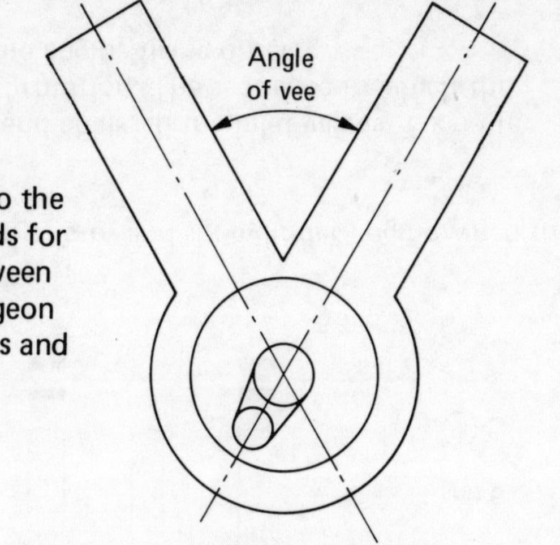


Twin-cylinder vee engine

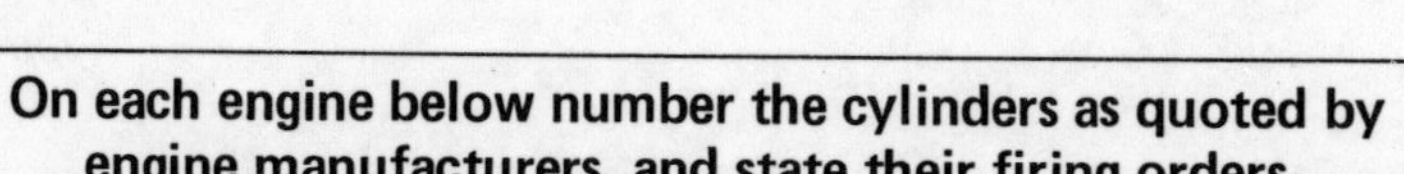

**On each engine below number the cylinders as quoted by engine manufacturers, and state their firing orders.**

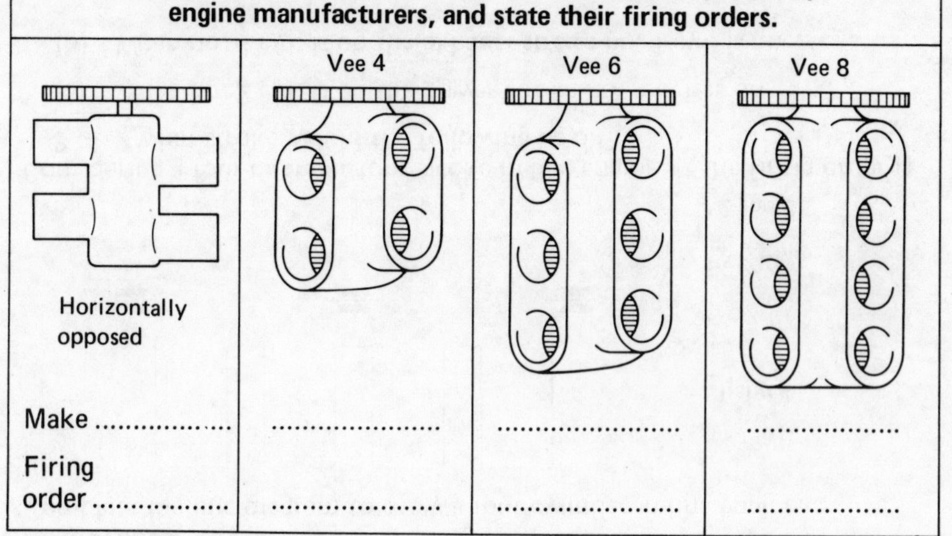


| Horizontally opposed | Vee 4 | Vee 6 | Vee 8 |
|---|---|---|---|
| Make .................. | .................... | ...................... | .................. |
| Firing order .................. | .................... | ...................... | .................. |

APPLIED STUDIES

A1: 21

# ENGINE TERMS

Explain the meaning of the following terms:

t.d.c. ..........................................................................................................

..........................................................................................................................

b.d.c. ..........................................................................................................

..........................................................................................................................

Bore ............................................................................................................

Stroke ..........................................................................................................

..........................................................................................................................

Cylinder capacity ........................................................................................

..........................................................................................................................

Engine capacity ...........................................................................................

..........................................................................................................................

Complete the lettered drawings below to show:
on (a) cylinder bore, on (b) piston at t.d.c. and (by shading) the clearance volume and on (c) the stroke, and (by shading) the swept volume.

(a) (b) 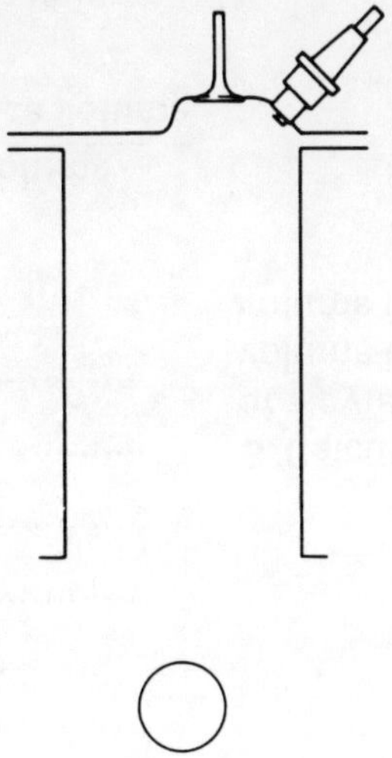 (c)

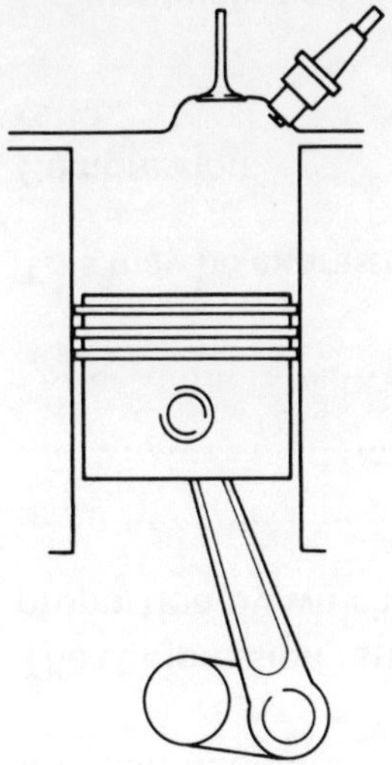

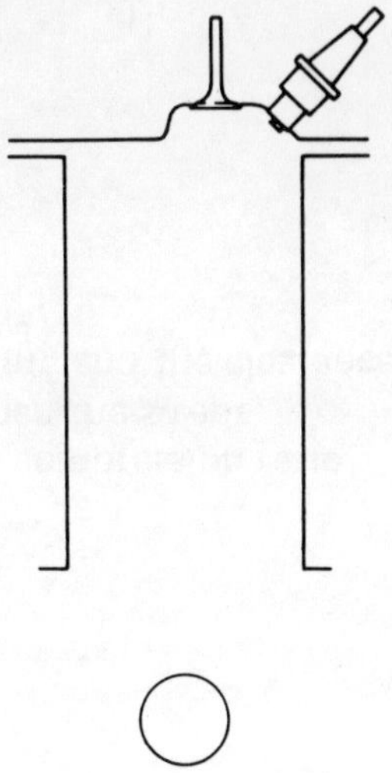

The swept volume of a cylinder in a four-cylinder engine is 249 $cm^3$. Calculate the total volume of the engine.

This engine would be known as a ..................... litre engine.

The swept volume of a cylinder in a six-cylinder engine is 332 $cm^3$. Calculate the total volume of the engine

This engine would be known as a ..................... litre engine.

The total volume of a four-cylinder engine is 1498 $cm^3$. Calculate the swept volume of one cylinder.

This engine would be known as a ........................ litre engine.

The cross sectional area of the piston crown is 48.5 $cm^2$ and the stroke is 12 cm. Calculate the swept volume of the cylinder and the capacity when it has six cylinders.

This engine would be known as a ........................ litre engine.

# CYLINDER SWEPT VOLUME

The volume of an engine cylinder is found by multiplying the area of the cylinder by the distance moved by the piston (stroke).

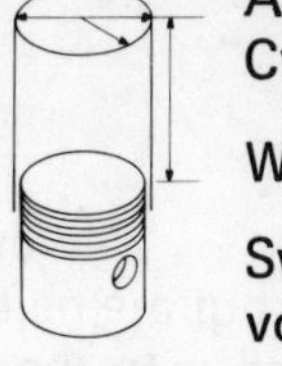

Area of Cylinder $= \frac{\pi d^2}{4}$ or $\pi r^2$

Where $d$ = cylinder bore

Swept volume =

Insert the appropriate dimension abbreviations on the drawing. For example calculate the swept volume of an engine cylinder having a bore diameter of 84 mm and a stroke of 90 mm.

Take $\pi$ as $\frac{22}{7}$

(Since engine capacity is quoted in cubic centimetres ($cm^3$) sometimes written as ccs the basic dimensions should be first converted to cm.)

Therefore bore 84 mm = 8.4 cm
stroke 90 mm = 9.0 cm

Swept volume = $\pi r^2$ x stroke

$= \frac{22}{7} \times 4.2 \times 4.2 \times 9$

$= \frac{22}{7_1} \times 4.2^{0.6} \times 4.2 \times 9$

$= 498.96\ cm^3$

If this cylinder was from a four cylinder engine it would be a ..............................litre engine.

1. Calculate the swept volume of an engine cylinder having a bore diameter of 70 mm and a stroke of 100 mm.

2. Calculate the swept volume of an engine cylinder having a bore diameter of 80 mm and a stroke of 70 mm.

3. Calculate the capacity of a four-cylinder engine whose bore and stroke are both 90 mm.



# COMPRESSION RATIO

The engine cylinders below have a compression ratio of ......................

10 cm³
t.d.c.
90 cm³
b.d.c.
(b) (a)

The clearance volume is ................

................................................

................................................

The compression ratio is the proportion by which ......................

................................................

................................................

................................................

This may be expressed as

$$\text{Compression ratio} = \frac{\text{Total volume}}{\text{Clearance volume}}$$

$$= \frac{\text{Swept volume + Clearance volume}}{\text{Clearance volume}}$$

$$CR = \frac{SV + CV}{CV}$$

1. Calculate the compression ratio of a cylinder when the swept volume is 720 $cm^3$ and the clearance volume is 90 $cm^3$.

=

2. Calculate the compression ratio of a cylinder when the swept volume is 518 $cm^3$ and the clearance volume is 74 $cm^3$.

3. Calculate the compression ratio of a cylinder when the swept volume is 900 $cm^3$ and the clearance volume is 60 $cm^3$.

This engine would be ....................

................................................



(continued on next page)

A1: 23

4. Calculate the compression ratio of an engine whose bore and stroke dimensions are 100 mm and 70 mm, respectively, when the clearance volume is 75 $cm^3$.

**Investigation**

Examine data books to determine the compression ratio of various engines.

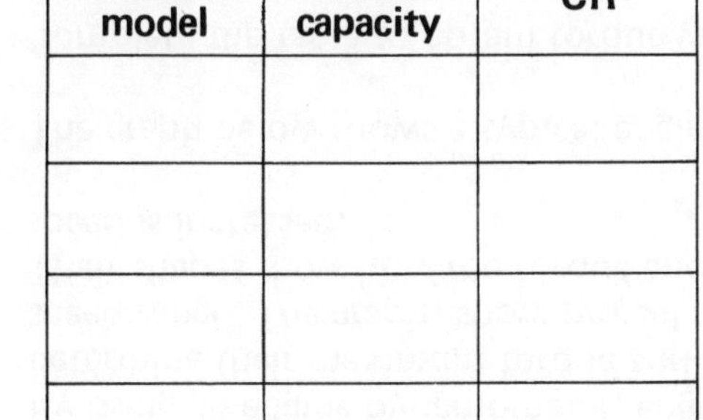

| Vehicle model | Engine capacity | CR |
|---|---|---|
| | | |
| | | |
| | | |
| | | |

A1: 24

# VALVE OPENING PERIODS

In terms of crankshaft rotation the valves are open for a period greater than the actual named stroke (see the diagrams below).

The theoretical valve open period lasts as long as the engine stroke and, measured in crankshaft degrees, this would be

..................................................

Below are shown separately the valve open periods measured in crankshaft degrees.

State which valve is represented by each diagram, indicate the opening and closing points and measure in degrees the total valve open period.

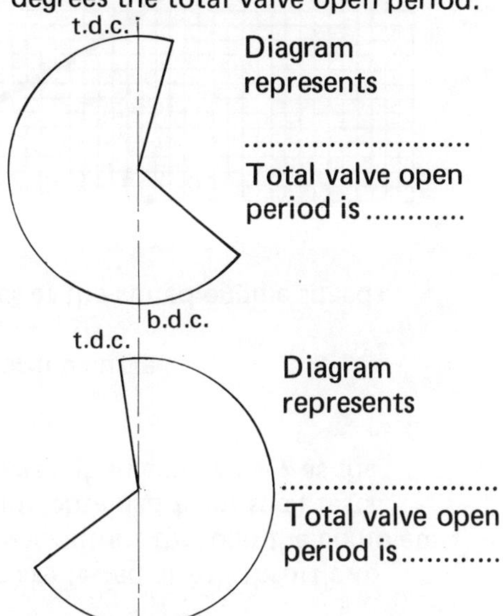


Diagram represents

.........................

Total valve open period is ...........

Diagram represents

.........................

Total valve open period is ...........

1. Calculate total valve opening period from the two valve timing diagrams below.

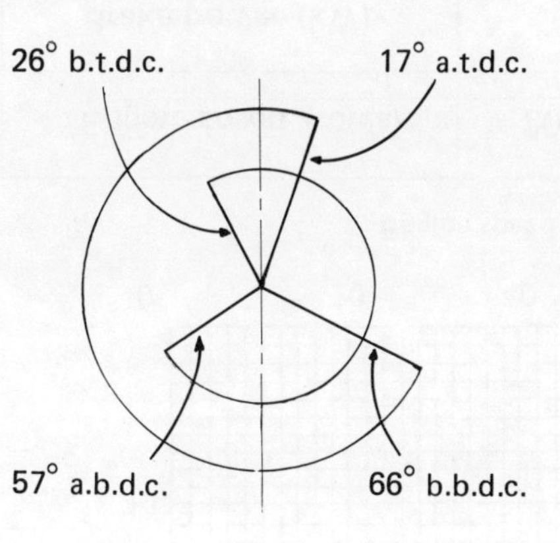


Inlet valve open period = ...........  Exhaust valve open period = ................

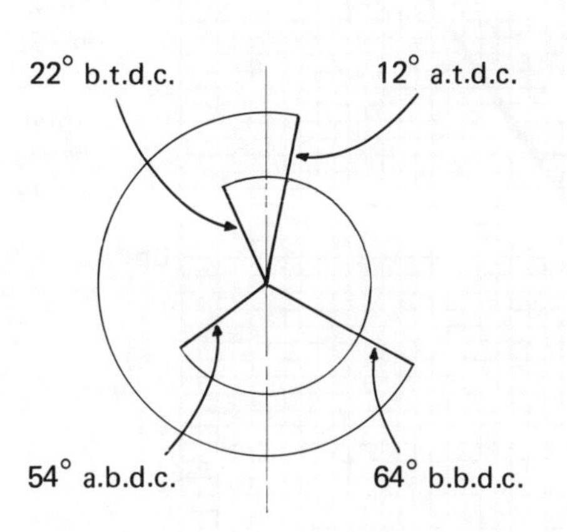


Inlet valve open period = ...........  Exhaust valve open period = ................

2. State the valve overlap and calculate in °a.t.d.c. the point when the inlet valve is fully open.

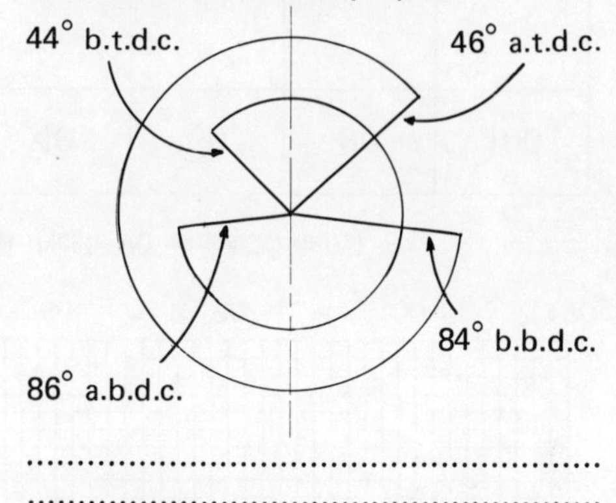


..................................................

..................................................

**Investigation**

Using valve timing data calculate the total valve open period for two engines.

| Engine | | 1 | 2 |
|---|---|---|---|
| Inlet valve | Opens °b.t.d.c | | |
| | Closes °a.b.d.c. | | |
| Actual stroke | | | |
| Total valve open period | | | |
| Exhaust valve | Opens °b.b.d.c. | | |
| | Closes °a.t.d.c. | | |
| Actual stroke | | | |
| Total valve open period | | | |

# ENGINE TORQUE AND POWER OUTPUTS

By using an engine dynamometer, engines are tested at full throttle to determine their maximum torque and power output through the complete speed range. The graphs show typical results obtained from such tests. Their shapes show how the torque and power of an engine vary as the speed is increased.

The graph below shows a typical engine torque curve.

Complete the table to obtain torque values at the stated engine speeds.

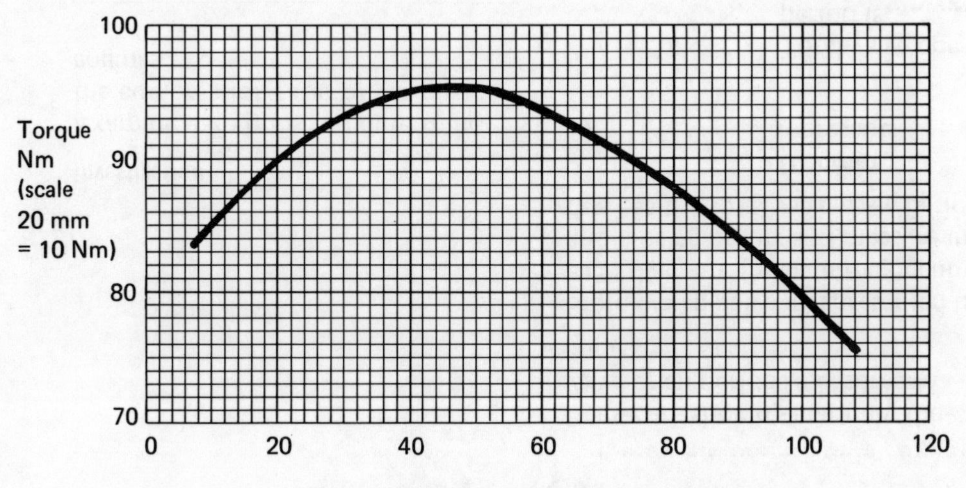


| **Engine speed** (rev/s) | 20 | 40 | 60 | 80 | 100 |
|---|---|---|---|---|---|
| **Torque** (Nm) | | | | | |

Maximum torque occurred at a speed of ..................................................

The graph shows a typical engine brake power curve.
Complete the table to obtain brake power values at the stated engine speeds.

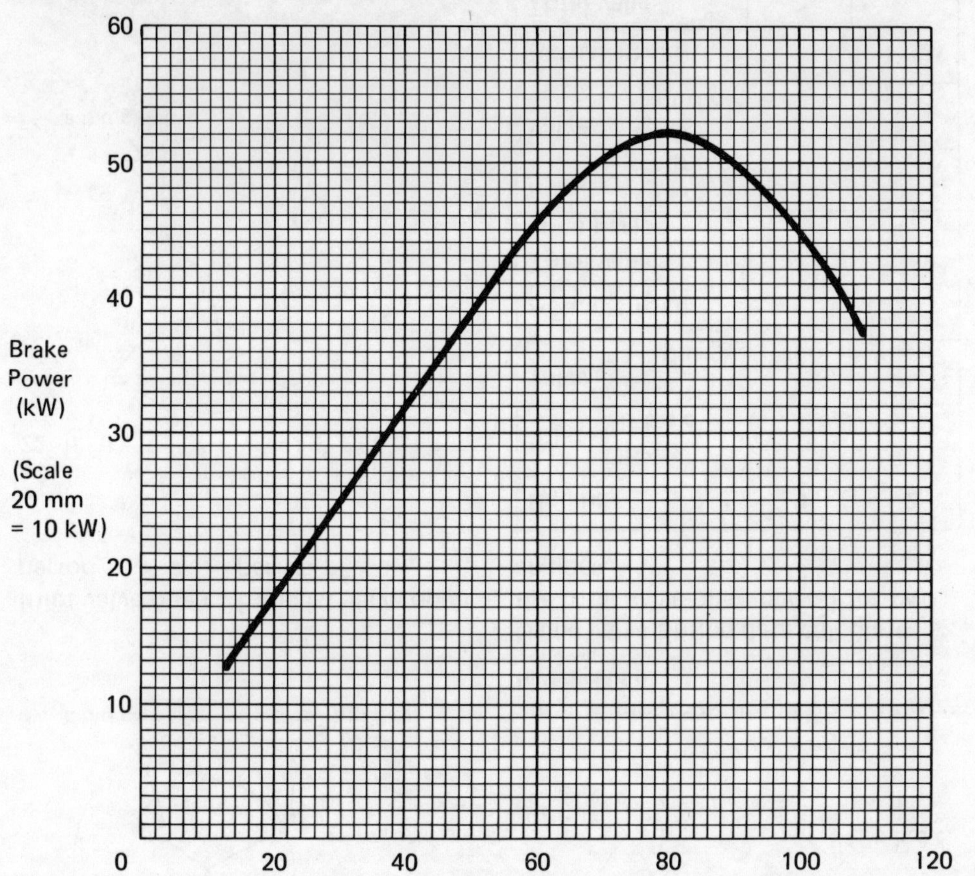


| **Engine speed** (rev/s) | 20 | 40 | 60 | 80 | 100 |
|---|---|---|---|---|---|
| **Brake power** (kW) | | | | | |

Maximum brake power occurred at a speed of ..................................................

A1: 26

# TEMPERATURE, PRESSURE, VOLUME

Heating a gas can cause a temperature, pressure and volume increase for example in an engine cylinder. For simplicity these effects can be considered as follows:

**Heating at constant pressure**

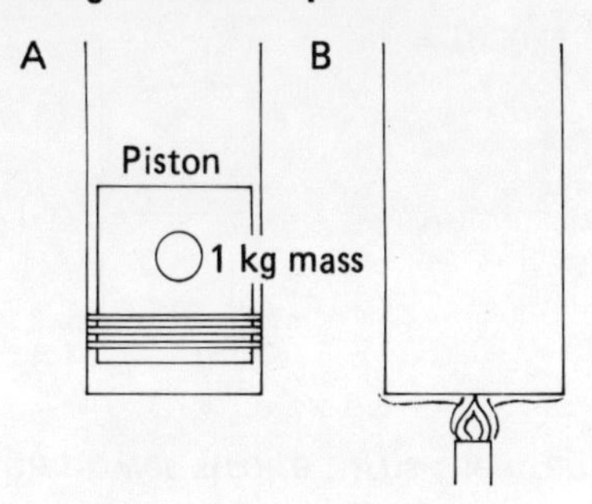


A shows air trapped in a gas-tight cylinder.
Show on drawing B the effect caused by heating the air and allowing the pressure to remain constant.

This effect proves the basic statement that:

The volume .............................. as the temperature ........................ if the pressure is kept ....................................

**Heating at constant volume**

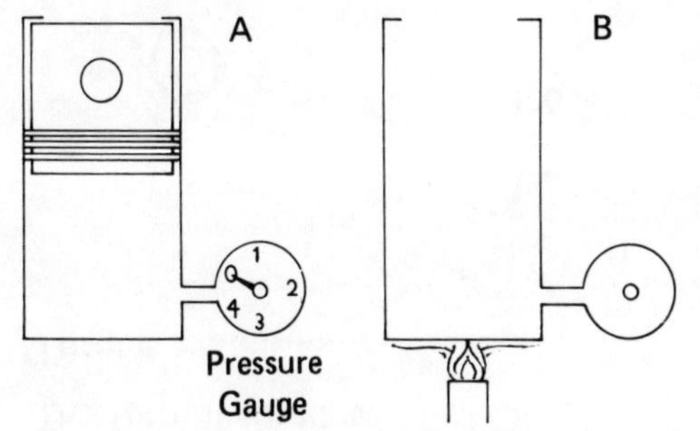


A shows both air and piston fixed in a cylinder.
Complete drawing B to show the effect caused by heating such an arrangement.

This effect proves the basic statement that:

The pressure..........................as the .................................. increases, if the volume is kept .................................

A1: 27

# EFFECTS OF HEAT ON ENGINE COMPONENTS

The heat created in an engine causes all the metal parts to ............................

Thus, moving parts must be designed to have a running ..............................

otherwise ......................................may occur.

Name engine parts which must be given clearance and state the effect of running with no clearance.

| Engine Part | Effect of no clearance |
|---|---|
| | |
| | |
| | |
| | |

A1: 28

# USE OF HEAT WHEN FITTING COMPONENTS

State TWO common examples where heat is used as an aid to fitting or assembling engine components.

1. ..........................................................................................

2. ..........................................................................................

Why is use of heat considered to be the best way of fitting these components?

..........................................................................................

..........................................................................................

..........................................................................................

..........................................................................................

## A1: 29 ENGINE TORQUE

When a turning force is applied to a spanner the spanner is said to be applying a torque.

The formula used is:

Torque = ......................................

0.1 m

100 N

The torque applied to the spanner shown is:

Torque = ......................................

......................................................

In an engine a similar situation occurs when the average force during the power stroke turns the crank.

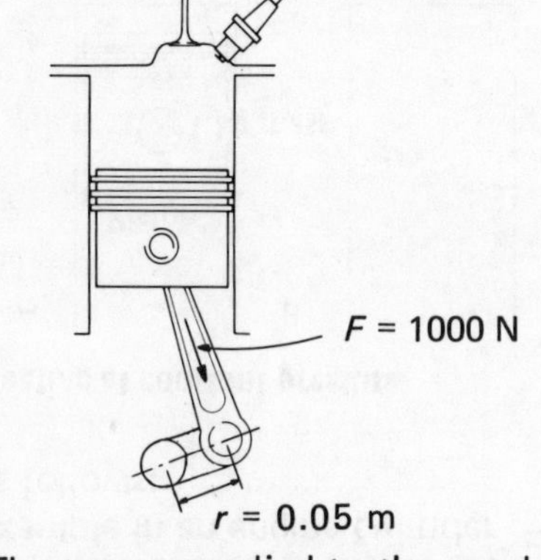


The torque applied to the crank is:

......................................................

## A1: 30 WORK DONE

Work is done when a force moves an object through a distance in the direction of the applied force.

The formula used is:

Work done = ................................

The units, however, are usually expressed differently to the torque units.

......................................................

......................................................

......................................................

......................................................

......................................................

......................................................

In an engine during the power stroke the work done is a product of the (average) force on the piston and the engine stroke.

F = 600 N

Stroke = 0.12 m

The work done is:

......................................................

## A1: 31 ENGINE POWER

Both the engine torque and the work done during the power stroke can be expressed in terms of power.

Power is the.................................

of doing ......................................

It is defined as...............................

......................................................

......................................................

The unit of power is:

......................................................

......................................................

Power produced when moving in a straight line is usually expressed as:

Power = ..................................

= ..................................

while power produced when rotating, for example the brake power produced from an engine, is expressed as:

......................................................

Calculate the power of an engine when rotating at 50 rev/s and developing a torque of 77 Nm.

**Problems**

1. Calculate the torque applied to the crankshaft when an average force of 1200 N is applied to an engine having a stroke of 0.14 m.

2. Calculate the work done during the power stroke when an average force of 1500 N is applied to the piston.
Engine stroke = 110 mm

3. An engine running at 4800 rev/min develops a torque of 98 Nm. Calculate the brake power of the engine at this speed.

# GASKETS AND THEIR APPLICATION

Joining surfaces of an engine normally require the use of a gasket.

.....................................................................................................................

.....................................................................................................................

.....................................................................................................................

The function of a gasket is ..........................................................................

.....................................................................................................................

.....................................................................................................................

.....................................................................................................................

.....................................................................................................................

**Investigation**

Examine various gaskets fitted to an engine, for example a new 'decoke' and engine sump set, and complete the following table.

| Gasket | Material | Reason for choice of material |
|---|---|---|
| Cylinder head | | |
| | | |
| | | |
| | | |
| | | |
| | | |
| | | |
| | | |
| | | |
| | | |
| | | |
| | | |
| | | |
| | | |

**Sealing compounds**

In many cases in addition to gaskets, sealing compounds are used.

There are two basic types.

| | Types | Typical use |
|---|---|---|
| 1. | | |
| | | |
| | | |
| 2. | | |
| | | |
| | | |

**'Instant' gasket**

A gasket compound made from silicone (room temperature vulcanising) rubber can be used to completely replace some cork and paper gaskets.

.....................................................................................................................

.....................................................................................................................

.....................................................................................................................

.....................................................................................................................

.....................................................................................................................

.....................................................................................................................

.....................................................................................................................

.....................................................................................................................

Other compounds are used to lock studs, nuts and screws, retain gears on shafts and bearing cups in housings.
The compound will take up wear if it is not greater than 0.125 mm.

*List typical engine examples*

1. ...................................................... 3. ......................................................

2. ...................................................... 4. ......................................................

# A2.

# Cooling

# COOLING SYSTEMS

All types of internal combustion engines require some form of cooling.

Why is a cooling system necessary?

.......................................................................................................

.......................................................................................................

.......................................................................................................

.......................................................................................................

Any cooling system must be designed to prevent both under and over cooling.

There are two basic types of cooling systems:

1. ............................................ 2. ............................................

Two systems of water cooling can be considered.
The type now in very widespread use is generally called the:

.......................................................................................................

The one not now used which is called:

.......................................................................................................

# AIR COOLING

This type of cooling is popular for motor cycles and is used on some small cars.

On what basic principle does air cooling rely?

.......................................................................................................

.......................................................................................................

.......................................................................................................

.......................................................................................................

.......................................................................................................

A motor-cycle engine is not usually enclosed; the passage of air over the cylinders when the cycle is in motion provides an adequate cooling flow.

**Investigation**

Examine an air-cooled cylinder barrel and head. Add to the outline cylinder below the cylinder head, showing the cooling fins and the fins on the barrel. Show how the fins vary in length.

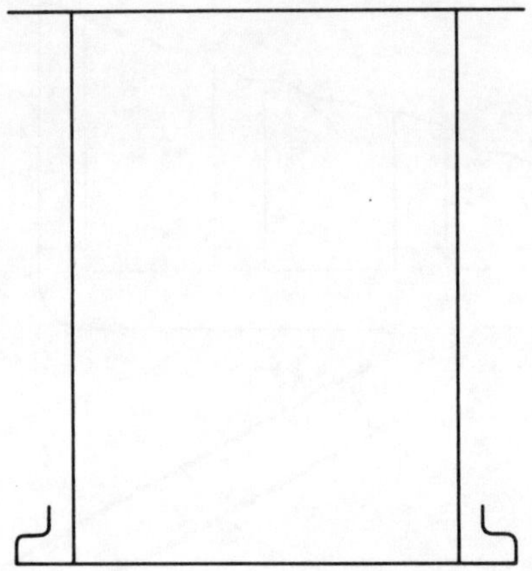

What is the reason for this variation in the size and shape of the cooling fins?

.......................................................................................................

.......................................................................................................

.......................................................................................................

.......................................................................................................

What periodic cooling-system maintenance should be carried out on air-cooled engines?

.......................................................................................................

.......................................................................................................

*(continued on next page)*

On a multi-cylinder car engine the engine is enclosed and the air is directed over the cylinders with the aid of a fan, fan cowling and baffles.

**Investigation**

Inspect a four-cylinder air-cooled engine, complete with air-cooling system.

Vehicle make ................................ Model ..........................................

How is the air-cooling fan driven?

..........................................................................................................

..........................................................................................................

..........................................................................................................

Describe the direction of air flow over the engine cylinder cooling fins.

..........................................................................................................

..........................................................................................................

..........................................................................................................

..........................................................................................................

..........................................................................................................

What controls the flow of air to the cylinders during and after the engine warm-up period?

..........................................................................................................

..........................................................................................................

Complete the table below in respect of a variety of vehicles having air-cooled engines.

| Vehicle make | Model | Number of cylinders | Approximate engine capacity |
|---|---|---|---|
| | | | |
| | | | |
| | | | |
| | | | |

# THERMOSYPHON WATER COOLING SYSTEM

A2: 3, 5

The water-cooling system in many old vehicles used this principle

..........................................................................................................

..........................................................................................................

..........................................................................................................

..........................................................................................................

..........................................................................................................

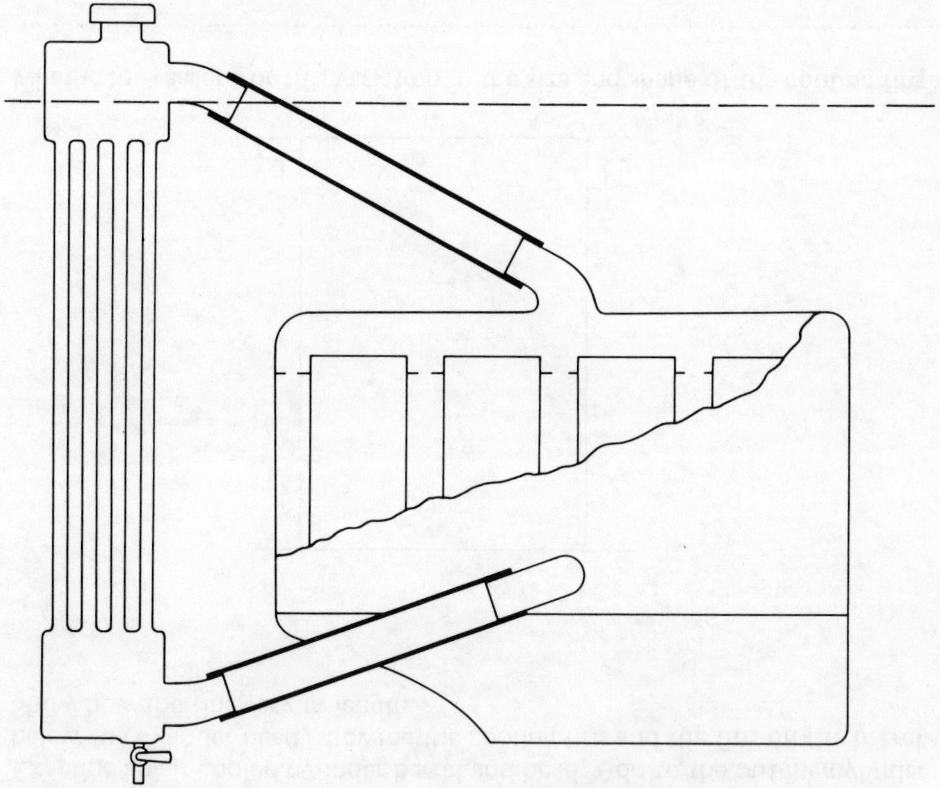

Name the main parts and show on this simple diagram the direction of the flow of water.

State what the dotted line through the header tank signifies.

List reasons why the thermosyphon system is not used on modern cars.

A2: 2, 3, 4

## PUMP-ASSISTED WATER COOLING SYSTEMS

On the diagram of the cooling system below, indicate the direction of water flow and identify the main components.

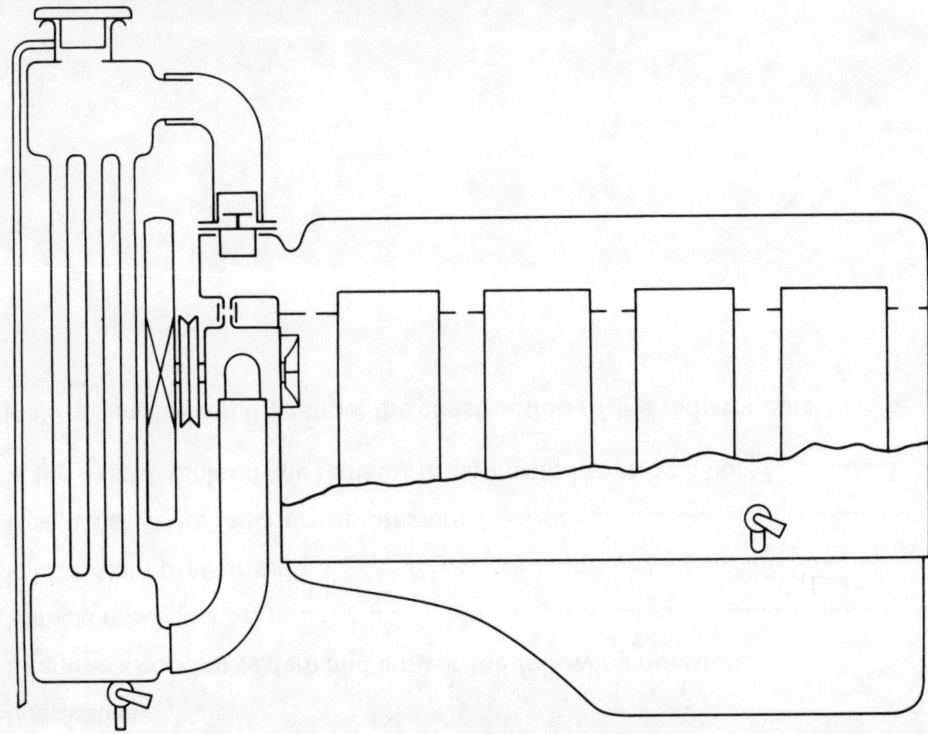

What are four advantages of air cooling over water cooling?

1.
2.
3.
4.

What are four advantages of water cooling over air cooling?

1.
2.
3.
4.

Describe the basic operation of the pump-assisted system.

A2: 2

**Investigation**

Examine a cooling system and answer the following questions.

Vehicle make ................................ Model ..................................................

Is its system pressurised?.........................................................................

If so, what is the radiator-cap pressure?..................................................

Is the header tank on the radiator or connected to it by a hose?.................

Make a simple sketch to show the construction of the radiator core (or element).

Examine the edges of the radiator hoses carefully and state from what materials the hoses are made ..........................................................................

Where is the water pump fitted?........................................ ..................

Is there any other water connection to the pump apart from the main one?

.........................................................................................................

If so, to where is it connected?...............................................................

.........................................................................................................

Where are the heater hoses connected to the engine?

(1) ..................................................................................................

(2) ..................................................................................................

Which one is the inlet supply to the heater? ..............................................

A2: 6,7

# THERMOSTAT

This is a temperature sensitive valve that controls water flow to the radiator.

There are two main reasons why it is fitted;

one is to ensure a rapid warm up when starting from cold.

The other main reason is ..........................................................................

.........................................................................................................

Examine a wax thermostat and state its operating temperature.....................

What would be the normal temperature of the coolant if the cooling system was fitted with this thermostat?..............................................................



Simplified diagram showing sectioned view of a wax thermostat.

Complete diagram to show thermostat in open position. Indicate direction of water flow and position of rubber and wax.

Explain how the thermostat is made to open

.........................................................................................................

.........................................................................................................

.........................................................................................................

.........................................................................................................

# PRESSURISED COOLING SYSTEM PRESSURE RADIATOR-CAP

When the engine is started the water is heated and it expands. Because the space for expansion is restricted, the system becomes pressurised. State five important reasons why this system is used.

..............................................................................................................

..............................................................................................................

..............................................................................................................

..............................................................................................................

..............................................................................................................

..............................................................................................................

..............................................................................................................

..............................................................................................................

..............................................................................................................

..............................................................................................................

What safety precautions must be observed when dealing with pressure caps?

..............................................................................................................

..............................................................................................................

..............................................................................................................

..............................................................................................................

..............................................................................................................

Suggest four faults that can prevent a cap operating correctly.

1. ..............................................................................................................
2. ..............................................................................................................
3. ..............................................................................................................
4. ..............................................................................................................

Name the essential parts of this typical radiator cap?

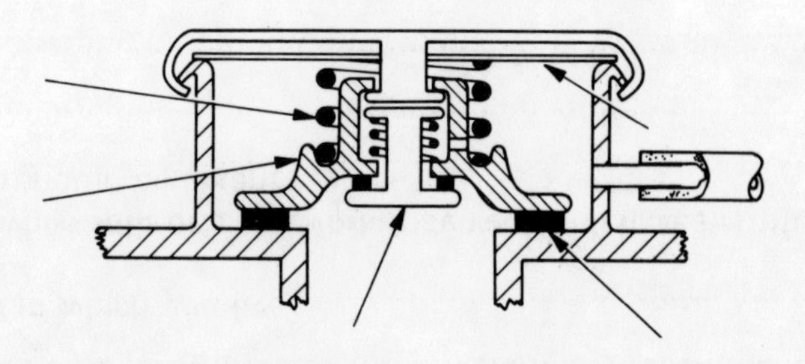

Explain how this type of cap maintains pressure in the system.

..............................................................................................................

..............................................................................................................

..............................................................................................................

How does the cap prevent a vacuum forming in the system as it goes cold?

..............................................................................................................

..............................................................................................................

..............................................................................................................

**Investigation**

Examine various caps and state at what pressure they should operate.

Use a pressure tester to check their condition.

| Make of car | Stated pressure of cap tested | Actual release pressure | State if cap maintained pressure for over 10 seconds |
|---|---|---|---|
| | | | |
| | | | |
| | | | |
| | | | |

A2: 11,12

## EXPANSION TANKS

Many modern cooling systems use an expansion tank. The layout will then be called, depending upon type, a sealed or semi-sealed system.

.................................................................................................

.................................................................................................

.................................................................................................

Explain how the system works.

.................................................................................................

.................................................................................................

.................................................................................................

.................................................................................................

.................................................................................................

.................................................................................................

Examine such a system and complete the sketch below to show where the expansion tank would be fitted. Show the recommended initial water level and name the main parts.

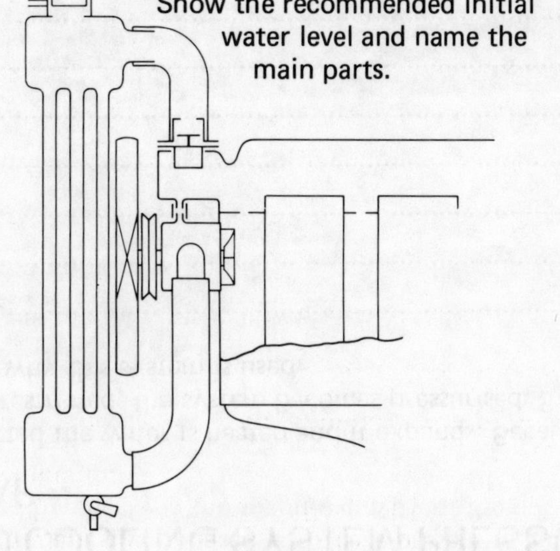

A2: 13

## EFFECTS OF FREEZING

When water freezes it increases in volume and this can cause a cylinder block to crack.

.................................................................................................

.................................................................................................

.................................................................................................

.................................................................................................

A2: 9,14,16

## ANTIFREEZE

If antifreeze is added to the water the temperature at which the mixture freezes can be progressively reduced.

Complete the following table in respect of an ethylene glycol-based antifreeze.

| Percentage antifreeze to water | °C at which mush begins to form | °C when mixture freezes solid | Comments on suitability for use |
|---|---|---|---|
| 10% | .................... | .................... | .................... |
| | | | .................... |
| 25% | .................... | .................... | .................... |
| 33.3% | .................... | .................... | .................... |

What proportion of antifreeze to water is normally recommended for use in the country in which you live? ..........................................

Antifreeze when spilt on paintwork may very well have harmful effects. What action should be taken?

.................................................................................................

.................................................................................................

.................................................................................................

*(continued on next page)*

A2: 15

The proportion of an eythylene glycol-based antifreeze present in a cooling system can be determined by checking the specific gravity of the coolant and by reference to its temperature.

.................................................................................................

.................................................................................................

.................................................................................................

.................................................................................................

.................................................................................................

Describe how the strength of antifreeze may be measured.

.................................................................................................

.................................................................................................

.................................................................................................

.................................................................................................

.................................................................................................

.................................................................................................

.................................................................................................

.................................................................................................

**Investigation**

Use manufacturer's test equipment to check antifreeze content on four vehicles.

| Vehicle make and model | Actual % antifreeze content present in cooling system | Water capacity from wall chart | 'Top up' amount of antifreeze required for a solution of 25% |
|---|---|---|---|
| | | | |
| | | | |
| | | | |
| | | | |

A2: 17

# COOLING-SYSTEM MAINTENANCE

Below is a check list for routine cooling-system maintenance. Examine a vehicle and complete the list.

Vehicle make ................................ Model ......................................

**Engine stopped**

| Item | √ | Comments |
|---|---|---|
| Coolant level | | |
| Coolant cleanliness | | |
| Evidence of leaks | | |
| Radiator cap (including pressure test) | | |
| Air passages through radiator | | |
| Top hose | | |
| Bottom hose | | |
| Heater hoses | | |
| By-pass and other hoses | | |
| Fan-belt tension | | |
| Fan-belt condition | | |
| Water-pump bearings | | |

**Engine running**

| Item | √ | Comments |
|---|---|---|
| Water pump, noisy operation | | |
| Thermostat operation | | |
| Pressure test of complete system | | |
| Evidence of external leakage | | |
| Evidence of cylinder leakage into cooling system | | |

# HEAT TRANSMISSION

Heat is one type of energy. A piston engine relies on heat for its principle of operation. Heat is transmitted in one (or more) of three ways.

.....................................................................................................

.....................................................................................................

.....................................................................................................

.....................................................................................................

.....................................................................................................

.....................................................................................................

.....................................................................................................

.....................................................................................................

The sketch below shows part of a motor-cycle engine. Add arrows showing the direction the heat path takes from the piston crown to the outside of the cylinder.

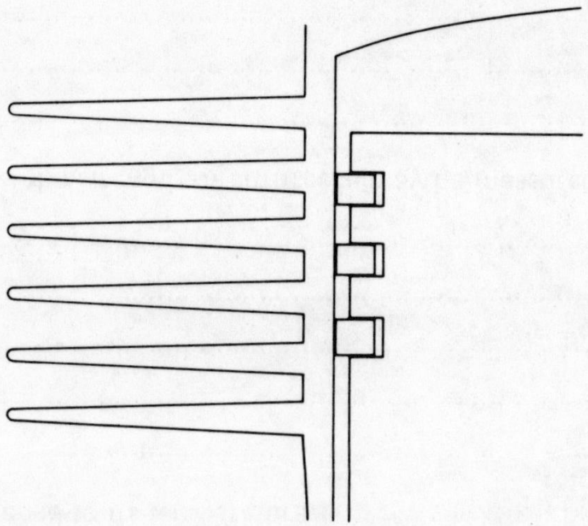

Heat flow, through the metal is by .....................................................

## Conduction

Pistons (and some cylinder heads and blocks) are made of aluminium alloy, instead of cast iron or steel. There are two reasons for the choice of this material. One is that it is lighter, the other is

.....................................................................................................

This leads to the fact that the rate of conduction varies

.....................................................................................................

.....................................................................................................

## Convection

Convection currents occur because of the difference in density between cold and hot water. In practical terms water density varies little through its complete liquid state, but cold water does have .............................. density than warm water.

What occurs to a quantity of water as its temperature rises?

.....................................................................................................

.....................................................................................................

The changes in density therefore directly produce ..............................

.....................................................................................................

## Radiation

Metal will lose heat at different rates according to:

1. .....................................................................................................

.....................................................................................................

2. .....................................................................................................

.....................................................................................................

3. .....................................................................................................

.....................................................................................................

# CONDUCTION

The amount of heat a material can transfer determines whether it is a good or bad conductor.

**Investigations**

Several types of equipment are available to demonstrate the relative heat conductivity of various materials. One is shown below. Conduct your test and list the order of heat (or thermal) conductivity of the rods. Show the position of the collars when the first one drops off.

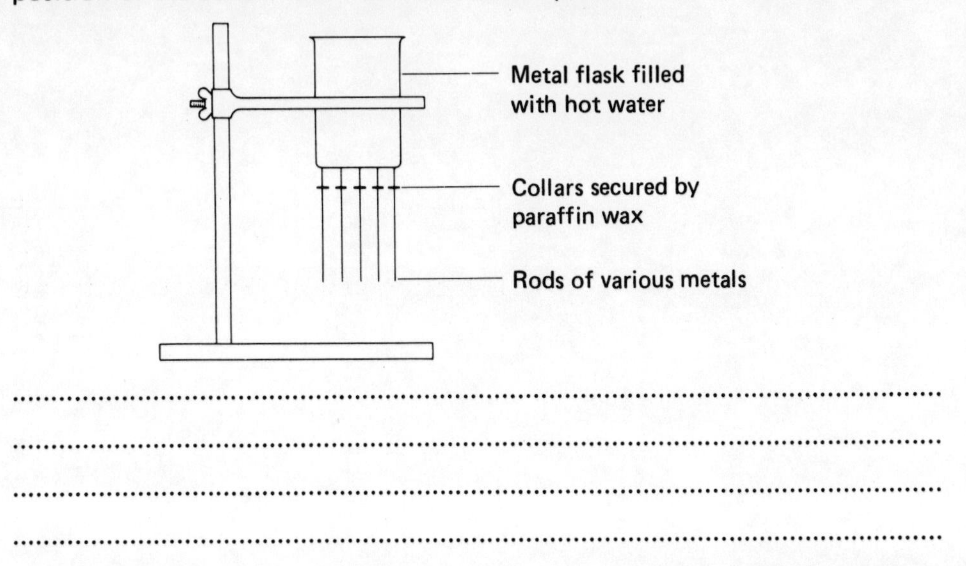


..................................................................................................

..................................................................................................

..................................................................................................

..................................................................................................

| Order of conductivity | Material | Where could this material be used on a vehicle? |
|---|---|---|
| 1. | | |
| 2. | | |
| 3. | | |
| 4. | | |
| 5. | | |

Water is a poor conductor of heat. To verify this hold at its lower end a fairly long narrow test tube filled with water. Heat the open end by means of a bunsen burner. Explain briefly your method and the results.

..................................................................................................

..................................................................................................

..................................................................................................

..................................................................................................

..................................................................................................

Make a sketch to show the equipment used to carry out the experiment.

What ensures the water in a vehicle's cooling system does not have this effect?

..................................................................................................

..................................................................................................

A2: 18,20,21

# CONVECTION

Give two examples of heat transfer by convection relating to a vehicle.

1. ............................................................

2. ............................................................

**Investigation**

Sketch a piece of simple apparatus by which it is possible to see the movement of a liquid when heated. Carry out the experiment and report on your observations.

............................................................

............................................................

............................................................

............................................................

............................................................

# RADIATION

Give two examples of heat transfer by radiation relating to a vehicle.

1. ............................................................

2. ............................................................

**Investigation**

The effect of colour on the transfer of heat by radiation.



Take readings over a period of 15 minutes. List the order of relative heat (thermal) radiation of the canisters, the best first.

1. ............................................................

2. ............................................................

3. ............................................................

Some motorists like to highly polish radiator header-tanks.

Explain why this is bad practice ............................................................

............................................................

In the interests of heat dissipation what would be the best colour for a vehicle radiator? ............................................................

# EXPANSION OF LIQUIDS

Liquids expand when heated and contract when cooled.

.................................................................................................................

.................................................................................................................

.................................................................................................................

.................................................................................................................

.................................................................................................................

.................................................................................................................

Name a very useful measuring instrument which uses the principle of the expansion of liquids ..............................................................................

Where on a motor vehicle must provision be made for the expansion of a liquid?..................................................................................................

When wax changes state from a solid to a liquid..................................occurs.

This effect is used to advantage in ...........................................................

**Investigation**

Verify that liquids expand when heated and contract when cooled, by conducting an experiment on equipment similar to that shown opposite. Each of the tubes has a bowl at its end. Typical liquids which may be used are alcohol, petrol, water, glycerol, turpentine and an antifreeze solution.

.................................................................................................................

.................................................................................................................

.................................................................................................................

.................................................................................................................

Name, above each tube, the liquid used.

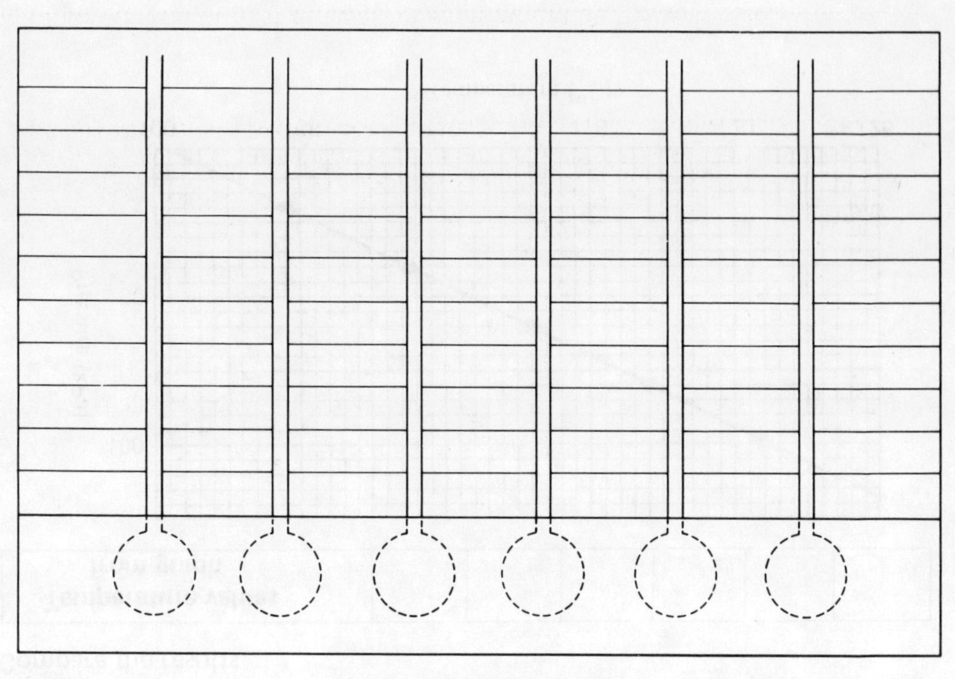

Trough containing hot water

Shade in the amount of expansion made by the liquid in each tube.

List the order of the expansion of the liquids.

| Order | Liquid |
|---|---|
| 1 | |
| 2 | |
| 3 | |
| 4 | |
| 5 | |
| 6 | |

.....................................

.....................................

.....................................

.....................................

.....................................

.....................................

.....................................

# EFFECTS OF PRESSURE ON THE BOILING POINT OF WATER

Although it is not obvious, the air around us has weight. Because of this it produces a pressure at sea level of 101.3 kN/m$^2$. At this pressure water boils at 100°C.

When pressure is lowered the temperature at which water boils ..........

When pressure is raised the boiling point is correspondingly ..........

This latter effect is used to advantage in the water cooling system of most vehicles.

..........

..........

..........

**Investigation**

Use suitable equipment (such as a radiator header tank) fitted with a pressure gauge and thermometer to show how the temperature of water can be increased above 100° C. Compare your results with those deduced from the graph opposite.

..........

..........

..........

..........

..........

..........

..........

Sketch the apparatus used.

*Results*

| **Pressure** (kPa) | 0 | 20 | 40 | 60 | 80 | 100 |
|---|---|---|---|---|---|---|
| **Temperature** (°C) | | | | | | |

Below is a graph obtained from a similar experiment. Using the graph obtain temperature values at the same pressures as the ones obtained experimentally. Compare the results.

| **Temperature values from graph** | | | | | | |
|---|---|---|---|---|---|---|

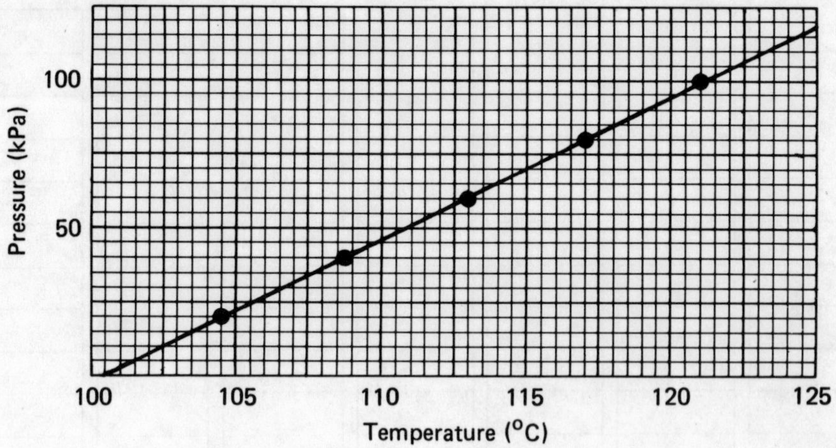

Pressure (kPa): 50, 100

Temperature (°C): 100, 105, 110, 115, 120, 125

..........

..........

A2: 23

**Investigation**

An experiment to show that water may be made to boil at different temperatures by altering the pressure is described below.
Conduct an experiment by boiling water in a flask. Allow it to boil for a few minutes then fit a stopper complete with a Celsius thermometer. Arrange the flask upside down as shown in the diagram and *carefully* pour cold water on to the top of the flask. Observe and record the results.

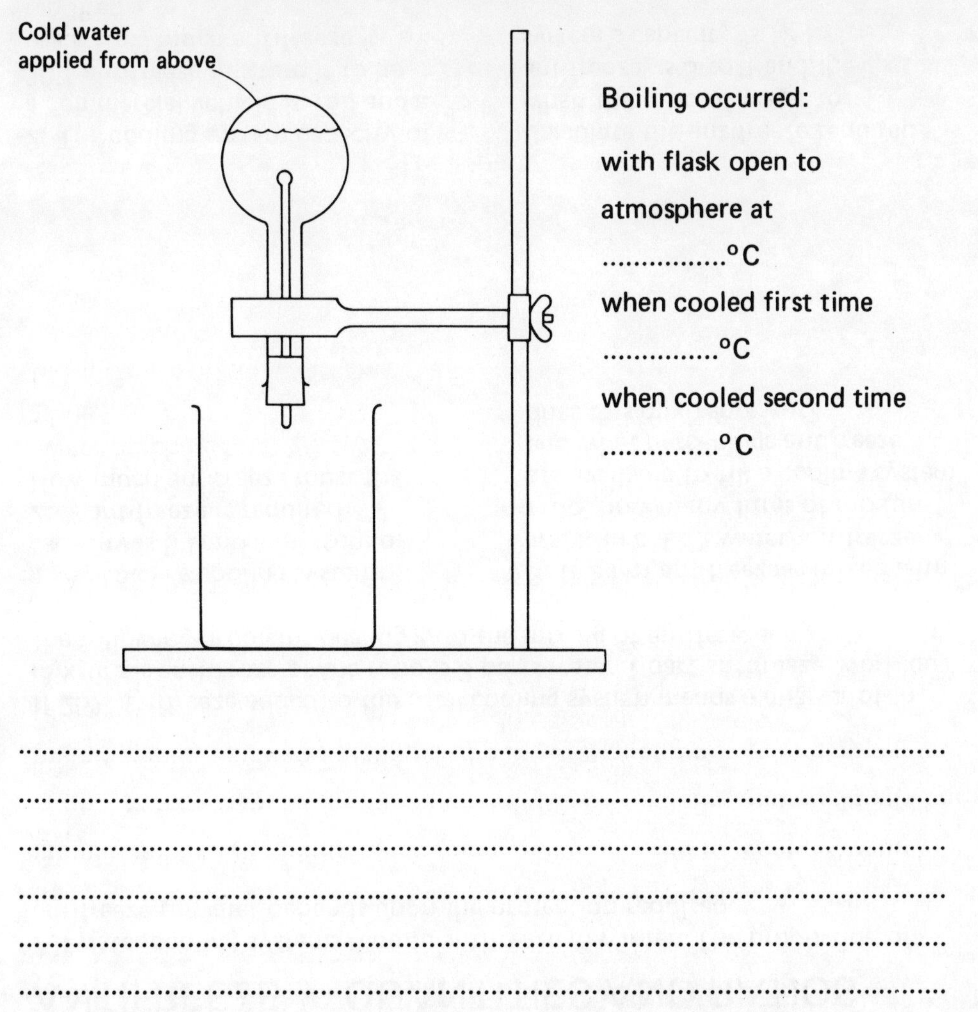


Boiling occurred:

with flask open to atmosphere at

................°C

when cooled first time

..............°C

when cooled second time

..............°C

..........................................................................................

..........................................................................................

..........................................................................................

..........................................................................................

..........................................................................................

..........................................................................................

A2: 25

# ELECTRICAL THERMOMETER

The temperature gauge fitted to modern engines is operated electronically.

The pick up unit used in an engine is called a ..............................................

Sketch such a unit naming the main parts, and show its electrical symbol.

Where in the engine is this unit fitted?

..........................................................................................

..........................................................................................

How does the unit operate?

..........................................................................................

..........................................................................................

..........................................................................................

..........................................................................................

..........................................................................................

..........................................................................................

..........................................................................................

..........................................................................................

Examine a temperature gauge on a vehicle and state the reading at normal running temperature.

..........................................................................................

A2: 16.26

# ANTIFREEZE – QUANTITIES AND RATIOS

All water cooling systems require antifreeze in winter. The proportion of antifreeze to water depends upon the protection required.

..........................................................................................

..........................................................................................

..........................................................................................

If 25% antifreeze added to the total cooling system means a quarter of the mixture is antifreeze or the ratio is 3 parts water 1 part antifreeze, work out the following problems dealing with the mixing of antifreeze.

1. A vehicle's cooling system capacity is 8 l and a mixture of 25% antifreeze is required. How much antifreeze must the owner purchase?

3. If 2 l of antifreeze is mixed with water in a 4 : 1 water/antifreeze ratio, how many litres of mixture are available to fill a cooling system and what percentage antifreeze does this mix represent?

2. The cooling system capacity of a commercial vehicle is 15 l and a 30% antifreeze mixture is to be used. How much antifreeze is required.

Calculate the antifreeze required when the ratio of water to antifreeze, is 3 to 1 and the system's capacity is 12 l.

Note: Antifreeze/water ratios can be as high as 50% (or 1 :  )

If a cooling system requires constant topping up and only plain water is added what effect will this have on

(a) the freezing point? ..........................................................................

..........................................................................................

(b) the boiling point of the solution? .........................................................

..........................................................................................

Shortly before they solidify due to cold, antifreeze solutions become 'mushy'. What precautions must the driver then observe?

..........................................................................................

..........................................................................................

..........................................................................................

..........................................................................................

**Investigation**

Place three flasks containing plain water, a 10% antifreeze solution and a 25% solution in a freezer to lower temperature. Then observe the effect on each solution.

| Flask | Temperature | Effect on contents |
|---|---|---|
| 1. Plain water | | |
| 2. 10% Antifreeze | | |
| 3. 25% Antifreeze | | |

# A3.

# Lubrication

A3: 1

When moving surfaces are in contact the friction created between those surfaces will cause heat and rapid wear. In an engine this effect is undesirable and must be controlled.

Explain briefly how friction is controlled in an engine.

..............................................................................................................

..............................................................................................................

..............................................................................................................

How would the lack of lubrication show itself in the running of an engine? For example if the engine was started without oil in the sump?

..............................................................................................................

..............................................................................................................

What effects would be caused by continual running with dirty oil?

..............................................................................................................

..............................................................................................................

..............................................................................................................

A3: 2

## VISCOSITY

The viscosity of an oil is a measure of its thckness (or body), or (more correctly) of its ..............................................................................

This property varies with temperature and for a specific oil:

When the temperature is low the oil will be ..........................................

When the temperature is high the oil will be .........................................

An oil said to be 'thin' is more properly described as a ...........................

................................and an oil described as 'thick' should be called a

..............................................................................................................

The viscosity of an oil is measured using a viscometer. This measures

..............................................................................................................

..............................................................................................................

A3: 3

## ENGINE OIL S.A.E. VISCOSITY CLASSIFICATION

The viscosity of an oil is expressed as a number prefixed by the letters S.A.E., for example S.A.E.30.

S.A.E. stands for the ............................................................. which is the American organisation that devised these viscosity standards.

State TWO typical engine oil viscosity numbers:

1. ................................................ 2. ................................................

Which oil has the lower viscosity?.......................................................

Modern oils often have two viscosity numbers, and are called

..............................................................................................................

The reason for two numbers is that two measuring standards are used, one at engine working temperature and the other at a very low temperature.

The working viscosity is calculated with the oil at 99°C (210° F) and the grade of oil is expressed as:

S.A.E. 20, 30, 40 or 50 etc.

The most viscous of the above being ...................................................

The second viscosity range is calculated at -18°C (0°F).

These are very low viscosity oils and have a suffix W (Winter) to indicate the measuring standard, for example

S.A.E. 5W, 10W, 20W.

The lowest viscosity there is ..............................................................

A modern multigrade oil is an oil whose viscosity meets the flow standards measured at both temperatures. This has many advantages:

..............................................................................................................

..............................................................................................................

..............................................................................................................

..............................................................................................................

Note: The S.A.E. number signifies only the viscosity of the oil at the specified temperature. It in no way indicates the quality of the oil.

# ENGINE LUBRICATION SYSTEM

Name the parts indicated, which make up the engine lubrication system.

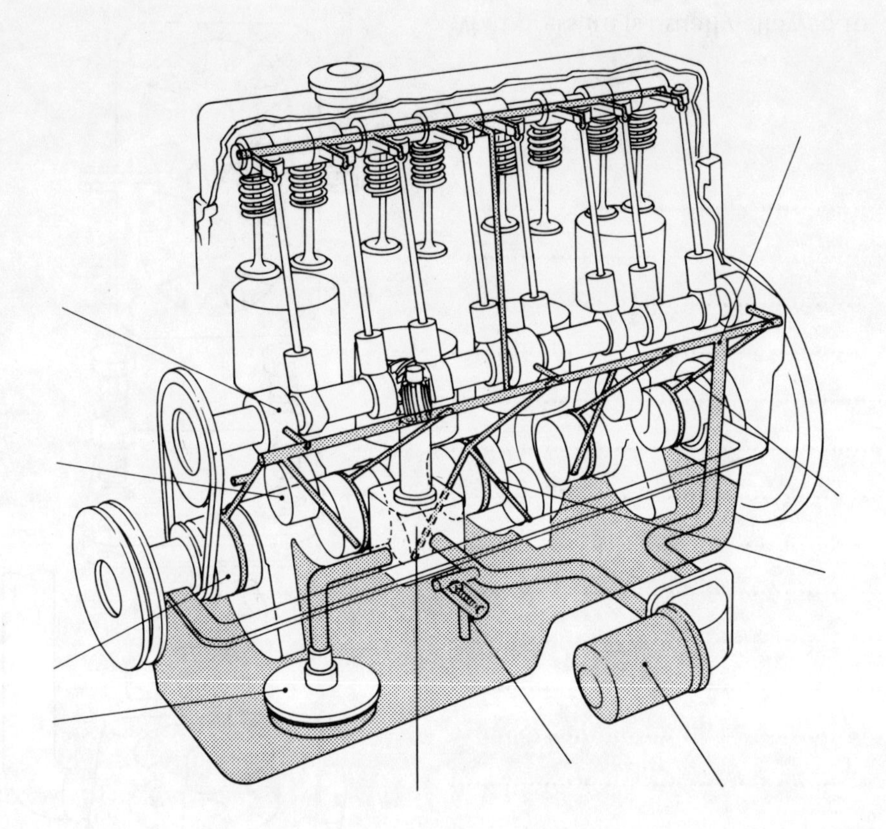

State FOUR functions provided by the oil:

..................................................................................................................

..................................................................................................................

State the purpose of the following items shown opposite.

Gauze filter ..................................................................................

..................................................................................................................

Oil pump ..................................................................................

..................................................................................................................

Relief valve ..................................................................................

..................................................................................................................

External (secondary) filter ..................................................................................

..................................................................................................................

Main gallery ..................................................................................

..................................................................................................................

**Investigation**

Examine an engine so as to determine the position of the oil passage-ways, filters, pump and pressure relief valves etc.

Engine make.......................................... Model ..........................................

| Component | Type | Position |
|---|---|---|
| Oil pump | .............. | .......................................................... |
| Primary filter | .............. | .......................................................... |
| Secondary filter | .............. | .......................................................... |
| Oil pressure relief valve | .............. | .......................................................... |
| Oil pressure indicator | .............. | .......................................................... |

# A3: 6 GEAR TYPE OIL PUMP

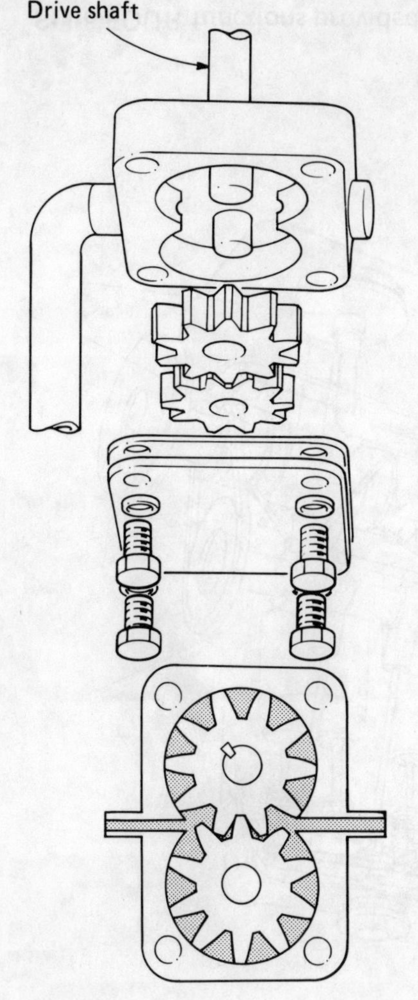


The simplest type of oil pump consists of a housing containing two gear wheels meshing closely together. Explain how the pump supplies and pressurises the oil.

..................................................
..................................................
..................................................
..................................................
..................................................
..................................................
..................................................
..................................................
..................................................
..................................................
..................................................
..................................................
..................................................
..................................................

What pressure is usually allowed to build up before the oil pressure relief valve opens.

..................................................
..................................................

Indicate the direction of gear rotation and oil flow. State which is the inlet and outlet.

# A3: 7 OIL FLOW THROUGH SYSTEM

The diagram below shows the main engine bearing surfaces and oil galleries drawn as simple blocks. Identify the components and show the direction of oil flow. Using dotted lines show the form of the camshaft and crankshaft and indicate the oil passages in the crankshaft.

State the sequence in which the oil is supplied from the oil pump to the various major parts.

..................................................
..................................................
..................................................
..................................................
..................................................
..................................................
..................................................
..................................................
..................................................

# METHODS OF LUBRICATING MAIN ENGINE PARTS

Oil is supplied to the moving parts of the engine by either full-film (forced) lubrication or splash.

On the sketch indicate and name four major parts that are supplied with full film lubrication, and three others lubricated by splash.

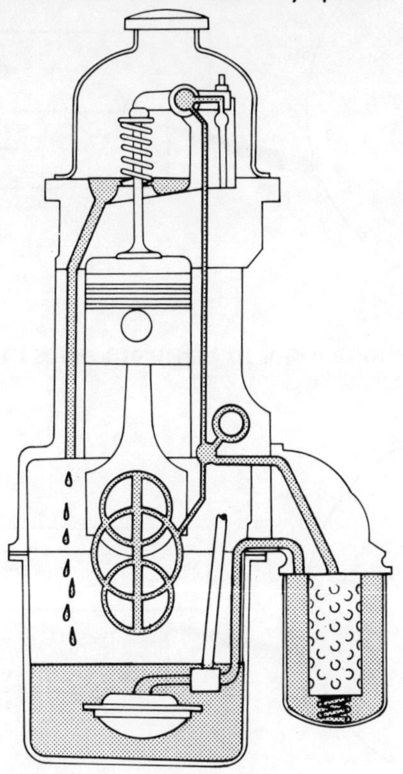

State FOUR items that are lubricated by splash

1. ............................................................................................................
2. ............................................................................................................
3. ............................................................................................................
4. ............................................................................................................



# RESTRICTION CONTROL OF OIL FLOW PAST PISTONS

The piston must form a moveable, gas- and oil-tight seal in the cylinder (although a very small amount of oil must pass the piston for lubrication purposes). To prevent gas leakage downwards and restrict oil leakage upwards the piston carries two types of rings.

These are ...................................... and ..............................................rings.

Complete the sketch to show the piston's sealing arrangement.

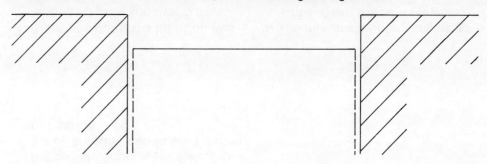

Sketch in section the two most common types of piston rings and state their function.

Type ........................................... Type ...........................................

........................................... ...........................................

........................................... ...........................................

........................................... ...........................................

## A3: 10 REDUCTION OF FRICTION BY LUBRICATION

When examined under a microscope, even apparently flat, smooth surfaces look like mountain ranges. For example this even applies to a newly-ground big end journal and its new shell bearings. The sketch below shows how two surfaces interlock with one another when they are dry.

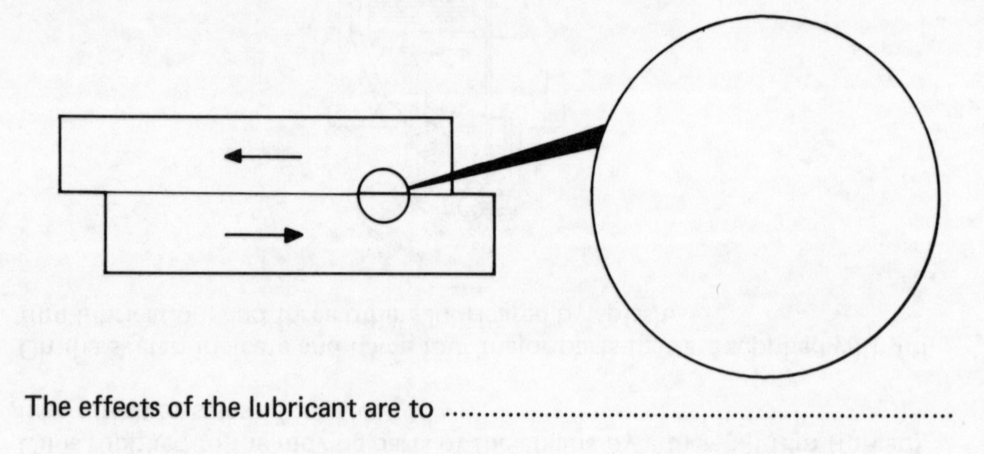

Complete the sketch to show the effect of lubrication.

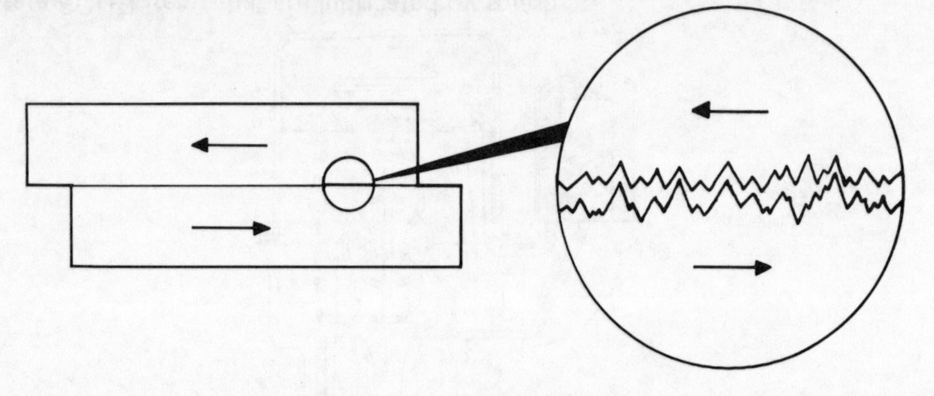

The effects of the lubricant are to ..............................................................

..............................................................................................

..............................................................................................

..............................................................................................

## A3: 14 OIL CONSUMPTION PROBLEMS

1. A vehicle requires topping up with 0.5 l of oil every 2000 km. The oil consumption in km/l would be

2. A driver purchases one 5 l can of oil and uses 3.5 l for an oil change. He runs the vehicle for 6000 km and uses the remainder of the oil for periodic topping up. Calculate the oil consumption in km/l during this period.

3. An engine burning a lot of oil was topped up daily and over 5 days required:

   1 l, 0.75 l, 1.5 l, 0.5 l, and 0.25 l.

   During this period the total mileage covered was 1000 km. Calculate the oil consumption in km/l.

4. If an engine oil consumption is 3000 km/l and the dipstick high level is 10 l and the low level is 7.5 l, how far can the vehicle safely travel before topping up with oil.

5. A vehicle requires topping up with 0.5 l of oil every 700 km. How much oil is used over a 10 000-km period?

6. The oil capacity of an engine is 4.75 l. When the oil level was checked it required 1.2 l of oil to correct the level. How much oil did the engine contain before topping up?

A3: 11

# TYPES OF OIL SEALING ARRANGEMENTS

Identify the types of engine oil sealing arrangements shown and label the parts indicated.

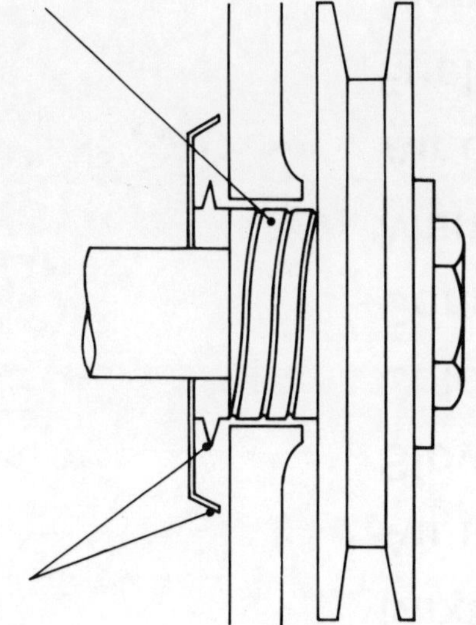

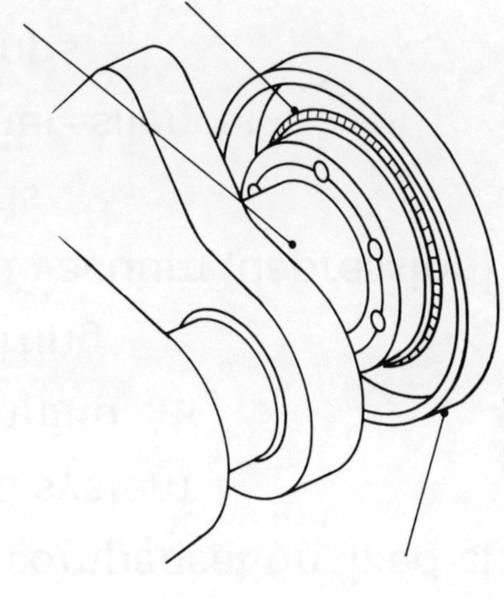

(1) ............................................ (2) ............................................

Explain how type (1) prevents oil leakage.

..........................................................................................................

..........................................................................................................

..........................................................................................................

..........................................................................................................

Explain the positioning of type (2) in relation to the oil it retains.

..........................................................................................................

..........................................................................................................

..........................................................................................................

..........................................................................................................

A3: 12

# CORRECT FITTING OF LIP TYPE SEAL

Show on the sketch a sectioned view of a lip type oil seal correctly fitted between the crankcase and crankshaft.

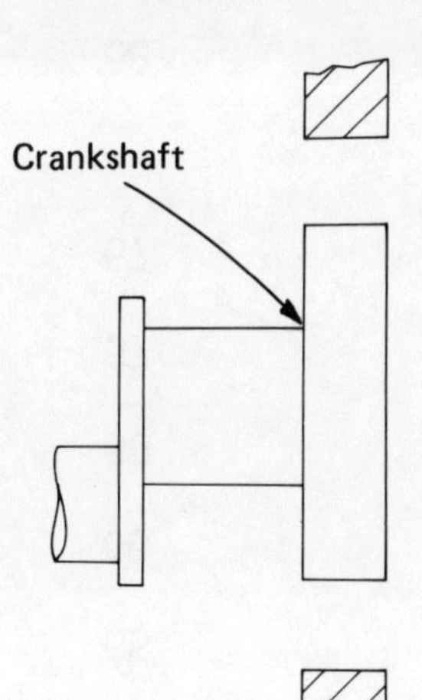


A3: 13

# TYPES OF LUBRICANTS AND LUBRICATION

Many types of lubricant and lubrication methods are available. Requirements depend on factors such as pressure, speed, material and operating temperatures and position.

..........................................................................................................

..........................................................................................................

..........................................................................................................

..........................................................................................................

..........................................................................................................

State below four different lubricants used on a vehicle and give examples of where they are employed.

| Lubricant | Where used |
|---|---|
| ............................................ | ............................................ |
| ............................................ | ............................................ |
| ............................................ | ............................................ |
| ............................................ | ............................................ |

# A4.

# Petrol Fuel System

# MIXTURES, AIR–FUEL RATIOS

In order to obtain correct combustion petrol and air must be mixed in correct proportions.

This ratio may vary depending upon the type of running the engine is doing but in view of economy and emission control must be kept within strict limits.

The chemically correct air–fuel ratio is ..................................................

10 : 1 would be a ........................ 18 : 1 would be a ..................................

Below is a graph showing air–fuel ratios for different car speeds.

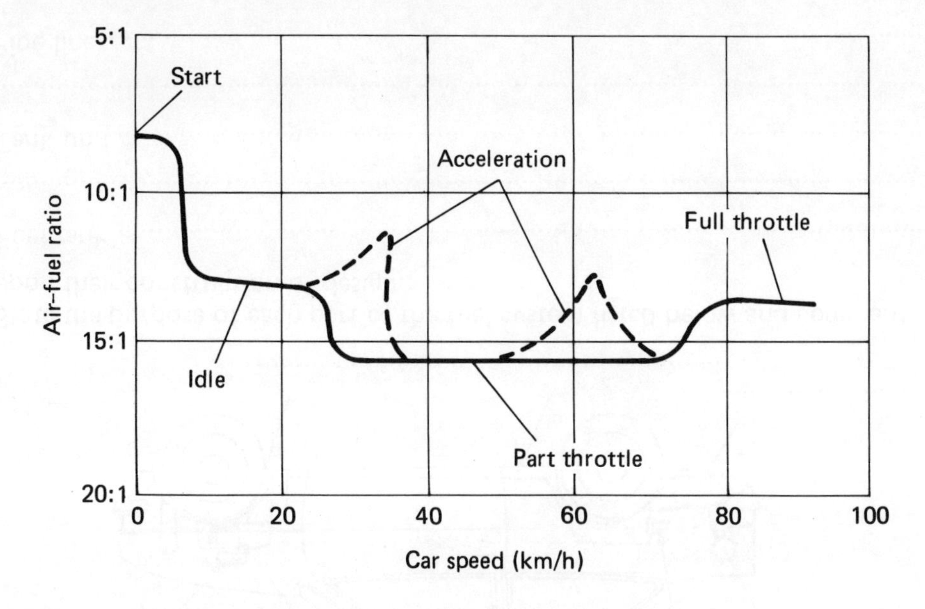


With the aid of the graph state typical air–fuel ratios for

Cold start .............................. Economical running ......................
Maximum power ................... Acceleration .................................

The values shown may vary with different engines, particularly the slow running value on modern engines.

If the carburettor is set incorrectly the mixture strength could be permanently weak or rich.
State TWO effects of running with a very weak mixture:

1. ........................................................................................................

........................................................................................................

2. ........................................................................................................

........................................................................................................

State TWO effects of running with a very rich mixture.

1. ........................................................................................................

2. ........................................................................................................



# SAFETY PRECAUTIONS

Petrol is a highly inflammable substance and exhaust gas may also be poisonous.

State personal safety precautions that must be observed when dealing with or working near:

1. Petrol

........................................................................................................

........................................................................................................

........................................................................................................

........................................................................................................

........................................................................................................

2. Exhaust gas

........................................................................................................

........................................................................................................

........................................................................................................

........................................................................................................

A4:5

# LAYOUT AND PURPOSE OF MAIN PARTS IN FUEL SYSTEM

Name the main parts of the fuel system layout shown.

..............................  ..............................

..............................  ..............................

..............................  ..............................  ..............................

State the purpose of each part of the fuel system listed below and comment upon their construction or design.

Fuel tank ..............................................................................................

..............................................................................................

Tank unit ..............................................................................................

..............................................................................................

Pipe line ..............................................................................................

..............................................................................................

Filters ..............................................................................................

..............................................................................................

Lift pump ..............................................................................................

..............................................................................................

Carburettor ..............................................................................................

..............................................................................................

Air cleaner ..............................................................................................

..............................................................................................

**Investigation**

Examine a fuel system layout and complete the table.

Make of vehicle .................................. Model ..................................

| Component | Type, position or material where applicable |
|---|---|
| Air cleaner or silencer | |
| Carburettor | |
| Filter | |
| Fuel pump | |
| Fuel pipes | |
| Fuel tank | |

A4:8

# IDENTIFICATION OF CARBURETTORS

State which is the horizontal and which is the downdraught carburettor.

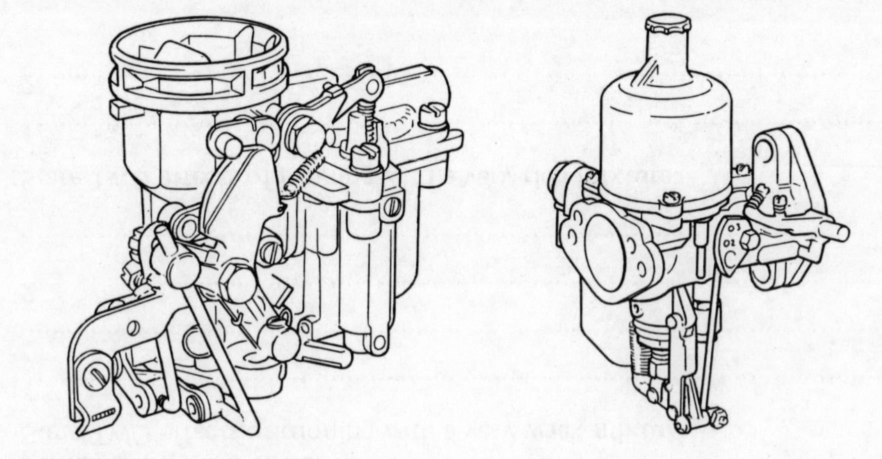

Type.................................. Type ..................................

# THE SIMPLE CARBURETTOR

A simple single-jet, fixed-choke carburettor has all the main features of a modern sophisticated carburettor.

Using the outlines as a guide, sketch below a line diagram of a simple carburettor. Label the major parts.

Fuel level

To engine

Explain the carburettor's basic operating principle.

................................................................................................

................................................................................................

................................................................................................

................................................................................................

................................................................................................

................................................................................................

................................................................................................

................................................................................................

The diagram below represents a simple venturi having air blown through by a fan. Show on the diagram the difference in water levels that would be produced in the pipes.

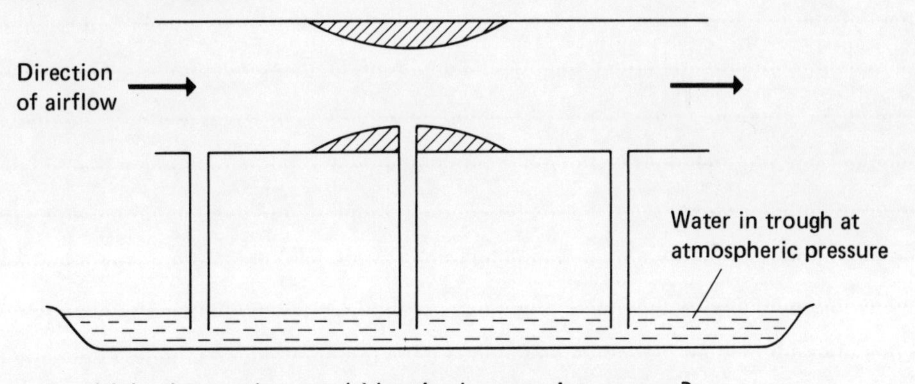


Across which pipe outlet would be the lowest air pressure?..........................

What is the function of the venturi or choke tube?

................................................................................................

................................................................................................

**Investigation**

Dismantle the float chamber of a carburettor. Examine the float and needle valve assembly.

State the material used for the various components.

| Component | Material |
|---|---|
| Float chamber | |
| Float | |
| Needle-valve seat | |
| Washer (if fitted) | |
| Needle | |

What is the function of the float and needle valve?

................................................................................................

................................................................................................

*(continued on next page)*

A4:9 A simple single-jet carburettor is not suitable for use on a modern variable speed engine. Why?

.................................................................................................

.................................................................................................

.................................................................................................

The graph below shows what would happen if a simple, single-jet carburettor was fitted to a variable-speed engine.

Mixture chemically correct at this point only
Petrol flow
Mixture too rich
Air flow
15:1
Flow of air and petrol increasing
Mixture too weak
Engine speed increasing

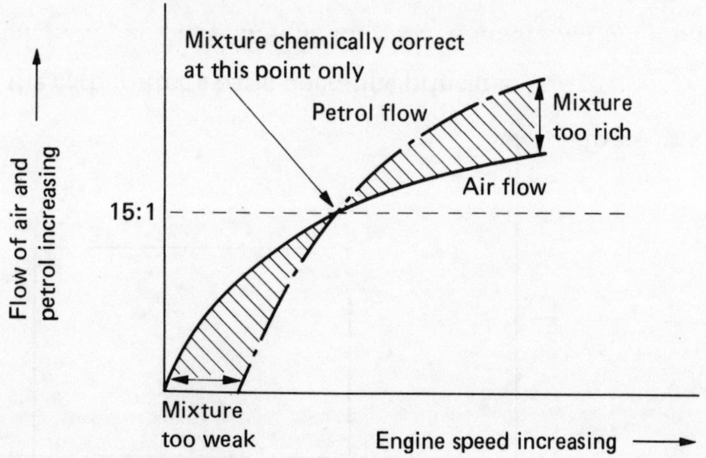

At low speeds the mixture strength would be ..........................................

At high speed the mixture strength would be ..........................................

## A4:10 MIXTURE COMPENSATION FIXED-CHOKE CARBURETTOR

To overcome the operating characteristics of the simple-jet system some form of compensation must be used to give satisfactory mixture control on a variable-speed engine.

The purpose of compensation is ..........................................

.................................................................................................

.................................................................................................

## A4:11 AIR BLEED SYSTEM

Examine a Solex type carburettor similar to that shown below and complete the drawing by adding the air correction jet and the emulsion tube. Indicate also the petrol level in the system.

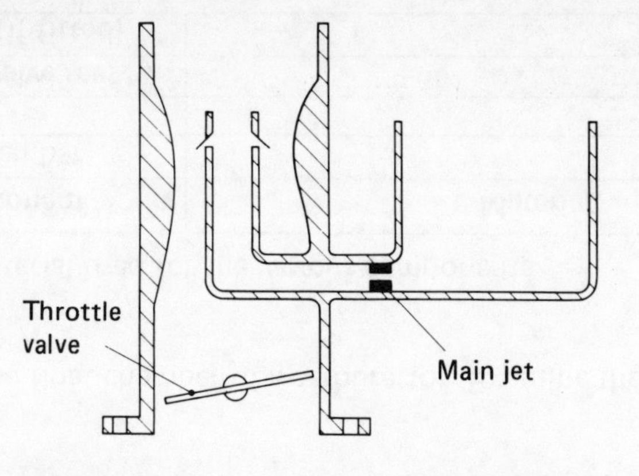


State the principle of operation of the air bleed system.

.................................................................................................

.................................................................................................

.................................................................................................

.................................................................................................

.................................................................................................

.................................................................................................

.................................................................................................

.................................................................................................

.................................................................................................

.................................................................................................

.................................................................................................

.................................................................................................

.................................................................................................

# SLOW RUNNING

To allow the engine to run at low speeds, it is necessary to use a mixture supply system which is completely separate from the main (and compensating) system. Why?

........................................................................................................................

........................................................................................................................

........................................................................................................................

........................................................................................................................

The fuel is usually supplied via an orifice situated at the edge of the throttle butterfly as shown below.

Complete the sketch to show a Solex slow running system. Add the idling air bleed jet, pilot jet and volume control screw. Indicate the air/fuel mixture flow and name the arrowed parts.

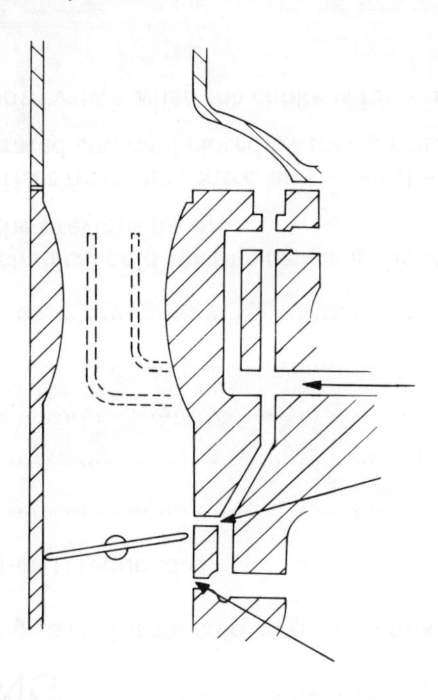

The operating principle of the slow running system is that

........................................................................................................................

........................................................................................................................

........................................................................................................................

........................................................................................................................

Why is a progression hole (or jet) necessary

........................................................................................................................

........................................................................................................................

........................................................................................................................

........................................................................................................................

........................................................................................................................

........................................................................................................................

........................................................................................................................

........................................................................................................................

........................................................................................................................

**Investigation**

Inspect a Solex carburettor similar to the one shown and if possible adjust the slow running on a similar carburettor.

Label on the drawing:

1. The throttle stop and volume control screw.

2. The cold start mechanism, including choke flap.

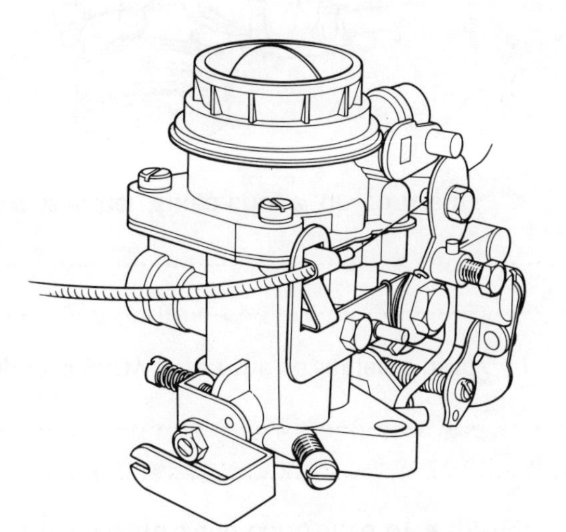

A4:15,17

# COLD STARTING

When the engine is being started from cold a very rich mixture is required.

The reason why extra fuel is required is:

..............................................................................................

..............................................................................................

..............................................................................................

..............................................................................................

..............................................................................................

The most common mechanical cold starting device is the strangler valve as shown below (and on the previous page).

The strangler valve is offset from the centre, and when the spindle is allowed to turn the valve is operated and held closed by spring pressure.

Show the position of both valves when the choke is fully operated.

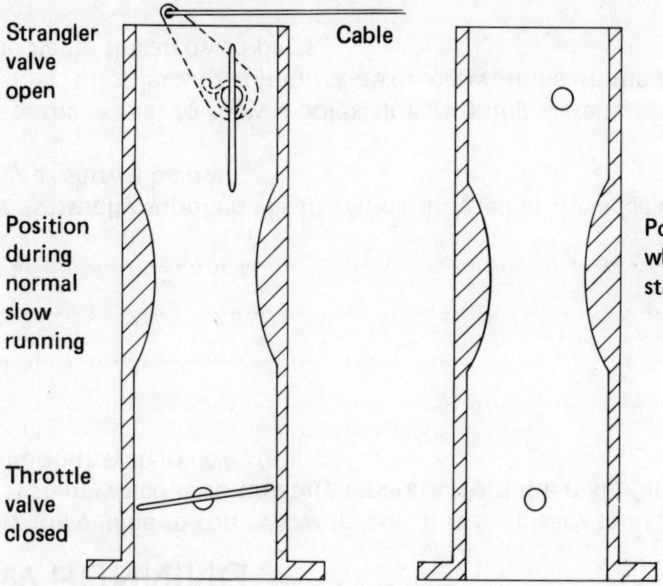

Strangler valve open

Cable

Position during normal slow running

Position when starting

Throttle valve closed

Why is the strangler valve offset from centre and controlled by a spring?

..............................................................................................

..............................................................................................

Why is the throttle made to open slightly when the strangler is used?

..............................................................................................

..............................................................................................

A4:18 Identify the carburettors below as either 'fixed choke' or 'constant depression' types.

..............................

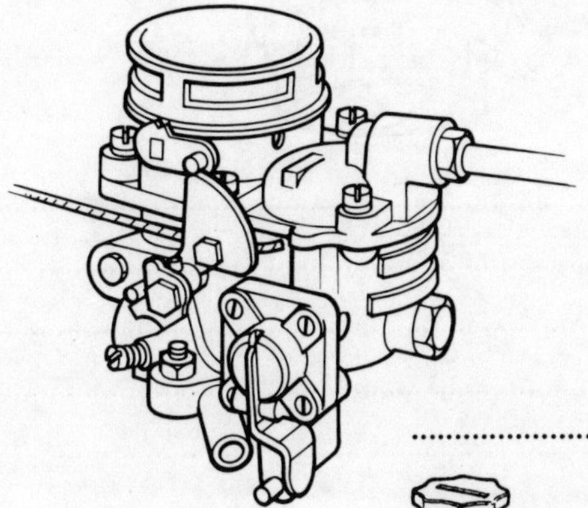

..............................

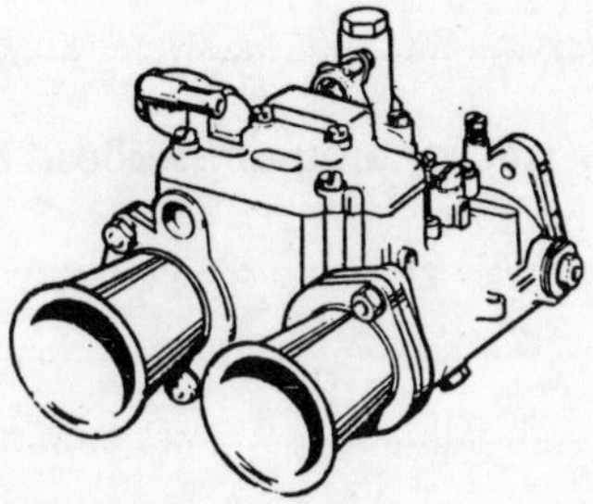

..............................

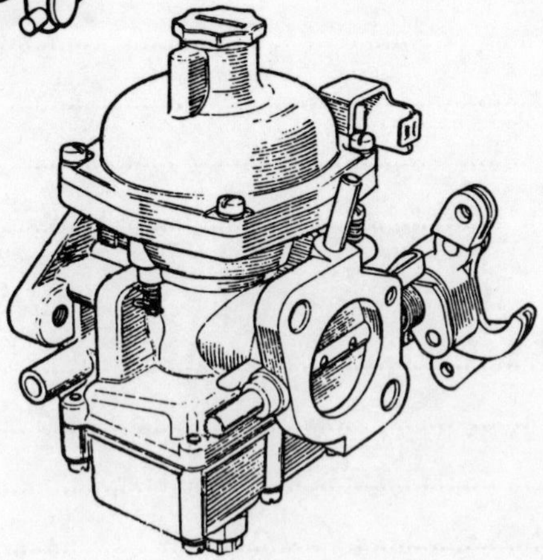

..............................

# CONSTANT VACUUM (DEPRESSION) CARBURETTOR

A4:19–21

A fixed-choke carburettor requires a main and compensating system, and a slow-running system containing many jets to maintain a fuel supply that is in step with the constant changing vacuum in the venturi as the engine alters speed. Variable-choke carburettors avoid this by altering the size of the venturi, according to the air flow.

Why is this type known as a constant-depression carburettor?

.................................................................................................................

.................................................................................................................

Why is no mixture compensation or correction necessary?

.................................................................................................................

.................................................................................................................

.................................................................................................................

.................................................................................................................

.................................................................................................................

Explain the carburettor's operation as the throttle is opened.

.................................................................................................................

.................................................................................................................

.................................................................................................................

.................................................................................................................

.................................................................................................................

.................................................................................................................

.................................................................................................................

.................................................................................................................

.................................................................................................................

The simplified sketch shows a constant-depression carburettor. The piston assembly and throttle valve are in the positions occupied when the engine is idling.

Name the arrowed parts.

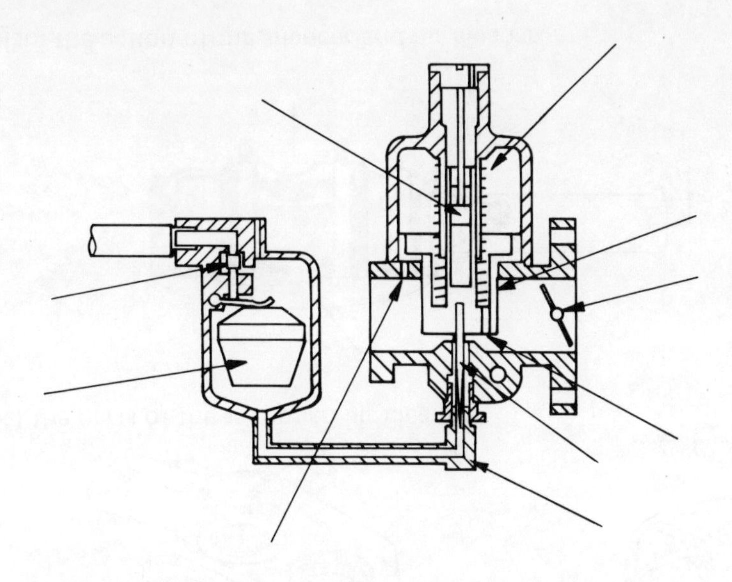

It is possible to lift the piston without opening the throttle valve. Why will that cause the mixture strength to weaken?

.................................................................................................................

A4:22

Ideally one carburettor should be used for each cylinder as is done with some racing cars. The compromise, however, is to use twin carburettors on 4 and 6 cylinder engines which allows a better fuel distribution due to the improved manifold design.

The main advantages of multi-carburation are:

.................................................................................................................

.................................................................................................................

.................................................................................................................

## A4:23,24 MANIFOLDS

The inlet manifold directs the flow of mixture into the cylinders and the exhaust manifold conducts the burnt gas from the cylinders to the exhaust system.

Why is some form of heating of the inlet manifold considered necessary?

..........................................................................................

..........................................................................................

**Investigation**

Examine engines with manifold arrangements similar to those shown below and note the method of heating the inlet manifold around the carburettor base.

..........................................................................................

..........................................................................................

..........................................................................................

..........................................................................................

..........................................................................................

Uniflow engine (Ford)

..........................................................................................

..........................................................................................

..........................................................................................

..........................................................................................

..........................................................................................

Crossflow engine (Ford)

## A4:25 AIR CLEANER—SILENCER

Most modern air cleaner–silencers are of the paper element type; an alternative is the oil-without wire mesh type.

Identify the air cleaners shown.

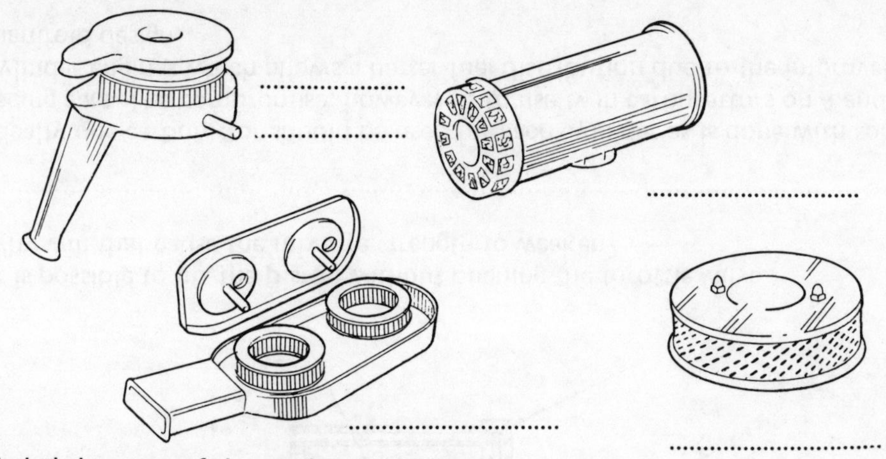

..........................................................................................

..........................................................................................

..........................................................................................

..........................................................................................

Label the parts of the sectioned air cleaner.

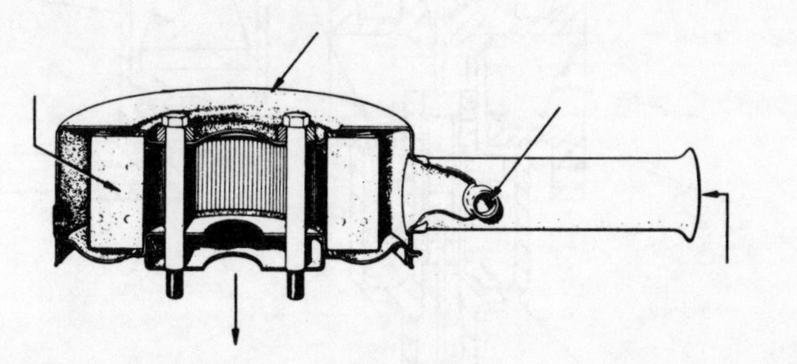

Explain the action of the silencer and air cleaner.

..........................................................................................

..........................................................................................

..........................................................................................

..........................................................................................

# FUEL PUMPS

Identify the type of fuel pumps shown. Name the arrowed parts.

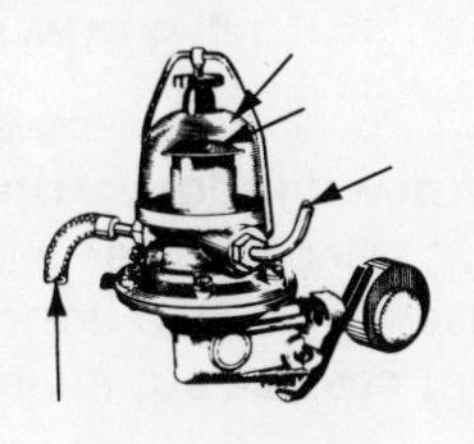

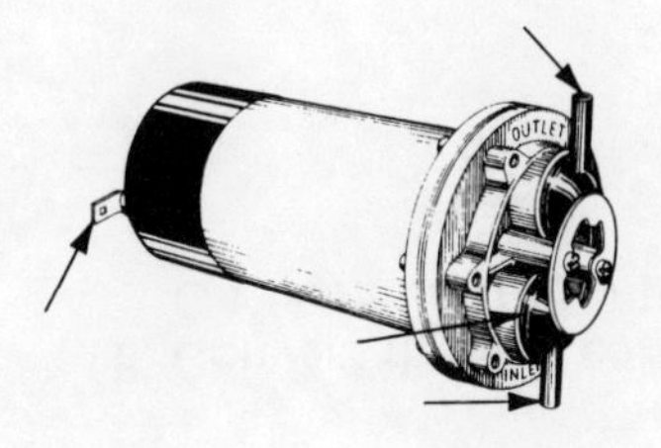


# MECHANICAL FUEL PUMP

State the basic operation of the fuel pump shown.
Indicate the flow of fuel through the pump.

........................................................

........................................................

........................................................

........................................................

........................................................

........................................................

........................................................

........................................................

........................................................

........................................................

........................................................

........................................................

........................................................

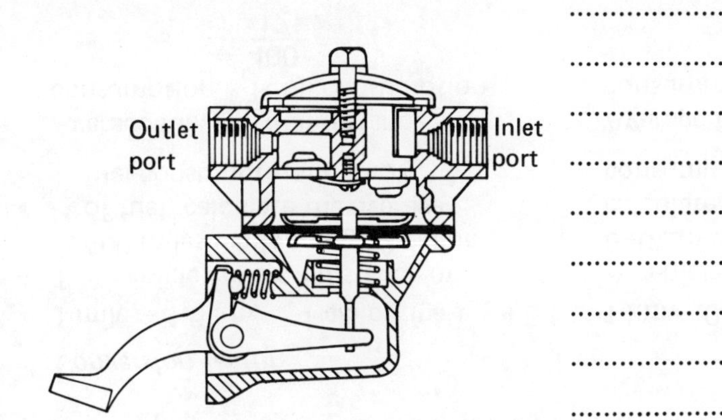


What occurs when the carburettor is full?

........................................................

........................................................

........................................................

## Investigation

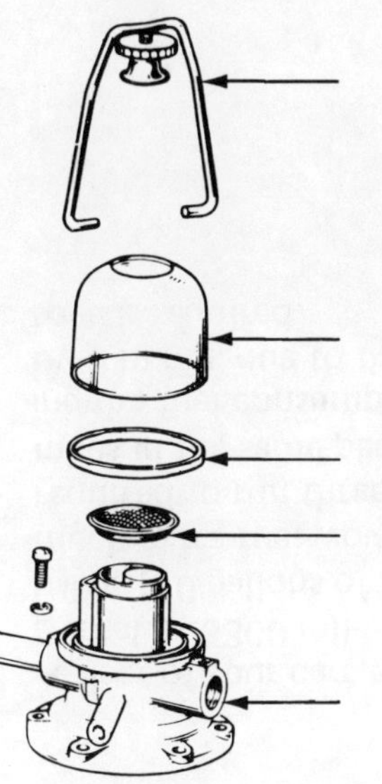

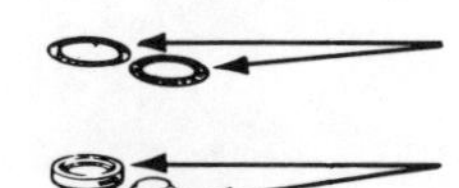

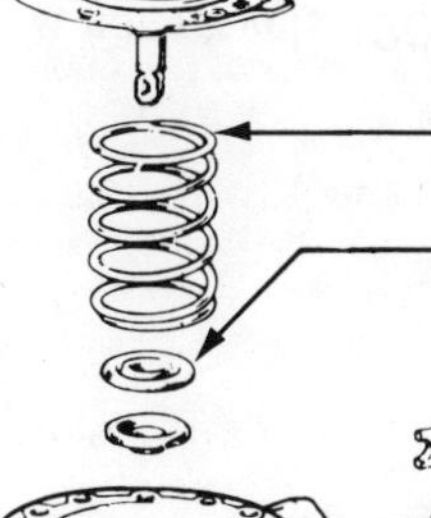

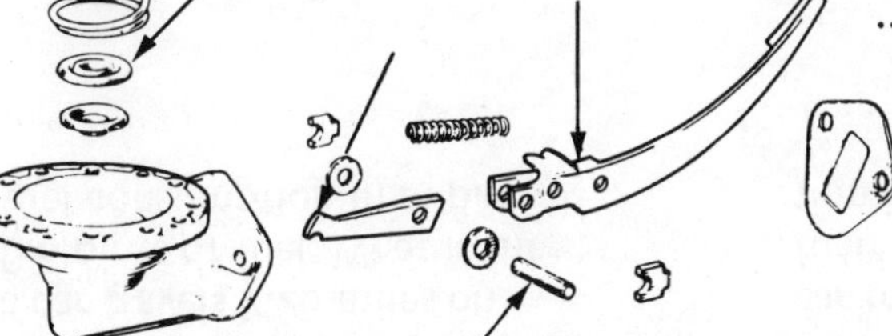

Dismantle a pump similar to the one shown.
Name the parts arrowed on the drawing.

Type of pump dismantled:

........................................................

From what was the bowl gasket made?

........................................................

How were the valves held in the upper body?

........................................................

........................................................

........................................................

........................................................

........................................................

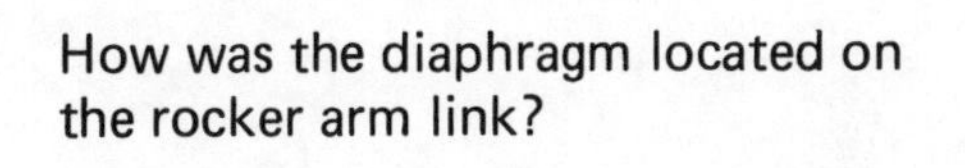

How was the diaphragm located on the rocker arm link?

........................................................

........................................................

........................................................

........................................................

........................................................

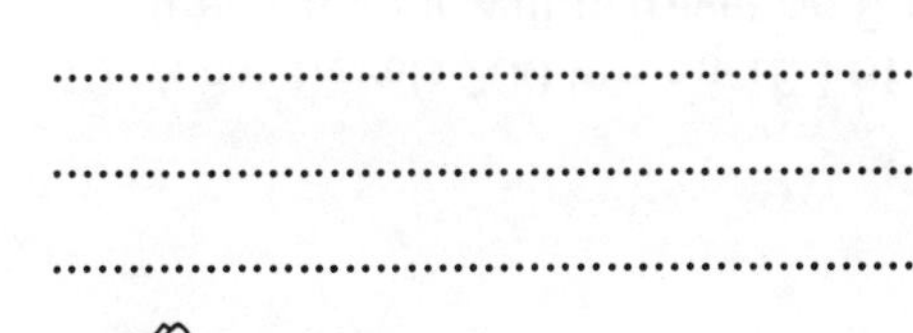

# FUEL CONSUMPTION PROBLEMS

When calculating the fuel consumption of a vehicle it is usual to obtain the value in miles per gallon (m.p.g.).
The alternative system used on the Continent is kilometres/litre or litres/100 km.
Since this dual system is likely to continue indefinitely the problems on this page have been designed to include British and Continental practice.

*Conversion factors*

1 mile ≏ 1.6 km    1 gallon (gal) ≏ 4.5 l    1 km ≏ 0.625 miles    1 l ≏ 0.22 gal

1. A vehicle covers a distance of 400 miles while using 12 gallons of fuel, calculate the average fuel consumption in m.p.g.

$$\text{Average fuel consumption} = \frac{\text{Total distance}}{\text{Total consumption}} = \frac{400}{12}$$

= ................

2. A vehicle covers a distance of 640 km while using 54 l of fuel, calculate the average fuel consumption in km/l.

$$\text{Average fuel consumption} = \frac{\text{Total distance}}{\text{Total consumption}} = \frac{640}{54}$$

= .............

3. A vehicle covers a distance of 700 miles while using 30 gallons of fuel. Calculate the average fuel consumption in m.p.g.

4. Convert the values in Q3 to km and l and calculate the average fuel consumption in km/l.

5. Calculate the average fuel consumption over a 10-week period when a vehicle covers 2400 miles. The driver tops up with fuel as follows:

2 times with 8 gal =
5 times with 6 gal =
5 times with 5 gal =
3 times with 3 gal =

6. Convert the fuel consumption in Q4 from km/l to l/100 km.

7. During a fuel consumption test a car travels 2.25 miles on 0.5 pints of fuel. What is the fuel consumption in m.p.g.

8. During a fuel consumption test a car travels 3.2 km on 0.25 l of fuel. What is the fuel consumption in l/100 km.

9. A car travels 120 miles on 4.5 gallons of fuel, how far will it travel on 8 gallons.

10. A car travels 200 km on 16 l of fuel, how far will it travel on 9 l.

11. A fleet of four cars travel a total of 3300 miles in one week, using 110 gallons of fuel. How much extra fuel would be required to run three cars 3000 miles in the same period assuming the fuel consumptions increase by 5 m.p.g. due to the increased speeds required.

12. A car travels 110 miles on 4 gallons of fuel. What distance (in km) will it travel on 12 l of fuel.

# A5.

# Engine Electrical System

A5: 1,2,3,6

# IGNITION SYSTEM

The coil-ignition system must provide, at a precise time, a high voltage spark that will jump the plug gap inside the combustion chamber and ignite the compressed mixture.

The system may be considered to be made up of two parts:

1. Low-tension (primary) circuit—LT

2. High-tension (secondary) circuit—HT

..........................................................................................

..........................................................................................

..........................................................................................

..........................................................................................

..........................................................................................

..........................................................................................

..........................................................................................

..........................................................................................

..........................................................................................

..........................................................................................

..........................................................................................

..........................................................................................

..........................................................................................

..........................................................................................

..........................................................................................

What is the firing order of the system shown opposite, if the rotor turns anticlockwise?..........................................................................

Name the main parts of the simple coil-ignition system shown and identify the primary and secondary circuits leads.

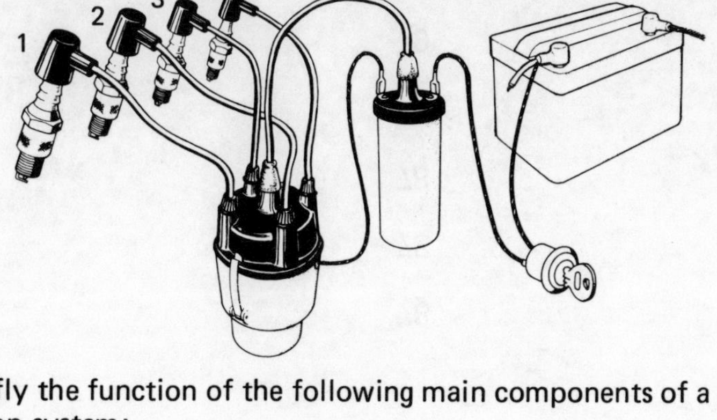


State briefly the function of the following main components of a coil-ignition system:

Battery

..........................................................................................

..........................................................................................

Ignition switch

..........................................................................................

..........................................................................................

Coil

..........................................................................................

..........................................................................................

Distributor

..........................................................................................

..........................................................................................

Sparking plugs

..........................................................................................

..........................................................................................

A5: 5

**Investigation**

Examine a coil-ignition system.

From observations complete the wiring diagrams opposite and list, in order, the main component parts through which the current in both primary and secondary circuits passes.

| Primary circuit | Secondary circuit |
|---|---|
| Battery | Coil |
| | |
| | |
| | |
| | |
| | |

A5: 4

# IGNITION COIL OUTPUT

The primary winding of the ignition coil is supplied at battery voltage (12 V) with a current of about 3 A. This supply builds up a magnetic field around both the primary and secondary coil windings.

Explain what happens to the output, when the distributor contact breaker points are opened.

..................................................................................................

..................................................................................................

..................................................................................................

..................................................................................................

..................................................................................................

..................................................................................................

Pictorial diagram

Sketch a rotor in the centre of the distributor cap, show its direction of rotation and state the firing order. Sketch in cables as appropriate.

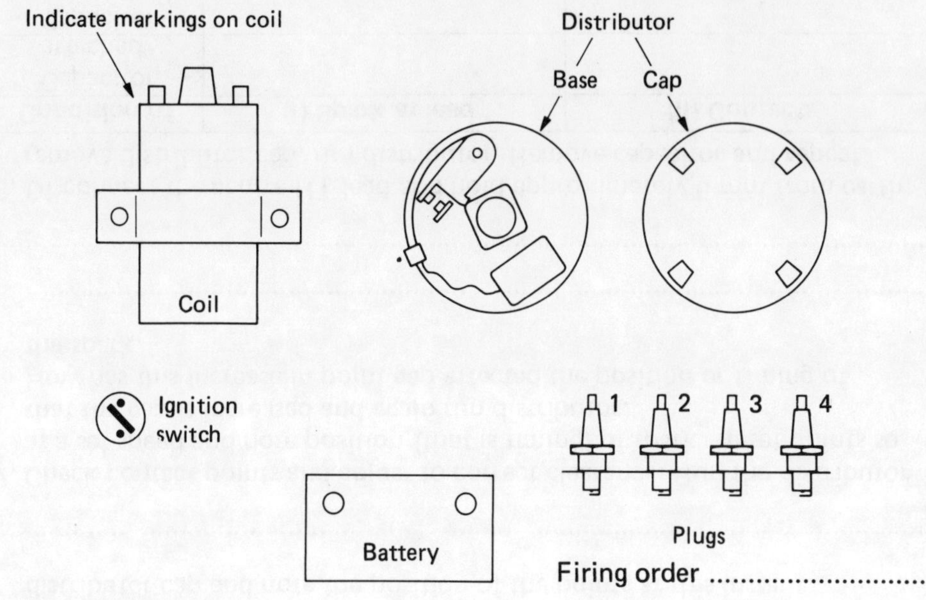


Theoretical diagram

Complete the diagram and identify the basic symbols shown.

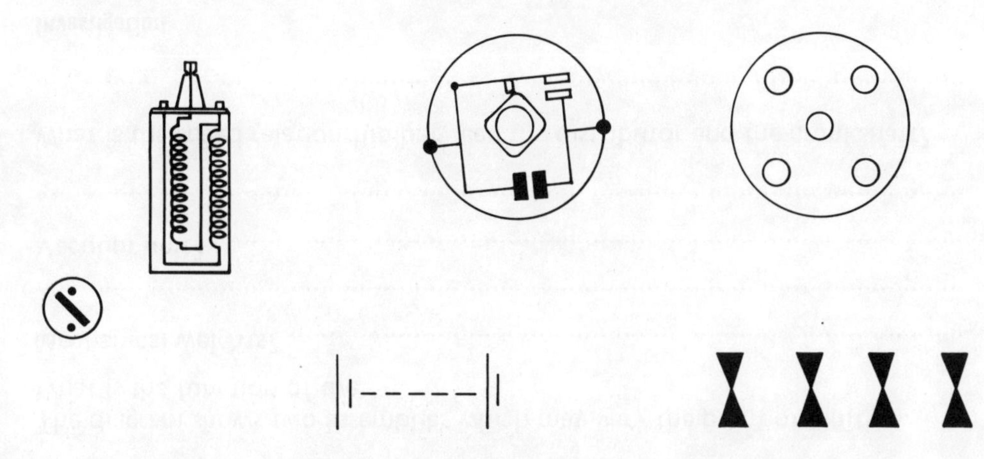

# DISTRIBUTOR

Name the main parts of the distributor unit shown.

For what type of engine would this unit be suitable? ....................................

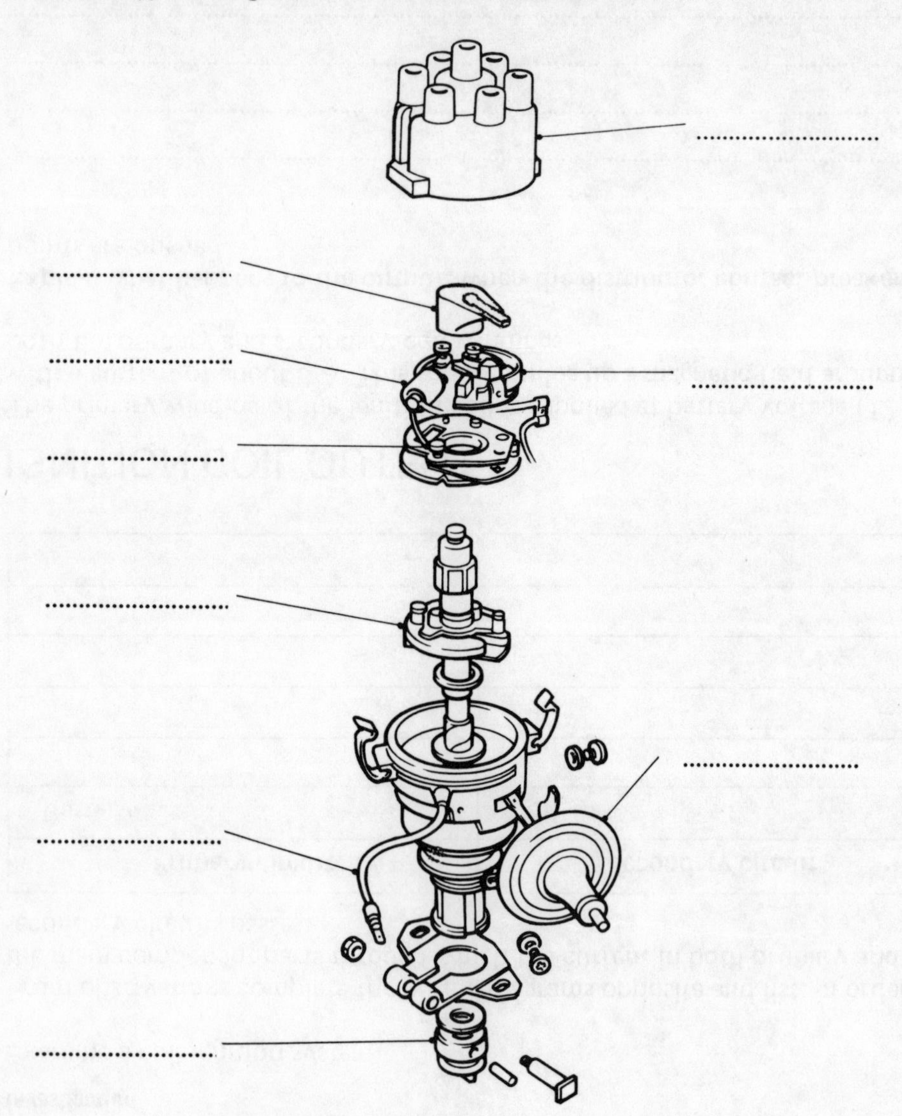

The diagram shows two assemblies which may vary the point of ignition.
What is the function of the:

Mechanical weights? ....................................................................................

..............................................................................................................

Vacuum unit? .............................................................................................

..............................................................................................................

What is the speed relationship between the distributor and the crankshaft?

..............................................................................................................

**Investigation**

Examine a coil-ignition system fitted to a distributor test unit.

1. Turn the distributor very slowly until the spark occurs. Remove the distributor cap and note the position of the points at this instant.

..............................................................................................................

2. Check contact points and adjust to correct clearance. Run the distributor at a set speed and note position (that is timing) of spark. Reset points so that the gap is increased and again run distributor.
How has this increase in point gap affected the position or timing of the spark.

..............................................................................................................

..............................................................................................................

3. Disconnect the centre HT lead and hold approximately 5 mm from earth, remove distributor cap, run distributor. Remove capacitor and repeat.

| Condition of | (i) Spark at lead | (ii) Contacts |
|---|---|---|
| Capacitor attached | | |
| Capacitor removed | | |

The function of the capacitor is:

..............................................................................................................

# SPARK PLUG AND IGNITION LEADS

Name the parts of the spark plug shown below:

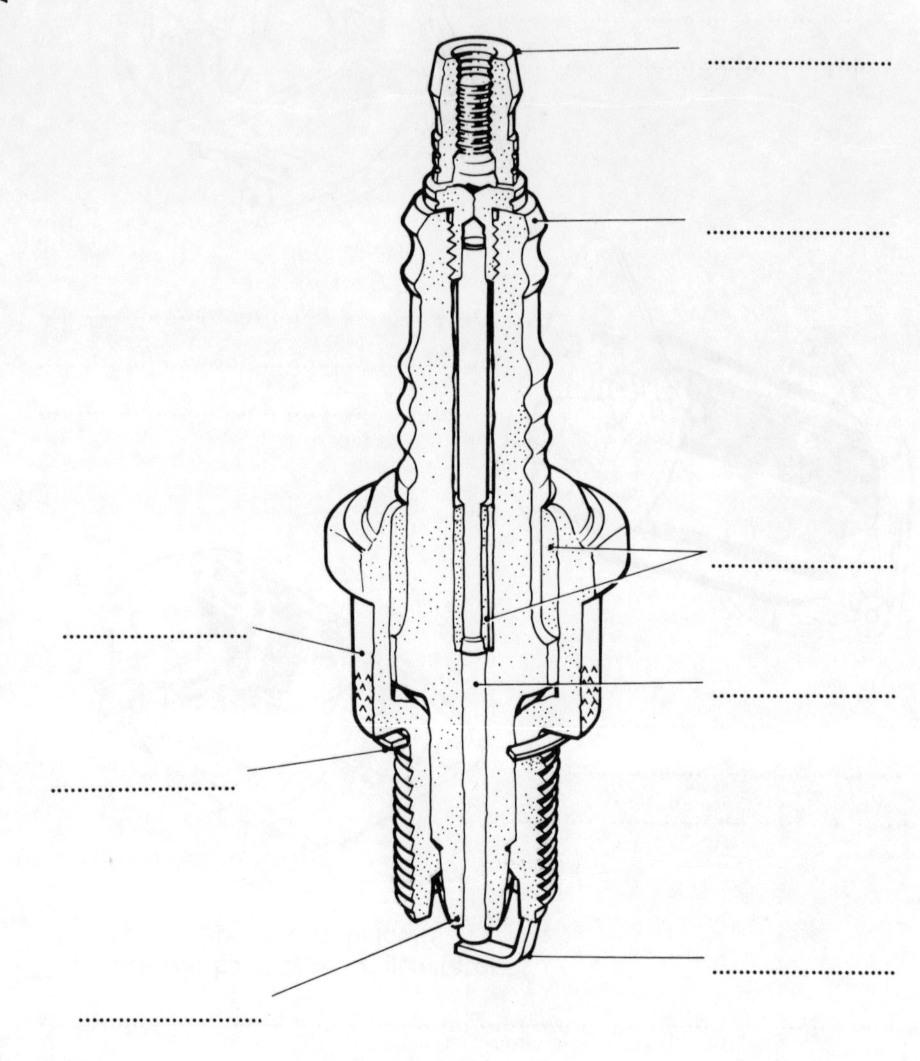

Indicate the plug diameter and gap.

The spark plug consists of a centre metal electrode which passes through a form of ceramic insulator. The lower part of the insulator is fixed to a metal case which screws into the cylinder head. This case forms the earth to the engine.

At normal atmospheric pressure the plug will readily spark with little voltage, but when in the running engine the voltage requirement may progressively increase, for example over a period it can rise from 7000 V to 15 000 V. State four factors affecting the voltage requirement of the plug:

1. ..........................................................................................

2. ..........................................................................................

3. ..........................................................................................

4. ..........................................................................................

What may cause a spark plug to foul and not spark?

1. ..........................................................................................

2. ..........................................................................................

3. ..........................................................................................

4. ..........................................................................................

List the routine maintenance that should be given to a spark plug:

1. ..........................................................................................

2. ..........................................................................................

3. ..........................................................................................

4. ..........................................................................................

Examine spark plug leads.
Two types of lead are commonly used. In one type the centre core is made of stranded wire.
What is used as the core of the second type of lead?

..........................................................................................

..........................................................................................

Both types are highly insulated. Why is this? ..........................................

..........................................................................................

# GENERATORS

The basic operation of a generator is to:

..............................................................................................

There are two basic types of generator.
Identify the types shown below.

..............................................................................................

..............................................................................................

..............................................................................................

What is the basic mechanical difference between a dynamo and alternator?
Examine various units.

..............................................................................................

..............................................................................................

..............................................................................................

..............................................................................................

..............................................................................................

The alternator has superseded the dynamo but there are still many dynamos in use.
What advantages does the alternator have when compared with the dynamo?

..............................................................................................

..............................................................................................

..............................................................................................

..............................................................................................

..............................................................................................

..............................................................................................

Although the alternator has these advantages missuse can cause instant failure.
What special care must be taken when fitting or removing an alternator or generally working on the vehicle?

..............................................................................................

..............................................................................................

..............................................................................................

..............................................................................................

..............................................................................................

..............................................................................................

..............................................................................................

..............................................................................................

# RECTIFICATION AND CONTROL

Both the dynamo and alternator produce alternating current and convert it to direct current.

This conversion is called ..........................................

The method by which the direct current is produced in the two machines is quite different.

Name the arrowed parts on both drawings and state the method of rectification.

Dynamo rectification

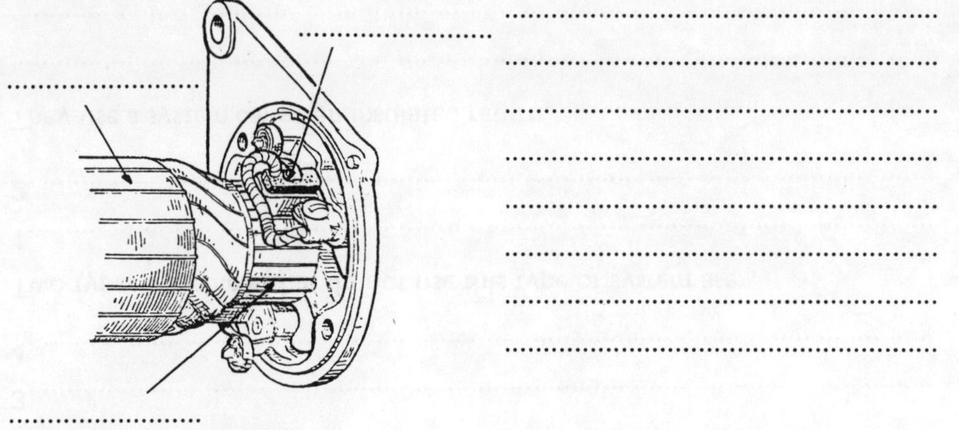

Alternator rectification

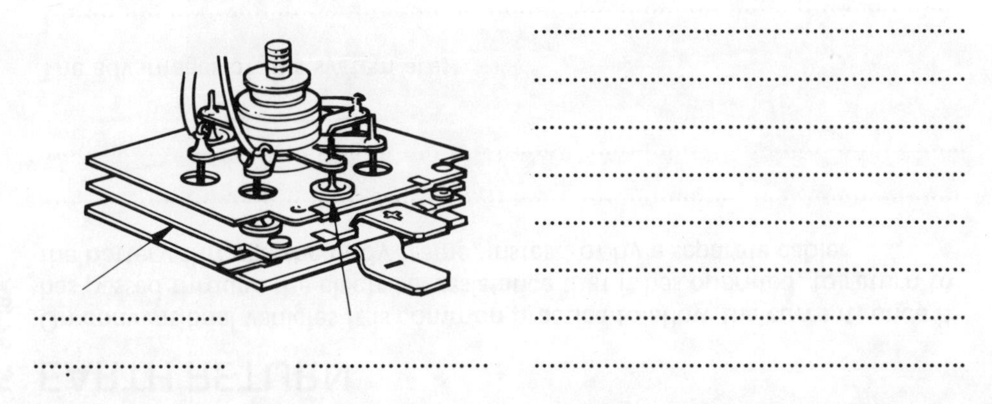

Both the dynamo and alternator need some form of current–voltage control. The unit that provides this control is the regulator.

What is the regulator's basic function?

..........................................

Fitted in the dynamo's control box is a cut-out. Why does the dynamo require such a unit?

..........................................

A control box for a dynamo includes:

1. ..............

2. ..............

3. ..............

The control unit for an alternator is a ..........................................

This contains ..............

A cut-out control is not required because:

..........................................

# EARTH RETURN

On conventional vehicles it is common practice to allow the current, once it has passed through the electrical resistance that it has operated, to return to the battery through the body frame, instead of by a separate cable.

...

...

The advantages of this system are:

1. ...
2. ...
3. ...
4. ...

Two types of vehicle that do not use this type of system are:

1. ...
2. ...

They use a system called an insulated return.

...

...

...

The system is used because ...

...

# STARTER MOTOR

Starter motors fitted to cars are usually one of the two types shown. What is the purpose of the starter motor?

...

...

Starter cables are of a heavy-duty type and they should be as short and of as large a cross section as possible. What is the reason for this?

...

...

Examine starter motors of the types shown and identify the arrowed parts.

Type (I)

...

Type (II)

...

Explain the mechanical operation of:

Type (I) ...

...

...

...

Type (II) ...

...

...

...

...

A5: 29–31

This diagram shows the components in an inertia-engaged starter circuit.

Sketch in the appropriate wiring, indicate which components need to be earthed and distinguish between the different types of cables.

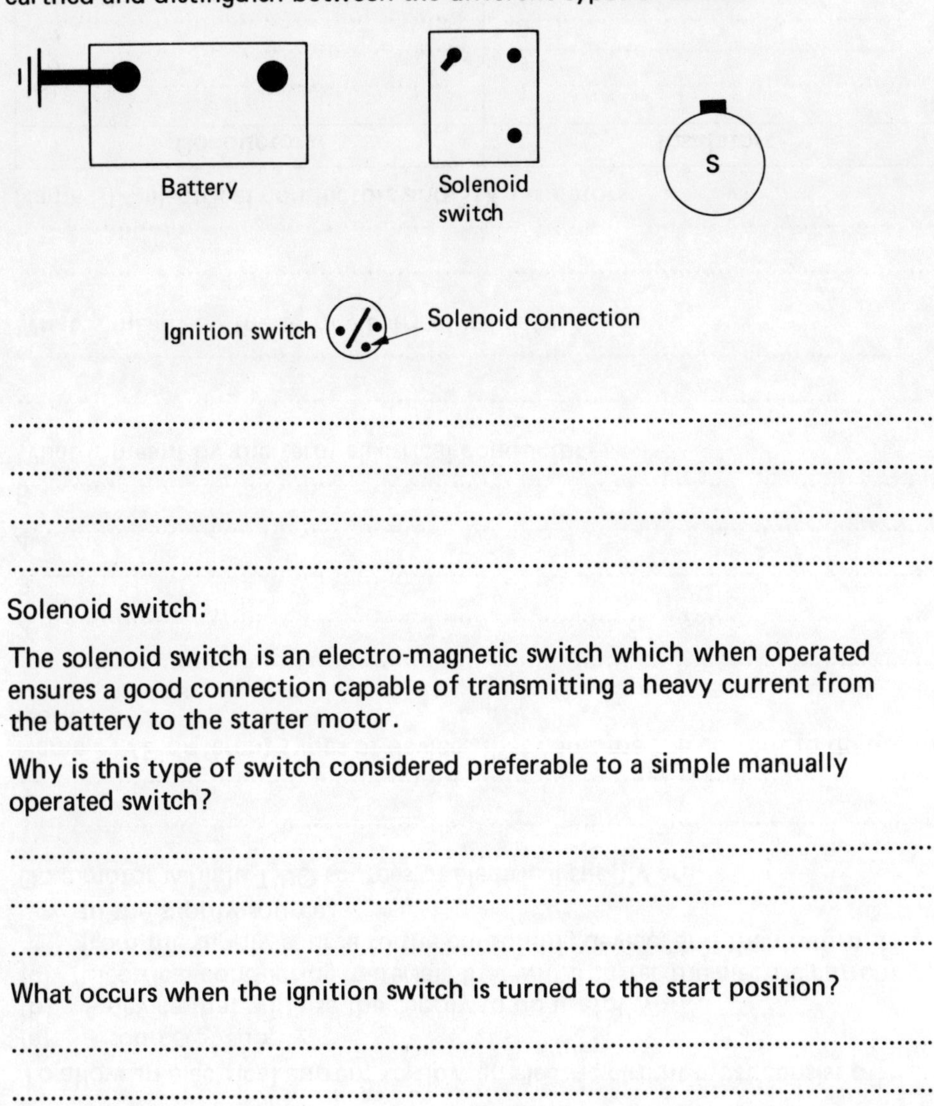


....................................................................................................

....................................................................................................

....................................................................................................

....................................................................................................

Solenoid switch:

The solenoid switch is an electro-magnetic switch which when operated ensures a good connection capable of transmitting a heavy current from the battery to the starter motor.

Why is this type of switch considered preferable to a simple manually operated switch?

....................................................................................................

....................................................................................................

....................................................................................................

What occurs when the ignition switch is turned to the start position?

....................................................................................................

....................................................................................................

....................................................................................................

**Investigation**

Examine a starter-motor circuit on a vehicle.

If possible use an induction ammeter to check the current flow when starting. (This type of ammeter simply clips around the cable.)

Examine the layout and answer the following questions.

Vehicle make .............................. Model ........................................

Type of starter motor ..............................................................................

Examine the cables and measure their diameters.

Cable diameter, battery to solenoid ......................................................

Cable diameter, ignition switch to solenoid ............................................

Why are the diameters different?...........................................................

....................................................................................................

State the position of the earth strap(s)

....................................................................................................

Why is the earth strap(s) required.........................................................

....................................................................................................

Clamp the ammeter on the cable between the battery and the solenoid switch.

Disconnect lead from ignition switch to coil (at the coil). This will prevent the engine from starting.

Operate starter motor:

State (i) the amount of current flowing ..........................................

(ii) the starter-motor direction of rotation ..........................................

Why is a normal ammeter not connected into the starter-motor circuit?

....................................................................................................

....................................................................................................

....................................................................................................

A5: 32–35

# ELECTRICAL CURRENT FLOW

To allow an electrical current to flow an electric circuit must consist of:

(a) A source of supply.
(b) A device that will use the supply to do useful work.
(c) Electrical conducting materials that will transfer the electric current from the supply source to the consuming device, and then return it to the supply source.

On a motor vehicle TWO sources of electrical supply are:

1. ..................................................

2. ..................................................

Name FIVE different types of devices that consume the current to do useful work:

1. ..................................................

2. ..................................................

3. ..................................................

4. ..................................................

5. ..................................................

What is meant by the term electrical conductor?

..................................................

..................................................

What is meant by the term electrical insulator?

..................................................

..................................................

Name SIX electrical conductors and SIX insulators:

| Conductors | Insulators |
|---|---|
| 1. .................... | 1. .................... |
| 2. .................... | 2. .................... |
| 3. .................... | 3. .................... |
| 4. .................... | 4. .................... |
| 5. .................... | 5. .................... |
| 6. .................... | 6. .................... |

# SHORT AND OPEN CIRCUITS

Two simple light circuits are shown, one is an open circuit, the other has a short circuit.
Identify, giving reasons for choice.

The circuit .................... The circuit ....................

.................... ....................

.................... ....................

What could be a probable cause and effect of the short circuit?

..................................................

..................................................

..................................................

# MAGNETS — LINES OF FORCE

Magnets act through lines of force. These lines of force stretch between the ends of a magnet and create a magnetic field. The two ends of a magnet are called .................... One end being the .................... and the other the .................... .

Using small bar magnets, a sheet of paper and iron filings, show the effects of the lines of force when the magnets are held in the positions shown.

A [n s] B [n s] [n s] C [s n] [n s]

The effects created by the magnets lead to the statements:

Like magnetic poles .................... Shown by sketch ....................

Unlike magnetic poles .................... Shown by sketch ....................

# PERMANENT AND ELECTRO-MAGNETS

There are two forms of magnets, permanent and electro-magnets.
What is the difference between a permanent and an electro-magnet?

........................................................................................................................

........................................................................................................................

........................................................................................................................

These two forms of magnetism lead to the important relationship between magnetism and electricity:

........................................................................................................................

........................................................................................................................

**Investigation**

To produce an electro-magnet:
Equipment
- Coil of insulated wire and iron bar suitable for passing through centre of coil
- Resistance
- Battery
- Screwdriver or bar for checking magnetism

Show sketch of apparatus used.

*Tests*

1. Test bar for magnetism
2. Pass current through coil
3. Test bar for magnetism
4. Attempt to pull bar out of coil. Switch off current.
5. Test bar for magnetism.

Effects of test were:

1. ..................................................
2. ..................................................
3. ..................................................
4. ..................................................
5. ..................................................

What forms the basic construction of an electro-magnetic?

........................................................................................................................

The core of the electro-magnet may be moving as shown or stationary (for example the ignition coil). In either case it is made from soft iron. Why is such a material used?

........................................................................................................................

........................................................................................................................

........................................................................................................................

........................................................................................................................

List FOUR motor vehicle components where an electro-magnet which produces movement is used.

1. ..................................................................................................................
2. ..................................................................................................................
3. ..................................................................................................................
4. ..................................................................................................................

# CONSTRUCTION OF A SOLENOID

The solenoid used for starter motor operation is a heavy duty type of electro-magnetic switch. With the aid of the sectioned sketch below describe the basic construction and operation of a solenoid switch.

..................................................

..................................................

..................................................

..................................................

..................................................

..................................................

..................................................

..................................................

..................................................

..................................................

# A6.

# Compression-Ignition Engines

A6: 1, 3, 5

# FOUR-STROKE CYCLE

The actual strokes, induction, compression, power and exhaust are exactly the same as in the spark-ignition engine.
The operating principle is, however, slightly different.

.................................................................................................

.................................................................................................

.................................................................................................

.................................................................................................

.................................................................................................

.................................................................................................

.................................................................................................

.................................................................................................

.................................................................................................

.................................................................................................

.................................................................................................

.................................................................................................

.................................................................................................

.................................................................................................

List the main operational differences of the compression-ignition engine when compared with the spark-ignition engine.

.................................................................................................

.................................................................................................

.................................................................................................

.................................................................................................

.................................................................................................

.................................................................................................

.................................................................................................

**Investigation**

Examine and compare the basic components of a spark-ignition and compression-ignition engine of similar size.

| Component | Ways in which compression ignition engine components differ from typical spark ignition engine components |
|---|---|
| Piston | ............................................<br>............................................ |
| Connecting Rod | ............................................<br>............................................ |
| Crankshaft | ............................................<br>............................................ |
| Cylinder Block | ............................................<br>............................................ |

Sketch within the outline of the cylinder shown, a typical piston in approximately the correct position for the events depicted. Indicate the shape of the combustion space and the number of piston rings.

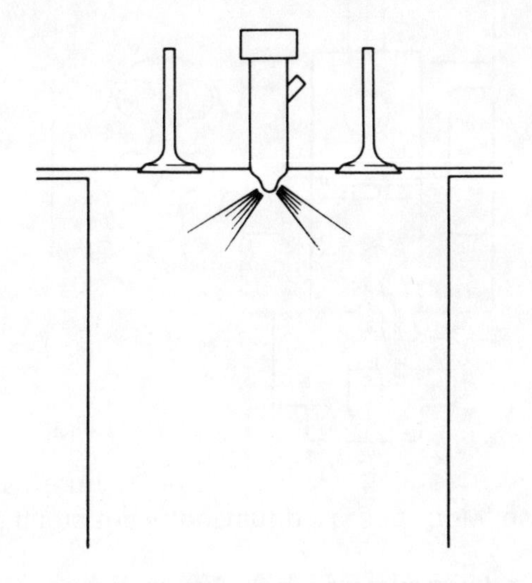

A6: 2

# COMPRESSION-IGNITION ENGINE

## ADVANTAGES

The compression-ignition engine has certain advantages when compared with the spark-ignition engine. List the main advantages.

A6: 4

## TWO-STROKE CYCLE

As with the four-stroke compression-ignition cycle, initially air only enters the cylinder.

In order to complete the cycle in two strokes the air must be forced into the cylinder by means of a pressure charger.

It is usual that air induction is through ports and exhaust by either ports or poppet valves.

Two alternative methods of arranging the pistons and ports are shown below.

On both drawings name the important parts and show, using arrows, the air flow through the system.

Fig. 1

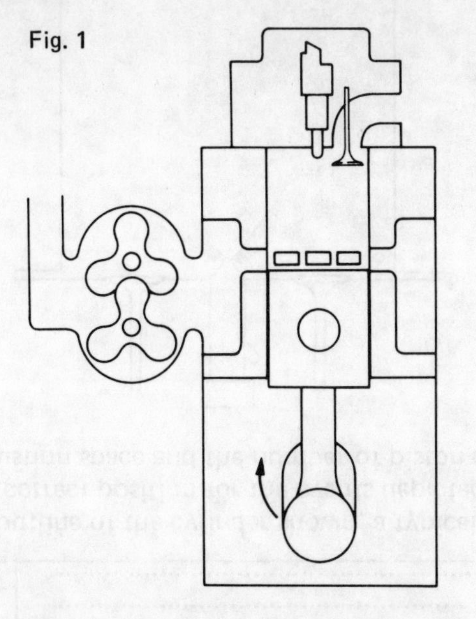

General Motors two-stroke compression-ignition engine.

Fig. 2

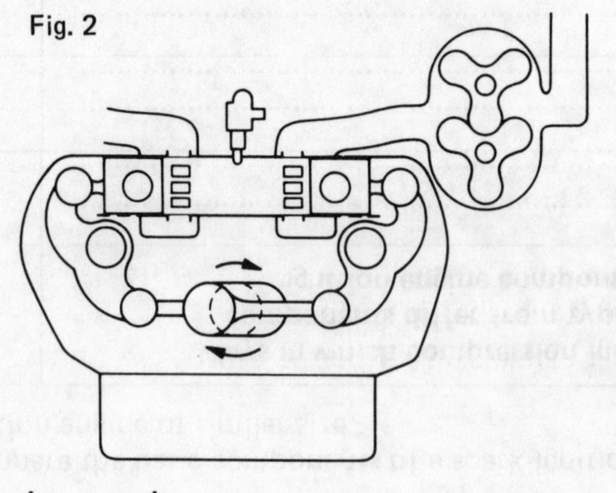

Commer opposed-piston engine.

## A6: 7 FUEL SYSTEM LAYOUT

The fuel system for the compression-ignition engine comprises:

Tank, pipelines, lift pump, filters, injection pump and injectors. Examine a vehicle fitted with a compression-ignition engine and add the fuel system components to the sketch below. Name the important parts.

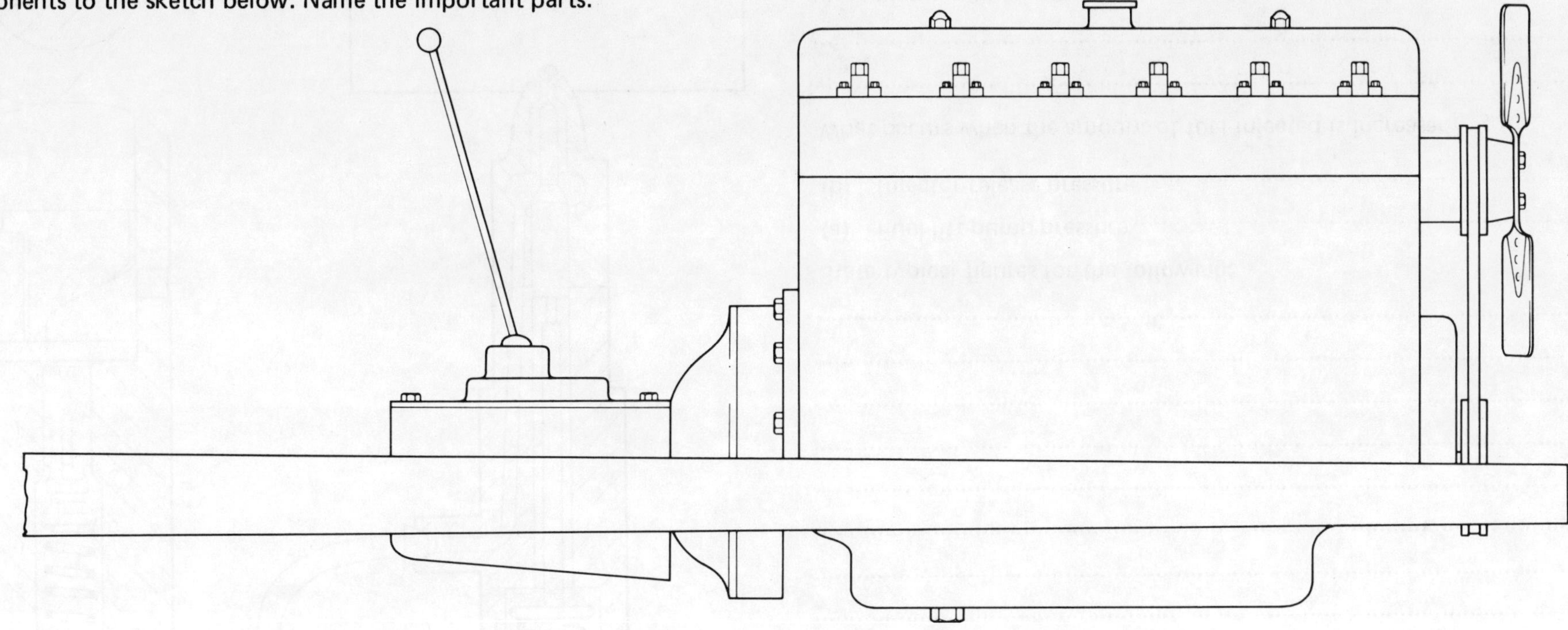

Inspect the pipelines and note whether there is a difference between the pipe from the tank to the lift pump and from the injection pump to the injectors. If so, state what the difference is, and why.

.............................................................................................................

.............................................................................................................

.............................................................................................................

State how the fuel tank is mounted.

.............................................................................................................

## A6: 6 FUEL FILTRATION

From the examination of the layout it will be found that there are more fuel filters or that they are larger than those of a petrol fuel system.

Why is a better fuel filteration system necessary?

.............................................................................................................

.............................................................................................................

.............................................................................................................

.............................................................................................................

A6: 8,11

# SINGLE-ELEMENT PUMP OPERATION

Add to this simplified diagram of an injector pump and injector, the names of the important parts; indicate the direction of fuel flow and show the type of spray pattern that the injector is likely to give.

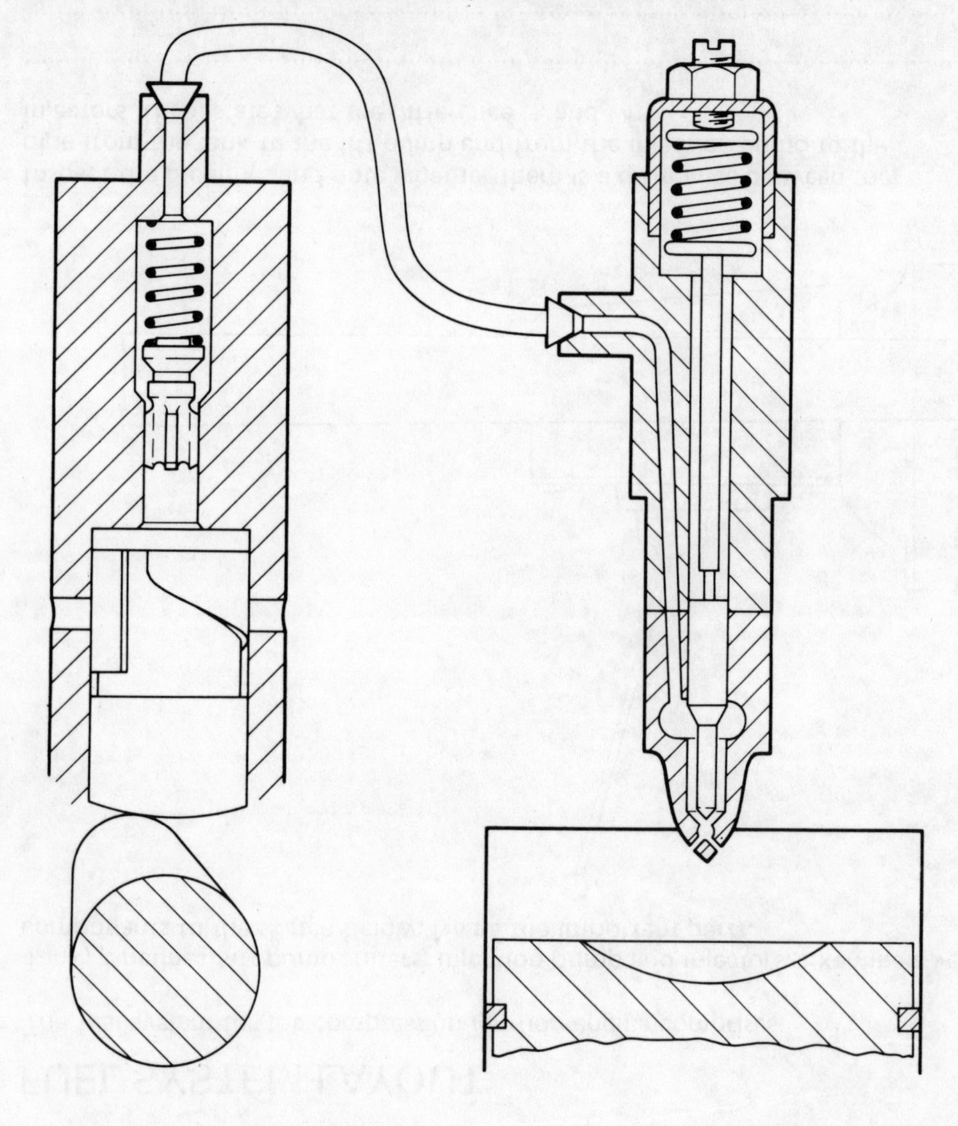

Explain the action of a single-plunger pump and injector.

..............................................................................................................

..............................................................................................................

..............................................................................................................

..............................................................................................................

..............................................................................................................

..............................................................................................................

..............................................................................................................

..............................................................................................................

..............................................................................................................

..............................................................................................................

..............................................................................................................

..............................................................................................................

..............................................................................................................

..............................................................................................................

..............................................................................................................

State typical figures for the following:

(a) Fuel lift-pump pressure ..............................................................

(b) Injector-release pressure ..............................................................

What occurs when the amount of fuel injected is increased?

..............................................................................................................

..............................................................................................................

..............................................................................................................

..............................................................................................................

..............................................................................................................

..............................................................................................................

A6: 9,10

# FUEL INJECTION

The fuel must be injected into the cylinder in the form of a finely atomised spray at very high pressures and at a precise time.

Why is such good atomisation necessary? ..........................................................

..........................................................................................................................

..........................................................................................................................

What would be the effect if the atomisation was poor? .......................................

..........................................................................................................................

..........................................................................................................................

What is the basic cause of black exhaust smoke? ................................................

..........................................................................................................................

..........................................................................................................................

..........................................................................................................................

..........................................................................................................................

..........................................................................................................................

A6: 12

# SAFETY PRECAUTIONS

When testing injectors what safety precautions must be observed?

..........................................................................................................................

Give TWO reasons why such precautions are necessary.

1. ......................................................................................................................

2. ......................................................................................................................

APPLIED STUDIES

A6: 14

# PRESSURE AND TEMPERATURE IN THE CYLINDER

When the piston ascends the cylinder on the compression stroke what effect does it have on the air?

..........................................................................................................................

..........................................................................................................................

A6: 13

# TYPES OF FUEL INJECTION PUMP

The rapid fuel pressure build-up to the point of injection is created by some form of jerk-pump. Usually an in-line or distributor type pump is used on small commercial vehicles.

Identify the common types of pump shown below.

..........................

..........................

..........................

..........................

..........................

..........................

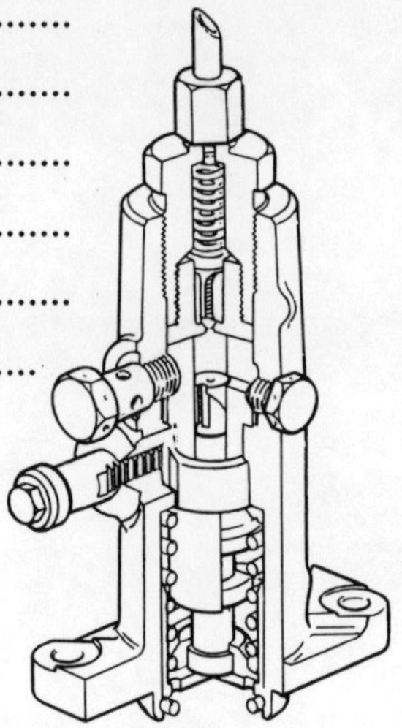

..........................

..........................

..........................

..........................

..........................

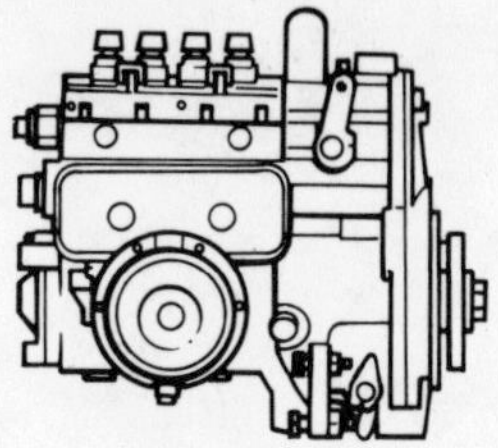

..........................

..........................

..........................

..........................

..........................

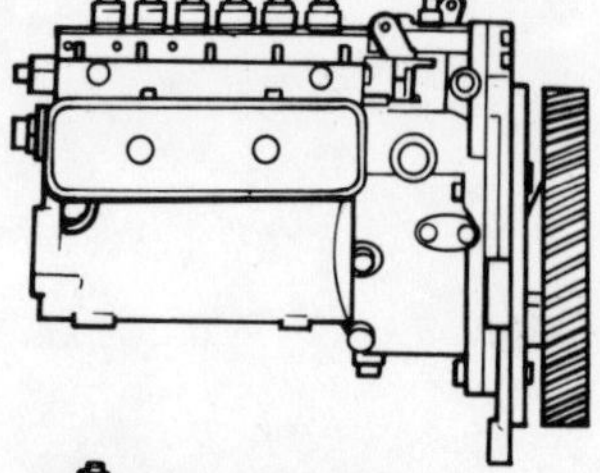

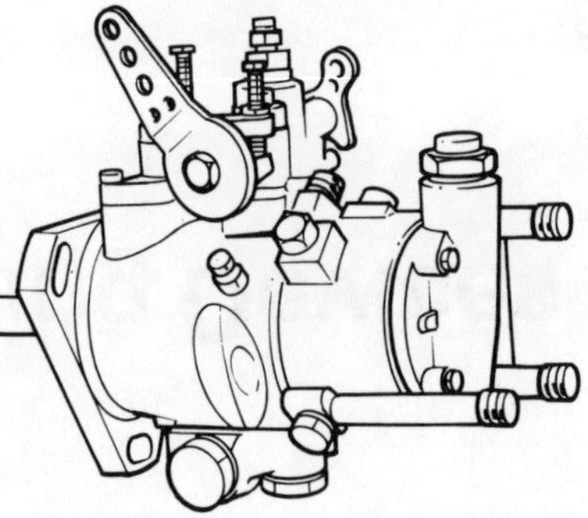

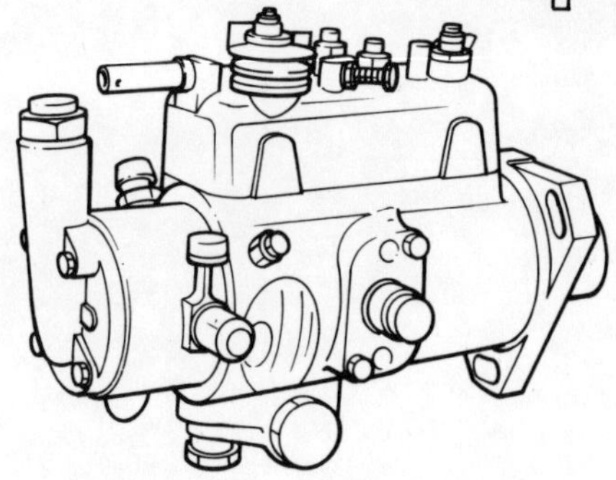

....................................................... .......................................................

....................................................... .......................................................

# A7.

# Fastening and Locking Devices

A7: 2,4

# SCREW THREADS

Screw threads may be external (male) for example bolts, studs, screws or internal (female) for example nuts, threaded holes. There are a number of screw thread forms that have been used on motor vehicles. The abbreviations for these are shown in the table below.

Complete the table to show what the abbreviations represent.

| | |
|---|---|
| BSW | British Standard Whitworth |
| BSF | |
| BSP | |
| BA | |
| UNC | |
| UNF | |

Complete the labelling on this sketch to show the main terms used in describing screw threads.

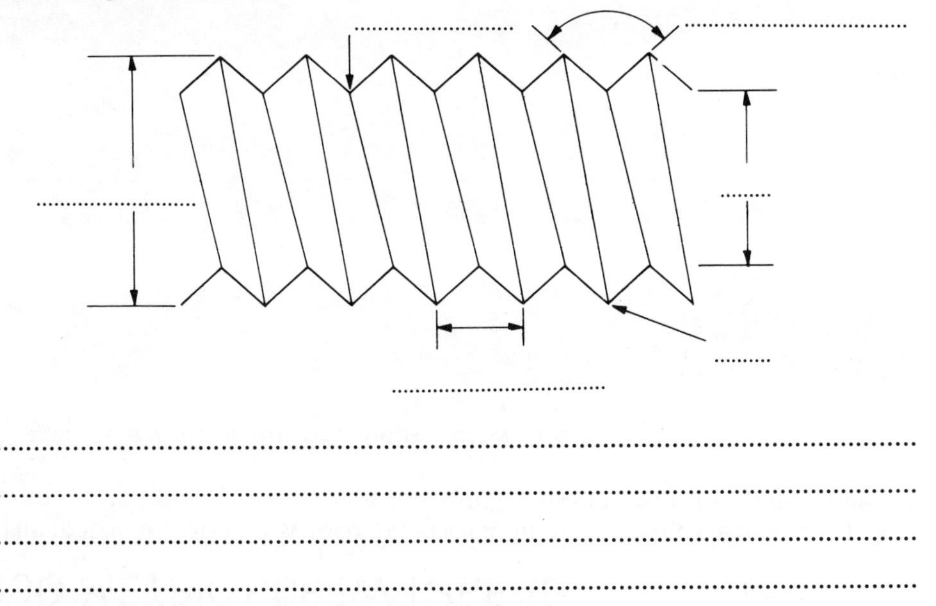

..............................................................................................

..............................................................................................

..............................................................................................

..............................................................................................

Define the term thread depth ..............................................................

..............................................................................................

Define the term LEAD used in connection with screw threads.

..............................................................................................

..............................................................................................

Fine pitch and course pitch screw threads are shown below, label the drawings accordingly.

.............................................. ..............................................

Complete these statements regarding course and fine threads such as those shown above.

(a) The thread having the greater pitch is the..................................thread.

(b) The greater thread depth is on the ...............................thread.

(c) For one turn of the nut on the fine thread it will move a........................ distance than would a nut on the .............................thread. Its...............................is less.

Why are course threads often used in soft alloys?

..............................................................................................

..............................................................................................

..............................................................................................

Why are fine threads very commonly used for most motor vehicle applications?

..............................................................................................

..............................................................................................

# ISO METRIC SCREW THREAD

The metric thread is now used extensively in motor vehicle engineering. As with unified threads a course or fine pitch is used to suit the application.

Sketch below the profile of a metric screw thread.

**Thread designation**

A thread designation such as M10 x 1.5 describes a metric thread, where;

M = ....................................

10 = ....................................

1.5 = ....................................

Refer to thread tables and give below the correct designation for 8 mm diameter fine and course metric threads.

Fine .................................... Course ....................................

State two places on a motor vehicle where 'left hand' threads are used.

1. ....................................

2. ....................................

**Cutting screw threads**

To cut an internal thread it is necessary first to drill a hole of the correct diameter. The thread is cut using a ..................... of the required thread form.

State the purpose of:

The taper tap ....................................

....................................

The second tap ....................................

The plug tap ....................................

....................................

....................................

The correct size of hole to be drilled for cutting a particular thread can be determined by referring to 'thread tables'. State a workshop method, other than using tables, to determine:

(a) the approximate drill size for cutting a thread, and
(b) the clearance hole diameter for a bolt to pass through.

(a) ....................................

....................................

(b) ....................................

....................................

For what purpose is a 'die-nut' used?

....................................

....................................

....................................

# LOCKING DEVICES

Most of the nuts and bolts used on motor vehicles are fitted with locking devices. This is to counteract the loosening effect caused by strain and vibration.

Name the types of locking device shown below.

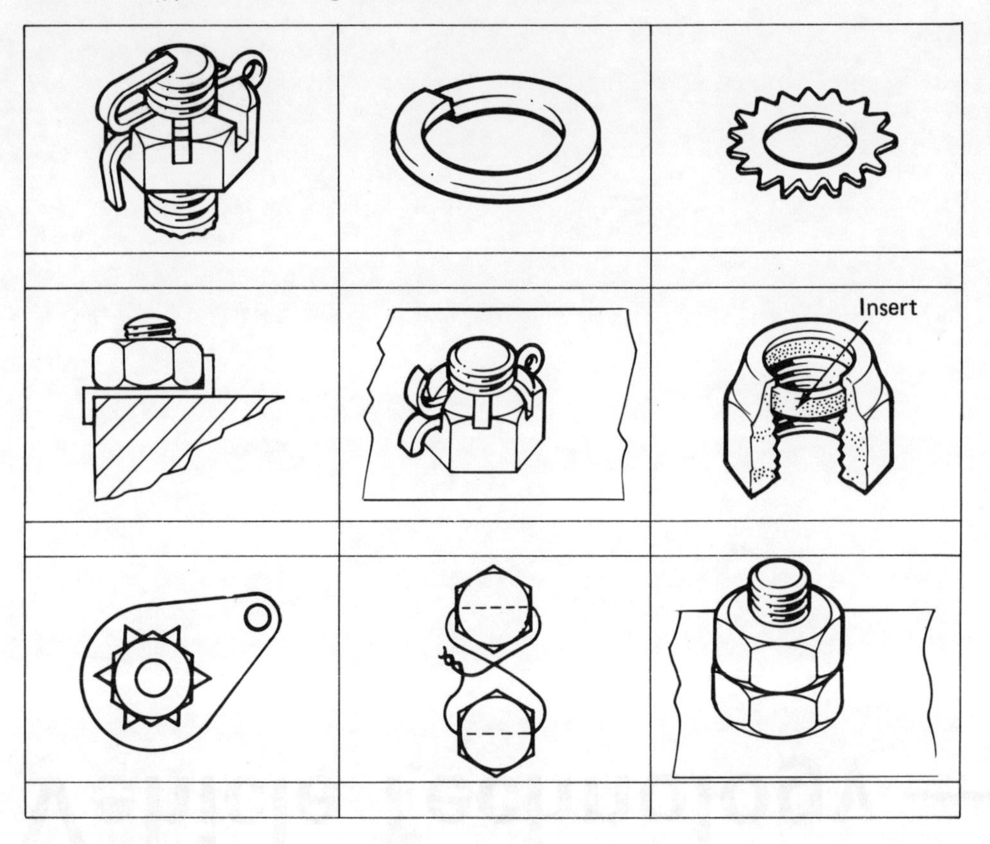


Describe an alternative method of locking nuts and bolts that is very often used in engine assembly.

..........................................................................................................

..........................................................................................................

**Investigation**

Examine a motor vehicle and complete the table below to give motor vehicle applications for the locking devices shown opposite.

| Locking device | Application |
|---|---|
| | |
| | |
| | |
| | |
| | |
| | |
| | |
| | |

Which of the above are:

Positive locking devices?..........................................................................

..........................................................................................................

Frictional locking devices?........................................................................

..........................................................................................................

SECTION B

# Vehicle Technology — Chassis Components

B1.

# Transmission: Clutch

# CLUTCH

**Function**

The clutch is a form of coupling which is used to connect the engine crank-shaft and flywheel assembly to the gearbox input or primary shaft.

One main function of the clutch is:
To allow the drive to be taken up gradually and smoothly as the vehicle moves off from rest.

State two more functions of the clutch.

1. ..............................................................................................

..............................................................................................

2. ..............................................................................................

..............................................................................................

# SINGLE-PLATE CLUTCH

There are many different types of clutch in use on road vehicles but by far the most popular is the single plate friction type. This type of clutch is operated by the driver depressing and releasing a pedal, it is used in conjunction with a *manual* type gearbox.

Name the type of clutch used with an automatic gearbox.

..............................................................................................

..............................................................................................

..............................................................................................

..............................................................................................

..............................................................................................

..............................................................................................

..............................................................................................

..............................................................................................

**Main features of operation (single-plate clutch)**

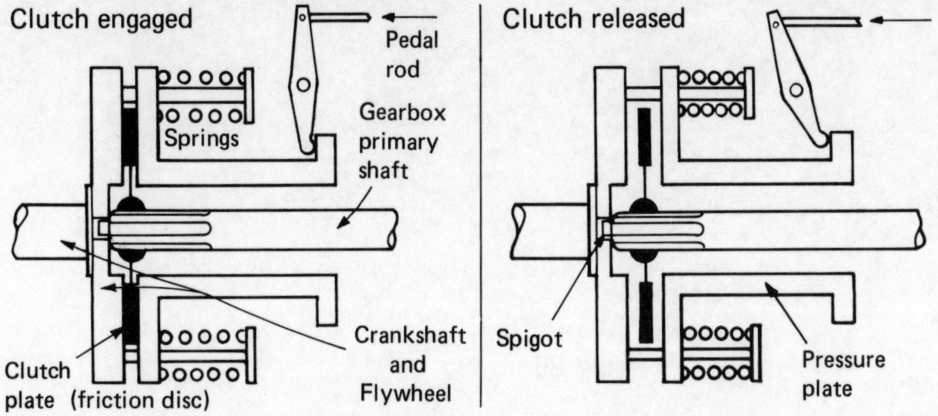

A very much simplified arrangement of a single-plate clutch is illustrated above above.

Study the two drawings and state:

1. How the drive is transmitted from the engine to the gearbox.

..............................................................................................

..............................................................................................

..............................................................................................

..............................................................................................

..............................................................................................

2. How the drive to the gearbox is disconnected when the clutch pedal is depressed?

..............................................................................................

..............................................................................................

..............................................................................................

State the most important single factor with regard to the transmission of drive through this type of clutch.

..............................................................................................

# THE MULTI–SPRING CLUTCH

The multi-spring type clutch, sometimes referred to as the coil-spring clutch, uses a number of coil springs to provide the necessary clamping force. A single-plate version of this type of clutch is shown below; complete the labelling on the drawing.

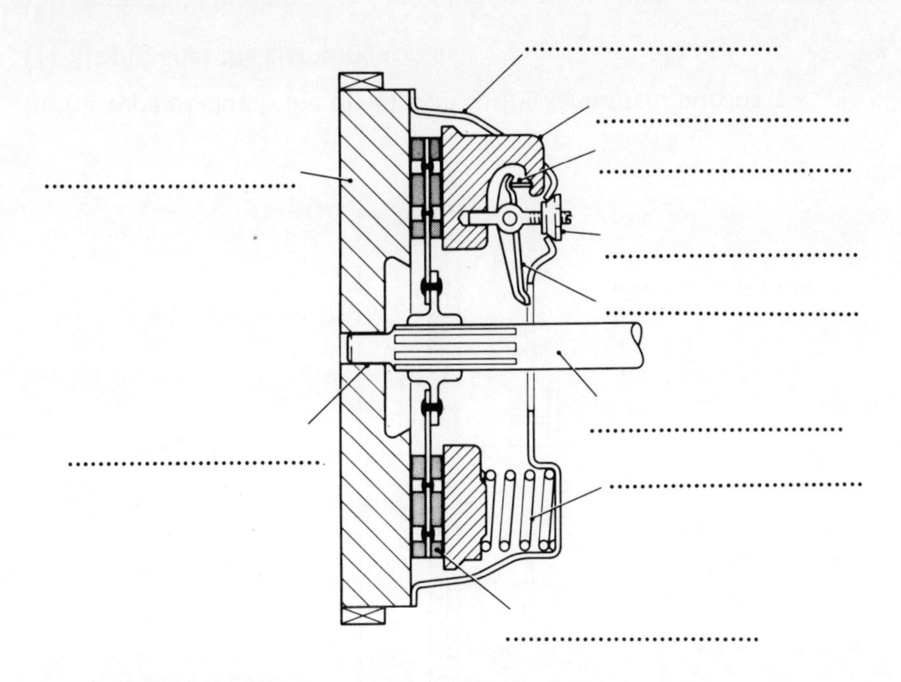

Some important points relating to the construction and operation of this clutch assembly are:

(a) The pressure plate is withdrawn against the springs by pivoting the

..........................................................................................................

(b) The clamping force depends on the .............................. of the springs, the amount that the springs are...................................... and the .............................. of springs.

(c) The clutch plate friction material is basically ......................................

**Investigation**

Examine a multi-spring type clutch pressure plate and a clutch plate.

(a) How many springs does the pressure plate have? ..................................

(b) Indicate on the circular outline below the relative positions of the coil springs and release levers. Along side it, sketch the clutch plate.

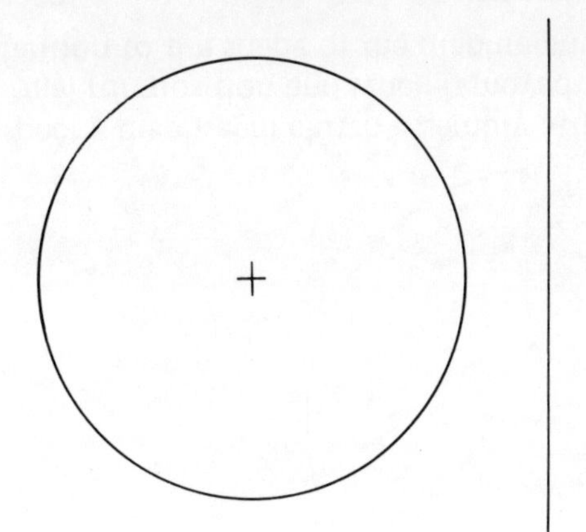

With a flywheel laid flat on a bench, rest on it the clutch plate and pressure plate in their normal working position without the securing bolts.

(c) By how much are the springs compressed when the pressure plate is bolted firmly in position? ..................................................................

(d) What is the thickness of the clutch lining?...........................................

(e) How is the lining secured to the clutch plate?

..........................................................................................................

(f) How does the thickness of the lining affect the clamping force provided by the coil springs, bearing in mind the fact that the force exerted by the springs increases as the springs are compressed?

..........................................................................................................

..........................................................................................................

# THE DIAPHRAGM SPRING CLUTCH



As an alternative to using a number of coil springs to provide the clamping force many clutches use a single *diaphragm* type spring. The diaphragm spring is rather like a saucer in shape with a hole in the centre.

A single plate clutch incorporating a diaphragm spring is shown below; complete the labelling on the drawing.

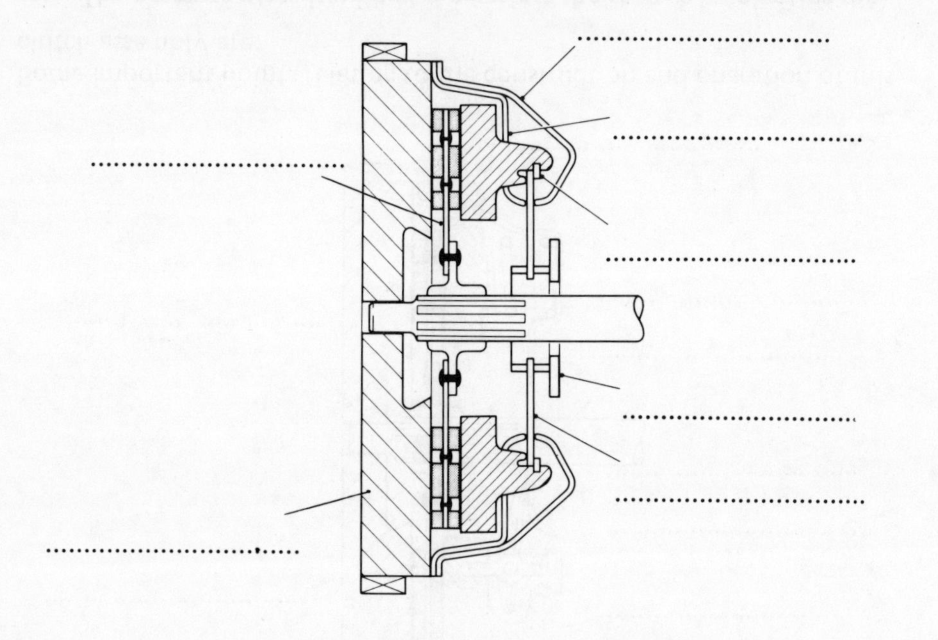

In this type of clutch the diaphragm spring serves two purposes:

(1) It provides the clamping force.

(2) ..............................................................................................

..............................................................................................

..............................................................................................

..............................................................................................

..............................................................................................

**Investigation**

Examine a diaphragm spring clutch assembly.

(a) How does the clutch pressure plate compare in size and weight to a similar diameter coil spring type?

..............................................................................................

..............................................................................................

(b) Which type of friction clutch has the least number of moving parts?

..............................................................................................

..............................................................................................

(c) Make a sketch of the diaphragm spring by completing the circular outline below.

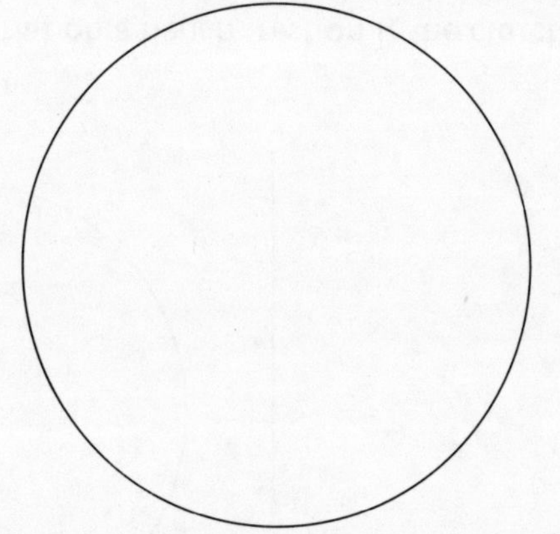

Inspect a diaphragm clutch assembly attached to an engine flywheel in the normal run position and when removed from the flywheel, paying particular attention to the shape of the diaphragm spring.

(d) Sketch below the shape (SIDE VIEW) of the diaphragm spring;

(1) in the normal run position and (2) when removed from the flywheel.

*Normal run position* *Removed from engine*

B1: 3, 5, 10, 11, 12

# METHODS OF OPERATING THE CLUTCH

The clutch can be controlled, from the pedal, either mechanically or hydraulically. In the mechanical system it is usually a cable or rod linkage that connects the pedal lever to the clutch release mechanism.

The main components in a hydraulic control system are shown below, complete the labelling.

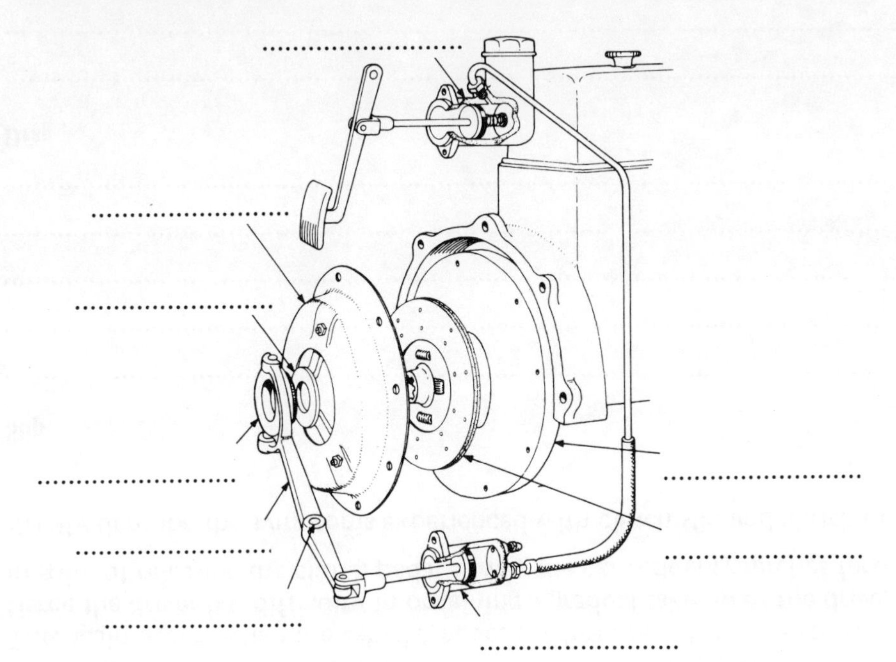

A clearance should be maintained between the release bearing and the clutch release plate giving an amount of *free play* in the control mechanism, this can be felt at the clutch pedal; why is this clearance necessary?

..........................................................................................

..........................................................................................

..........................................................................................

..........................................................................................

..........................................................................................

**Investigation**

Examine a vehicle equipped with a mechanically operated clutch control system and complete the sketches below to illustrate the mechanism between the clutch pedal and release bearing.

Clutch pedal

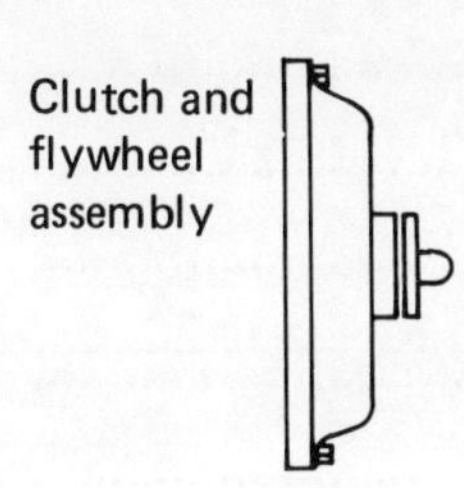


# MULTI-PLATE CLUTCHES

As the name implies multi-plate clutches use more than one clutch plate. They are found mainly on motor cycles and heavy goods vehicles.

(a) State the reason why multi-plate clutches are used.

..........................................................................................

..........................................................................................

..........................................................................................

(b) State one problem associated with the multi-plate clutch.

..........................................................................................

**Wet clutches**

Multi-plate clutches are very often *wet* clutches, how do these differ from dry clutches and why are they used?

..........................................................................................

..........................................................................................

..........................................................................................

# CLUTCH FAULTS

The four main faults associated with the clutch are;
*slip, drag, judder* and *fierceness*

**Judder**

This occurs when the vehicle moves off from rest, as the drive is taken up the whole car shudders until a positive drive is established. It is more pronounced when the vehicle is fully laden or starting on a hill.

**Fierceness**

This again occurs when the vehicle moves off from rest. If the clutch is fierce the driver has difficulty in obtaining a gradual take up of the drive, and in spite of releasing the clutch pedal slowly the car suddenly lurches forward.

Briefly describe the symptoms experienced with clutch slip and clutch drag.

**Slip**

......................................................................................................................

......................................................................................................................

......................................................................................................................

......................................................................................................................

......................................................................................................................

**Drag**

......................................................................................................................

......................................................................................................................

......................................................................................................................

......................................................................................................................

It is an inevitable consequence of design that sooner or later a clutch will begin to slip, this is therefore the most common fault experienced. Judder and fierceness are very often experienced at the same time, this is due to the fact that the same fault can create both symptoms.

**Causes and remedies**

(a) Complete the table below to indicate the causes of and remedies for the four clutch faults.

| Fault | Causes | Remedies |
| --- | --- | --- |
| Slip | .................................<br>.................................<br>.................................<br>................................. | .................................<br>.................................<br>.................................<br>................................. |
| Drag | .................................<br>.................................<br>.................................<br>................................. | .................................<br>.................................<br>.................................<br>................................. |
| Fierceness | .................................<br>.................................<br>.................................<br>................................. | .................................<br>.................................<br>.................................<br>................................. |
| Judder | .................................<br>.................................<br>.................................<br>................................. | .................................<br>.................................<br>.................................<br>................................. |

(b) Another common clutch fault is a squeak or grating sound when the clutch pedal is depressed; what causes this?

......................................................................................................................

......................................................................................................................

B1: 16, 17

# FRICTION

Friction is the resistance to motion produced when two surfaces in contact are made to slide over each other.

Some of the effects of friction are:

(a) ..........

(b) ..........

(c) ..........

The force $F$ required to move the block over the surface shown below must be sufficient to overcome the frictional resistance. It is known as the *force of friction*

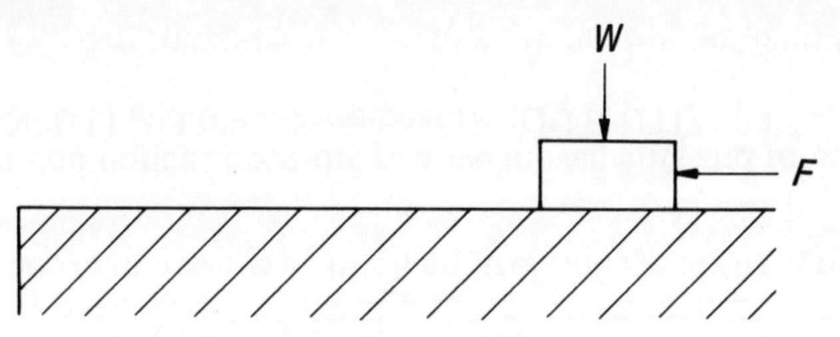


(a) State the two factors which affect the force of friction:

(1) ..........

(2) ..........

**Coefficient of friction**

For any two surfaces in contact the ratio $F/W$ is known as the *coefficient of friction* the symbol for which is the Greek letter $\mu$ (mu)

Hence $\mu = \frac{F}{W}$

The coefficient of friction is therefore an indication of the frictional 'quality' existing for any pair of surfaces in contact.

(b) What single factor has the greatest effect on the coefficient of friction?

..........

**Investigation**

Find the force required to move a loaded section of clutch lining at a steady rate on a clean, dry steel surface.

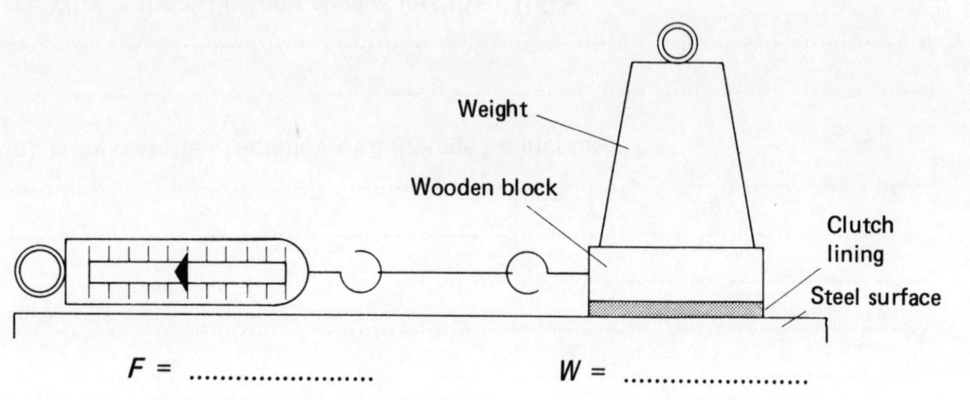


$F$ = .......... $W$ = ..........

Double the weight and repeat the test.

$F$ = .......... $W$ = ..........

(a) Does the force of friction ($F$) increase in proportion to the increase in weight?

..........

Repeat the tests using a section of the same clutch lining which has half the contact area.

(b) Does the reduction in contact area alter the resistance to motion?

..........

(c) When a clutch is slipping heat is generated, what is the reason for this?

..........

..........

(d) Why is a clutch friction lining likely to wear rapidly?

..........

..........

..........

# MECHANICAL LINKAGE

A mechanical linkage can be used to transmit movement and force from one part of the motor vehicle to another. The main components that make up a mechanical linkage are:

..........................................................................................

..........................................................................................

150 mm Clutch pedal Force 80 N 25 mm Release bearing Force 480 N Pivot Pivot Rod

The diagram above represents a clutch control linkage of the type used on some goods vehicles.

(a) What do you notice about the relative movements and forces at the pedal (INPUT) and the release bearing (OUTPUT)?

*Movements* ..........................................................................................

..........................................................................................

*Forces* ..........................................................................................

..........................................................................................

The relationship of movements and forces can be expressed as ratios.

$$\text{Force ratio} = \frac{\text{Force at output}}{\text{Force at input}} \text{ or } \frac{\text{Load}}{\text{Effort}}$$

$$\text{Movement ratio} = \underline{\qquad\qquad}$$

In the mechanism above:

$$FR = \underline{\qquad} = \qquad\qquad MR = \underline{\qquad} =$$

**Efficiency of the linkage**

It has been theoretically assumed that the linkage shown opposite is completely free from friction. In practice, however, friction is present in a mechanical linkage.

(b) Give three examples of the places within a linkage where friction would be present.

1. .................... 2. .................... 3. ....................

Some of the effort applied must therefore be used to overcome this friction.

(c) Which of the two ratios MR or FR will be affected by friction in the mechanism? ....................

The efficiency of a linkage is usually expressed as a percentage and is calculated:

$$\text{Efficiency} = \frac{\text{Force ratio}}{\text{Movement ratio}} \times \frac{100}{1}$$

(d) If it took 20 N to overcome friction in the linkage shown opposite, calculate:

(1) the force at the release bearing
(2) the force ratio
(3) the efficiency

..........................................................................................

..........................................................................................

..........................................................................................

..........................................................................................

..........................................................................................

..........................................................................................

(e) How can the efficiency of a linkage be increased?

..........................................................................................

..........................................................................................

(f) Why is the efficiency always less than 100%

..........................................................................................

..........................................................................................

B2.

# Transmission: Gearbox

B2: 1–4

# FUNCTION

In a motor vehicle the gearbox serves three purposes.

(1) To multiply (or increase) the torque (turning effort) being transmitted by the engine.

(2) ..................................................................................................

(3) ..................................................................................................

Under many operating conditions the torque requirement at the driving wheels is far in excess of the torque available from the engine.

(a) State four operating conditions under which the engine torque would need to be multiplied at the gearbox.

(1) When the vehicle is heavily laden.

(2) ..................................................................................................

(3) ..................................................................................................

(4) ..................................................................................................

**Types of gearbox**

The FOUR types of gearbox are:

(1) Sliding Mesh (2) Constant Mesh

(3) .................................... (4) ....................................

(b) Which of the four types of gearbox are used in most modern cars?

..................................................................................................

..................................................................................................

..................................................................................................

..................................................................................................

..................................................................................................

..................................................................................................

..................................................................................................

**Types of Gearing**

The spur gear, the helical gear and the double helical gear are all types of gears used in gearboxes.

By observation in the workshop complete the sketches below to show the tooth arrangement for each type.

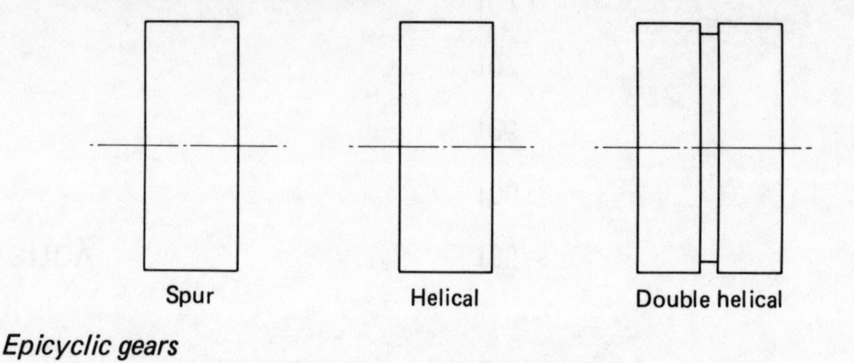


*Epicyclic gears*

The sketches below show a simple epicyclic gear train. This extremely compact arrangement of gears is used in

.............................................. and ..............................................

(c) Name the main parts of this gear train by completing the labelling on the drawing. Name the type of gearbox shown on the right.

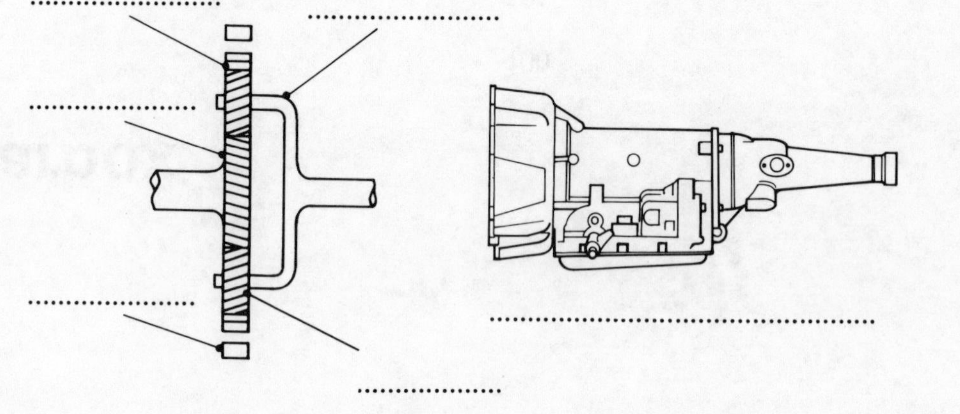

B2: 4,5,6

# SIMPLE SLIDING-MESH GEARBOX

The drawing below shows a three-speed sliding-mesh type of gearbox. To obtain the various gear ratios the gearbox layshaft is made up of different sized gearwheels which are connected in turn to the gearwheels on the mainshaft. The drive to the layshaft is through a pair of gearwheels which are permanently in mesh.

Complete the labelling on the drawing:

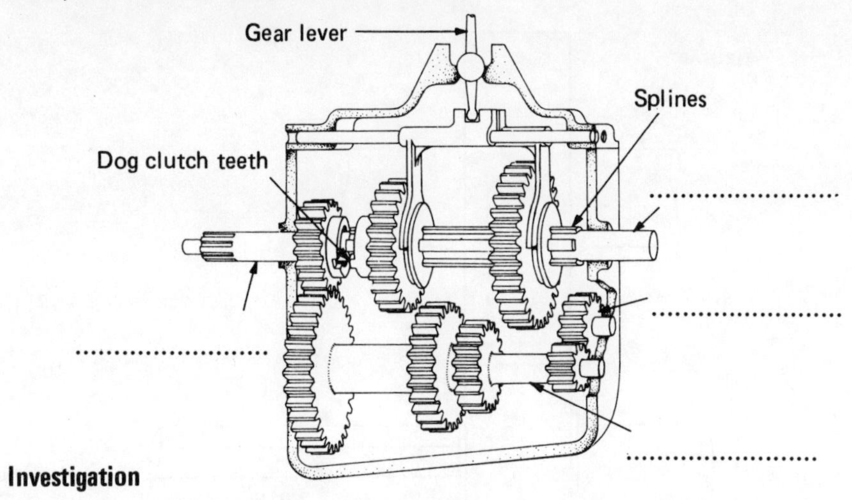


**Investigation**

Examine a sliding mesh gearbox and answer the following questions:

(a) What type of gearing is used? ........................................................

(b) How are the gears engaged to provide the various gear ratios?

..........................................................................................

..........................................................................................

..........................................................................................

..........................................................................................

(c) Why is the mainshaft splined?

..........................................................................................

..........................................................................................

(d) Show the power flow in 1st, 2nd and top gear by adding the mainshaft gearwheels and arrows to the drawings below. On the wheels in (4) show the direction of rotation; view the gear train from the rear of the gearbox.

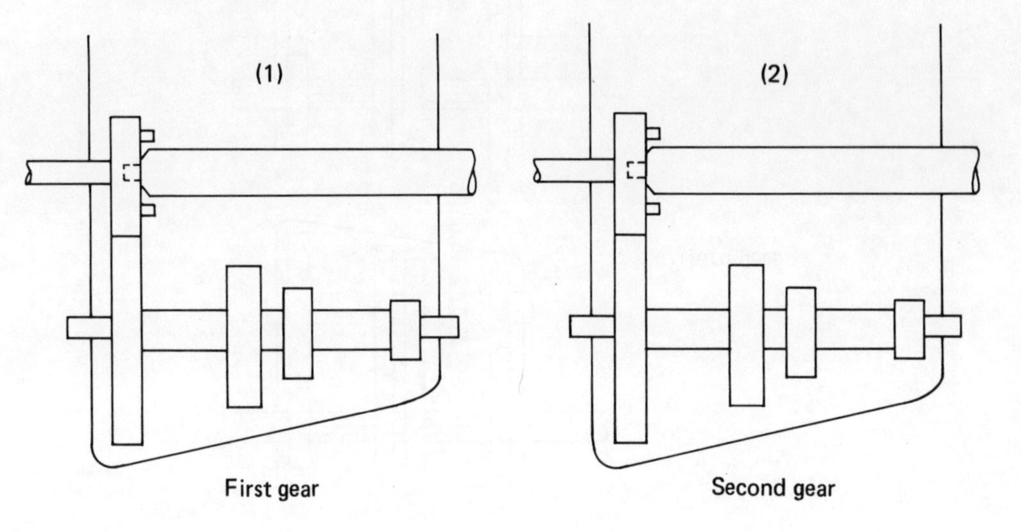


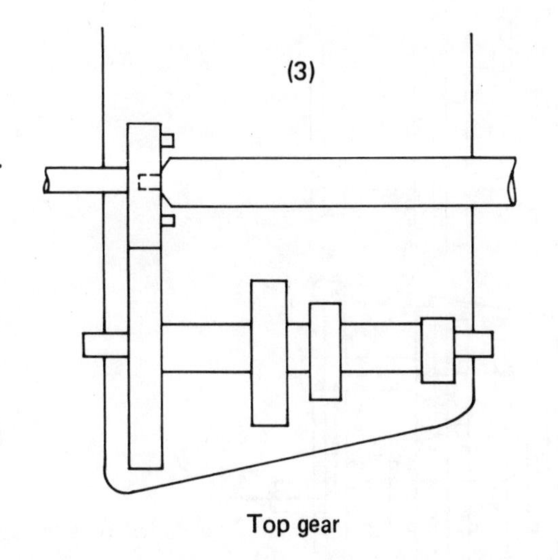


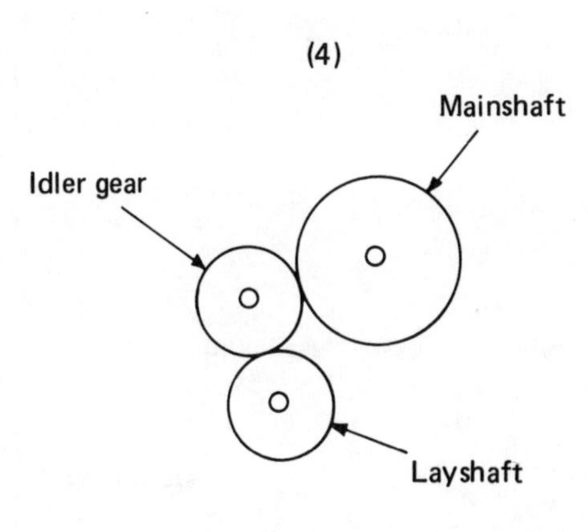

# CONSTANT-MESH GEARBOX

In the constant-mesh gearbox, as the name implies, the gearwheels are permanently in mesh. Constant meshing of the gears is achieved by allowing the mainshaft gearwheels to rotate on bushes. Dog clutches which are splined to the mainshaft, provide a positive connection, when required, to allow the drive to be transmitted to the output shaft.

Principle of operation:

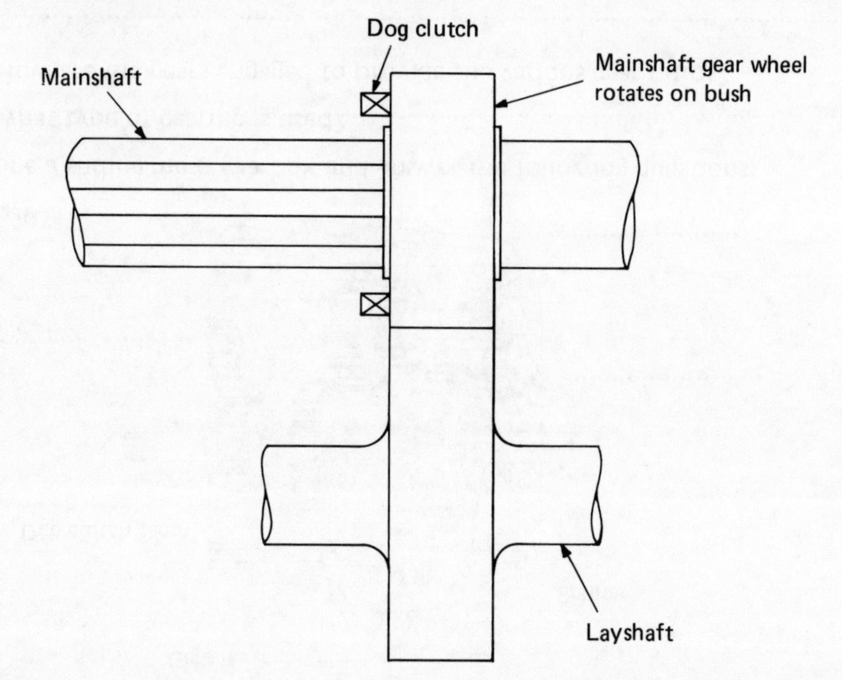


**Power flow**

(a) Complete the drawing above to show how a dog clutch member is used to connect the mainshaft gearwheel to the mainshaft and add arrows to indicate the power flow from the layshaft to the mainshaft.

(b) Add arrows to the drawings opposite to trace the power flow through the constant mesh gearbox in the gear positions shown. Sketch the dog clutches in their correct positions.

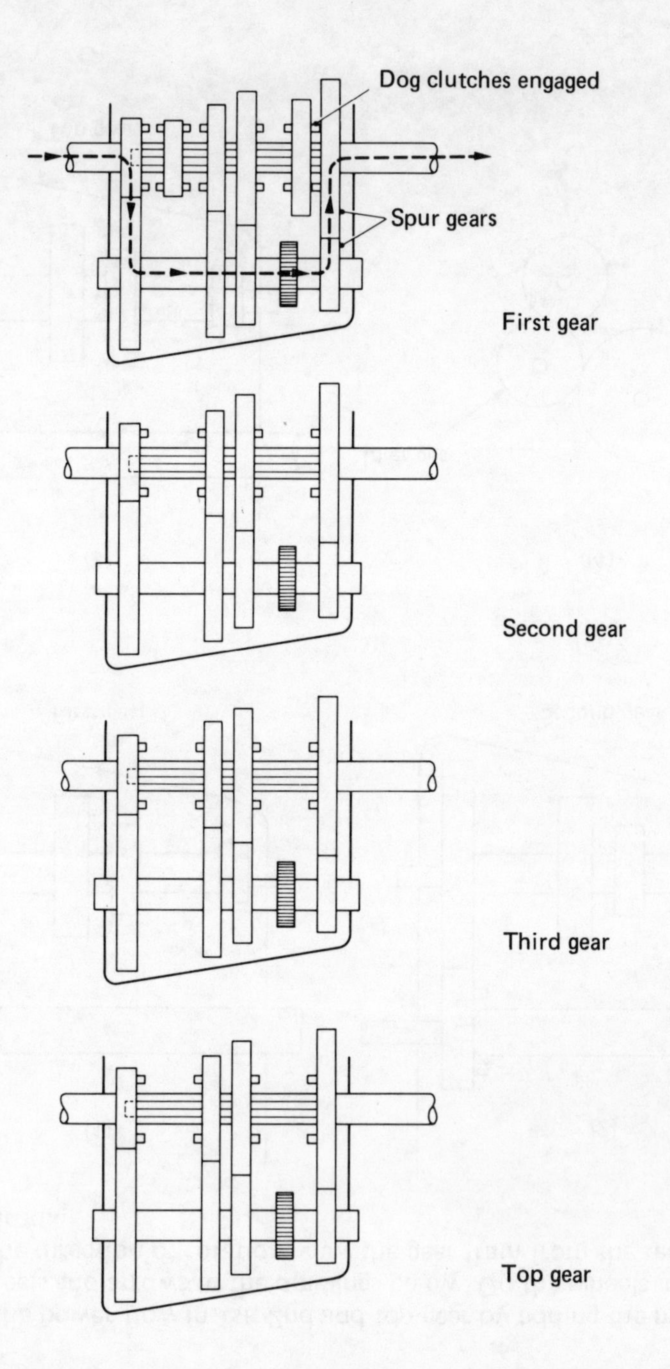

B2: 7,8,9,11,12

State three advantages of constant mesh over sliding mesh gears.

1. ..........

2. ..........

3. ..........

# SYNCHROMESH GEARBOX

The simple constant-mesh gearbox has been superseded by the synchromesh gearbox. In this type of gearbox 'synchronising' devices, which form part of the dog clutch members, overcome the problems associated with sliding or simple constant-mesh gearboxes, but the gearbox is more complicated and expensive.

State two advantages of synchromesh over simple constant-mesh.

1. ..........

2. ..........

Why does gear-changing require skill and experience when sliding-mesh or constant-mesh gearboxes are used?

..........

..........

..........

..........

..........

..........

# SELECTOR MECHANISM

When gears are selected the gearwheels or dog clutch members are moved into position by selector forks which are carried on shafts. Within the selector mechanism provision must be made to retain the selector forks in neutral or in the required gear position; the mechanism must also prevent engagement of two gears at the same time.

**Investigation**

Examine different types of selector mechanism and complete the simplified drawing below to include the selector fork and gear lever.

*Simple selector mechanism (side view)*

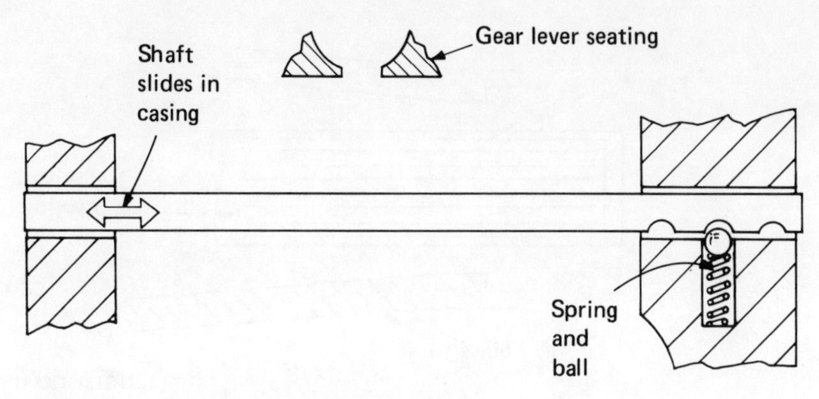


(a) What is the purpose of the spring and ball in the above drawing?

..........

(b) The drawing below shows a selector shaft 'interlock' mechanism. What is its purpose?

..........

..........

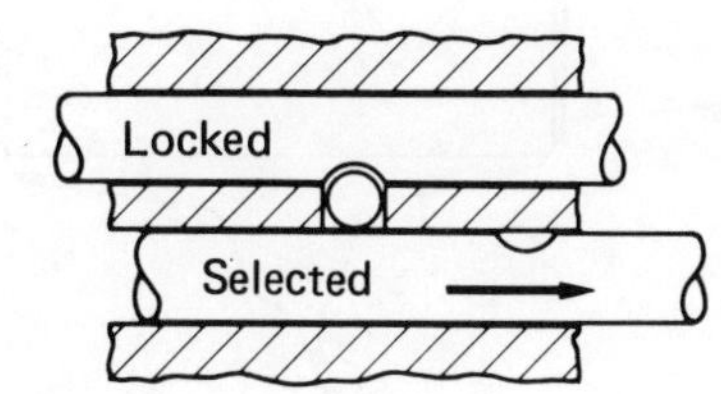


**Speedometer Drive**

From which shaft in the gearbox is the drive to the speedometer usually taken?

..........

# GEARBOX LUBRICATION

(a) How are the components in a gearbox usually lubricated?

(b) Approximately how much oil would an average family saloon car gearbox require?

(c) How is the oil level in a gearbox usually checked?

(d) What advantage has the level plug over a dipstick?

**Oil Sealing**

(e) A type of oil seal commonly used in gearboxes is shown below, name this type of seal and label the drawing.

(f) Add arrows to the gearbox outline below to indicate where oil seals would be positioned.

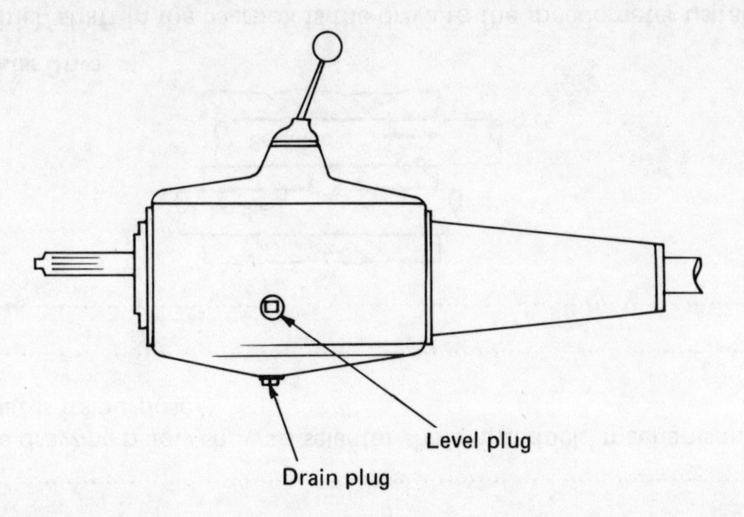


(g) Examine a gearbox and complete the drawing below to show an oil seal in position.

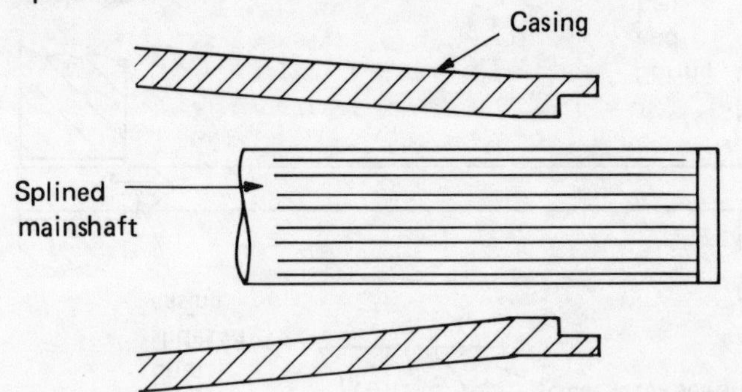


(h) How is the oil prevented from leaking between the joint faces in a gearbox?

# GEAR RATIO, TORQUE RATIO, EFFICIENCY

## Gear ratio

When two gearwheels are meshed to form a 'simple' gear train, the *gear ratio* can be expressed as a ratio of gear teeth or a ratio of gearwheel speeds.

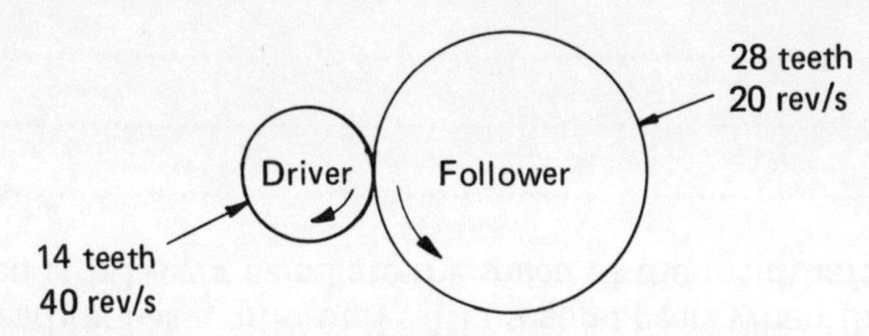


For the pair of gears represented above,

$$\text{Gear ratio} = \frac{\text{No. of teeth on follower}}{\text{No. of teeth on driver}} =$$

or using gear wheel speeds,

Gear ratio =

When speeds are used the ratio is sometimes expressed as

.................................................................................................................

(Note: see associated problems on next page.)

## Torque ratio

It has already been stated that the gearbox multiplies engine torque; thus the relationship between gearbox input torque and output torque can be expressed as a ratio.

Torque ratio =

It does not follow that the torque ratio will be the same as the gear ratio, this is due to the fact that some of the input torque is used to overcome friction in the gear assembly.

## Efficiency

The efficiency of a gear train is an indication of the friction present. This must therefore be taken into account when calculating the torque ratio.

(a) What would be the efficiency of a gear train if the gear ratio and torque ratio were the same?

.................................................................................................................

(b) How is efficiency calculated?

.................................................................................................................

.................................................................................................................

(c) State the effects of heavy oil in a gearbox compared with a thin oil on the following:

(1) Efficiency .................................................................................

(2) Torque ratio .................................................................................

(3) Gear ratio .................................................................................

(d) In second gear the gearbox input torque is 250 N m and the output torque is 400 N m. Calculate the efficiency of the gearbox if the second gear ratio is 2 : 1

Torque ratio =

Efficiency =

(e) State the gear ratios for a modern vehicle which is fitted with a four speed and reverse gearbox.

Vehicle make and model ............................................Year ................

Ratios

1st gear...........................2nd gear.......................3rd gear ...............

4th gear...........................reverse..........................

# CALCULATIONS: GEAR RATIO

(a) The input gear of a pair of gearwheels has 12 teeth and the output gear has 30 teeth; the gear ratio is:

(a) 2.5 : 1 (b) 2.75 : 1 (c) 3 : 1 (d) 18 : 1

Answer ........................

(b) The constant-mesh gearwheels in a sliding-mesh gearbox have 14 and 28 teeth respectively, calculate the gear ratio for this pair of gears and the speed of the layshaft when the primary shaft speed is 60 rev/s.

..........

..........

..........

..........

(c) With a vehicle in second gear and the engine speed at 70 rev/s, calculate the second gear ratio if the propellor shaft speed is 28 rev/s.

..........

..........

..........

(d) A gearbox has a ratio of 3 : 1 in second gear. When the primary shaft speed is 50 rev/s calculate the speed of the mainshaft.

..........

..........

..........

(e) Complete the table below.

| **Gear ratio** | **4.5 : 1** | **3 : 1** | |
|---|---|---|---|
| Input shaft speed (rev/s) | 54 | | 49.5 |
| Output shaft speed (rev/s) | | 15 | 18 |

# CALCULATIONS: TORQUE RATIO

(a) Calculate the efficiency of a gearbox given the following data: Third gear ratio 1.5 : 1, engine torque 250 N m, propellor shaft torque 350 N m.

..........

..........

..........

..........

(b) If the gear ratio of a simple gear train is 3 : 1 and the efficiency is 90% calculate the output torque and torque ratio when the input torque is 200 N m.

..........

..........

..........

..........

(c) In first gear the gear ratio is 4 : 1 and the efficiency of a gearbox is 85%, calculate the torque ratio when the torque transmitted by the engine is 350 N m.

..........

..........

..........

..........

..........

(d) Complete the table below.

| **Gear ratio** | **2.5 : 1** | **4 : 1** | |
|---|---|---|---|
| Torque ratio | 2.5 : 1 | | 6 : 1 |
| Efficiency | | 95% | 93.75% |

B2: 17,18

# WORK DONE AND POWER

When a vehicle is propelled along a road through a certain distance, the *work done* is the product of the propelling 'force' (N) and the 'distance' (m) through which the vehicle travels.

Hence:

Work done (N m) ........................................ x ................................................

If the time factor is taken into consideration that is the time taken to complete the distance, the *rate* of doing work can be calculated. The basis for this calculation being :

The *force* (N) multiplied by the *distance per second* moved by the vehicle.

The *rate of doing work* is known as ............................................................

*Work done* is the 'total quantity' of work done in moving the vehicle through a given distance, whereas

........................................................is the 'work done each second'.

Note: The same applies to all other machines, not just vehicles.

# EFFICIENCY

The power generated by the engine is transmitted to the vehicle's driving wheels via the transmission system. However, some of this power is used to overcome friction in the transmission system which results in the transmission *output power* being .......................... than transmission *input power.*

The power loss is therefore dependent upon the efficiency of the transmission.

What would be the transmission efficiency if input and output power were equal?

..............................................................................................................

# FRICTION AND LUBRICATION

When a gearbox is in operation, metal surfaces are continually sliding and rolling over each other. If these surfaces were dry and free from oil, heat would be generated and wear would take place. In fact under these conditions total seizure would rapidly occur.

(a) What is the fundamental cause of this?

..............................................................................................................

Smooth metal surfaces viewed through microscope

Sliding will cause the peaks and valleys to interlock giving rise to heat and wear on the surfaces.

**Investigation**

1. Place a metal block on a flat metal surface and push the block along the surface.
2. Place the block in a pool of lubricating oil on the surface and push the block along.

(b) What effect had the oil?

..............................................................................................................

(c) Why does the oil have this effect?

..............................................................................................................

..............................................................................................................

If metal to metal contact is to be avoided in a gearbox the lubricating oil must withstand *extreme pressure* without the oil film breaking down.

(d) Where do these extreme pressures occur in a gearbox?

..............................................................................................................

(e) Name the type of lubricant to suit gearbox lubrication and give an example of one such type.

.................................................................... ........................

# B3.

# Transmission: Propellor Shafts and Drive Shafts

B3: 1,2,3,5

# PROPELLOR SHAFTS AND DRIVE SHAFTS

On a vehicle of conventional layout the purpose of the propellor shaft is to transmit the drive from the ....................................to the ........................... ..................................... Drive shafts (or half shafts) transmit the drive from the ................................ to the .................................................................

(a) Give three examples of vehicle layouts in which external drive shafts may be used as opposed to conventional type half shafts enclosed in the axle casing.

1. Front engine, rear wheel drive with 'independent' rear suspension.

2. ..........................................................................................

3. ..........................................................................................

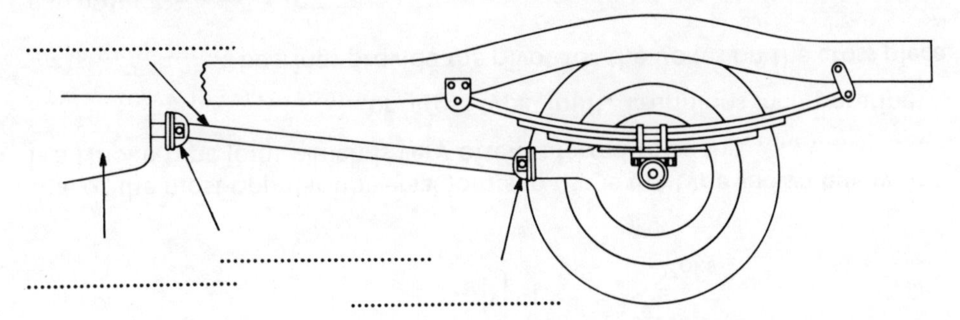

(b) Complete the labelling on the 'open' type propellor shaft arrangement shown above.

(c) Why is it necessary to have a universal joint at both ends of the propellor shaft?

..........................................................................................

..........................................................................................

..........................................................................................

Universal joints are also used on drive shafts to allow for the rise and fall of the road wheels relative to the final drive assembly on cars with independent rear suspension.

As the rear axle swings up and down with spring deflection the distance between the gearbox and axle varies. It is therefore necessary to enable the propellor shaft to effectively vary in length. The splined *'sliding joint'* in a propellor shaft assembly provides this facility.

**Investigation**

Examine a vehicle and make a sketch below to show the propellor shaft sliding joint arrangement.

(b) Is the propellor shaft solid or tubular?

..........................................................................................

(c) State three advantages to be gained by using a tubular shaft.

1. ..........................................................................................

..........................................................................................

..........................................................................................

2. ..........................................................................................

3. ..........................................................................................

# UNIVERSAL JOINTS

*Hooke-type*

In the Hooke-type universal joint two yokes (Y pieces) are connected to a centre 'cross' piece. By allowing the yokes to hinge or pivot on the cross piece the drive can be transmitted through varying angles.

(a) Complete the drawing of the simplified Hooke-type joint below:

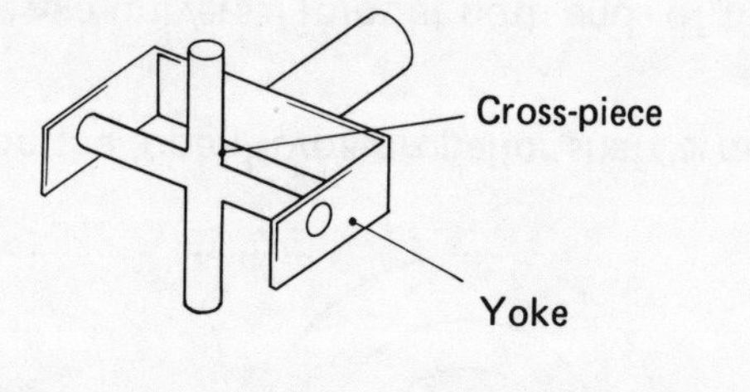


One of the most popular universal joints in use is the type shown below, it is a Hooke-type joint which is very often referred to as the........................

..........................................or 'cross type' joint. Trunnions incorporating

..........................bearings provide the pivot for the yokes on the cross piece.

Label the drawing.

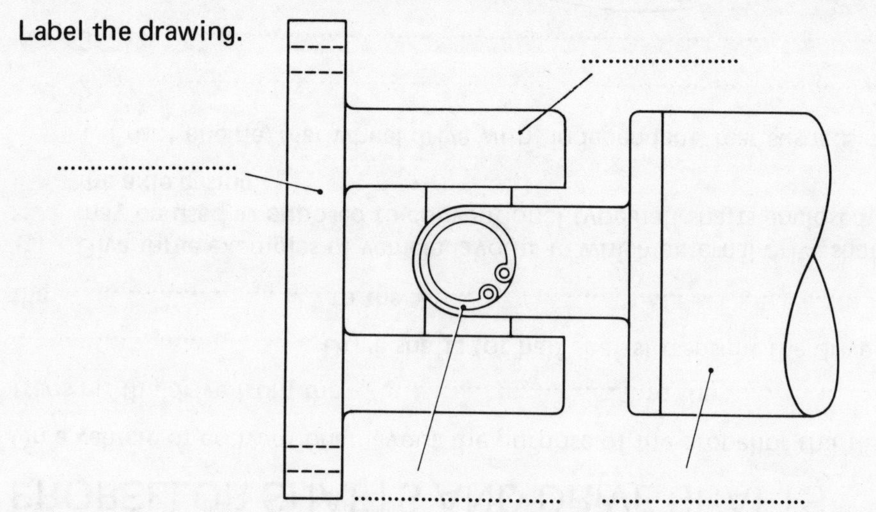

Two other types of universal joint in use are the 'Layrub' type and the 'Doughnut' type. A vital feature of these two types of joint that provides flexibility is the use of ..........................................................................................
Examine two such joints and in the spaces below make suitably labelled sketches.

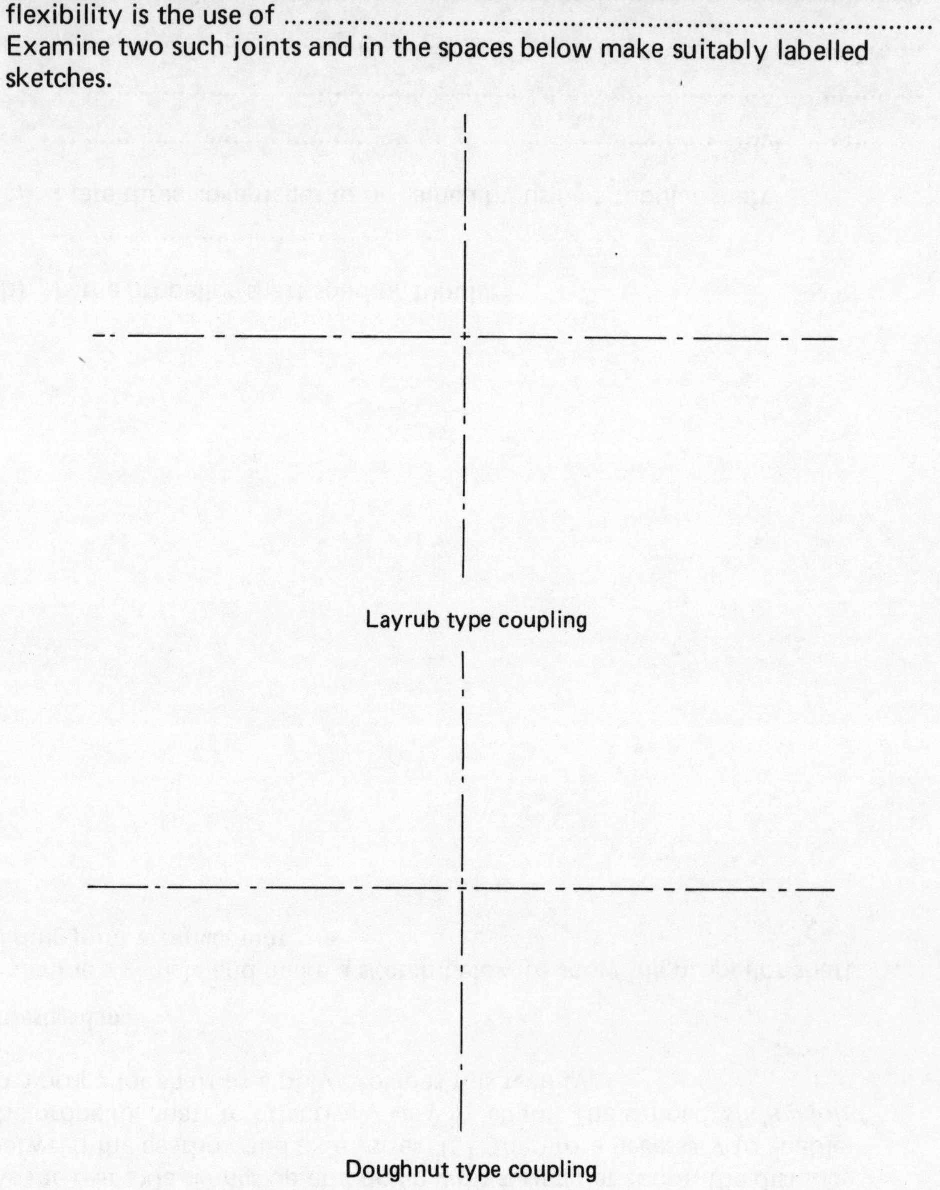

# PROPELLOR SHAFT CENTRE BEARING

A two-piece propellor shaft is used on many modern vehicles. With this arrangement two shafts transmit the drive from the gearbox to the final drive. A chassis-mounted centre-bearing providing support for the shafts.

Examine a vehicle fitted with a two-piece propellor shaft assembly and complete the drawing below to illustrate the arrangement.

Vehicle make .................................... Model .........................................

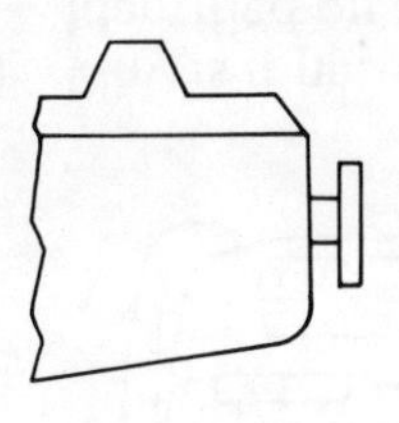

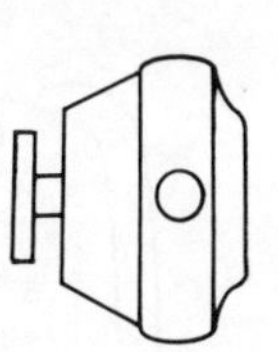

What are the reasons for using divided or two-piece type propellor shafts?

..........................................................................................................................

..........................................................................................................................

..........................................................................................................................

..........................................................................................................................

..........................................................................................................................

..........................................................................................................................

..........................................................................................................................

..........................................................................................................................

..........................................................................................................................

..........................................................................................................................

# THE TRANSMISSION OF CONSTANT ANGULAR VELOCITY

When two shafts are aligned and connected by a universal joint as shown in (a), constant velocity will be transmitted from shaft *x* to shaft *y*.

(a)

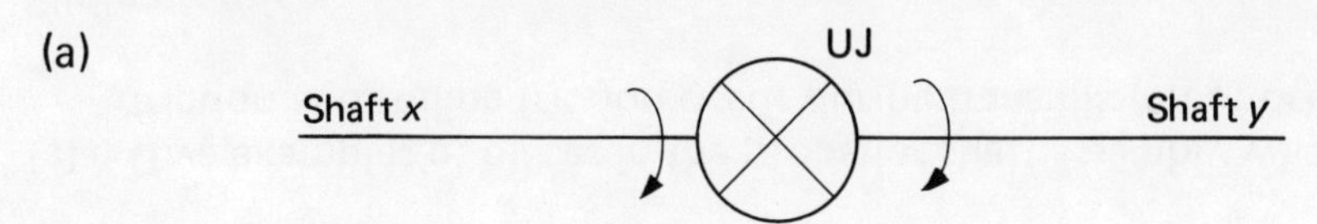


If shaft *y* swings through an angle as shown in (b) its velocity can vary, that is it can accelerate and decelerate in spite of the fact that shaft *x* rotates at constant velocity.

(b)

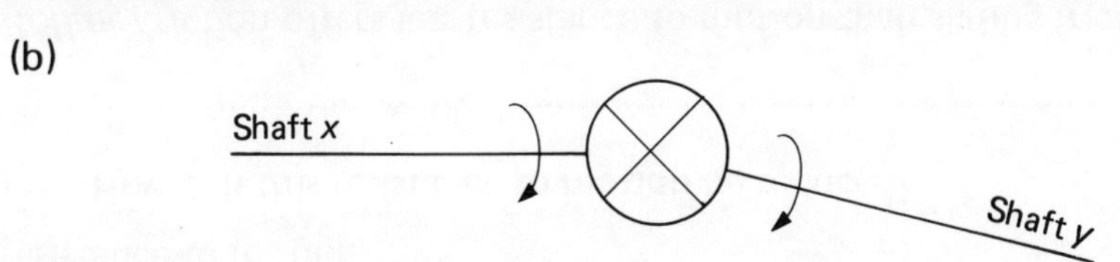


This problem occurs when a 'Hookes' or 'Cross' type joint is used and results in vibrations being set up. The problem is overcome in a propellor shaft assembly by correctly aligning the universal joints relative to each other.

Examine a propellor shaft on which one universal joint is splined to the shaft and draw it below to show the relative position of the universal joints.

The joint is on the correct spline when ..........................................................................

...........................................................................................................................

# CONSTANT VELOCITY JOINTS

Certain types of universal joints are known as 'constant velocity' joints.

(a) What is the purpose of a constant velocity joint?

..........................................................................................

..........................................................................................

(b) Which of the universal joints on the vehicle layout shown would normally be constant velocity type joints?

..........................................................................................

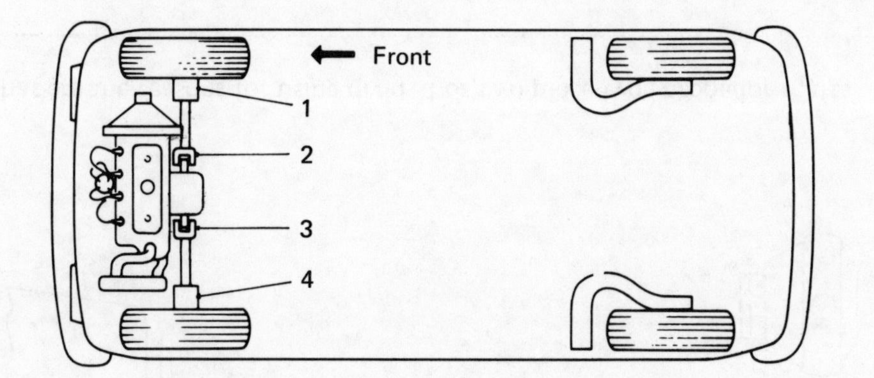


(c) Why is it necessary to use constant velocity joints in the position identified on the drawing above

..........................................................................................

..........................................................................................

(d) Name four modern vehicles in which constant velocity joints are used.

..........................................................................................

..........................................................................................

..........................................................................................

..........................................................................................

# APPLIED STUDIES

It has already been established that the propellor shaft on a vehicle is of tubular construction. The shaft must be sufficiently rigid in structure to resist bending which would cause vibration. Certain factors affect the ability of a shaft to resist bending. List below three of these factors.

1. ..........................................................................................

2. ..........................................................................................

3. ..........................................................................................

## FRICTION

When a shaft rotates in a plain bearing or bush the surfaces in contact are *sliding* over each other. It is sliding friction therefore which produces the resistance to motion.

(a) How can this resistance to motion be reduced?

..........................................................................................

*Rolling* friction offers less resistance to motion than sliding friction. This advantage is put to good effect in many motor vehicle applications.

(b) In which design of bearing is rolling friction a feature of operation?

..........................................................................................

(c) Give examples of places in the propellor shaft assembly where sliding friction and rolling friction occur during transmission of drive.

Sliding friction

..........................................................................................

Rolling friction

..........................................................................................

B4.

# Transmission: Final Drive

# THE FINAL DRIVE

The final drive consists basically of a pair of gears which provide a permanent gear reduction thereby multiplying the torque being transmitted from the gearbox.

In most transmission arrangements (for example front engine with rear live axle) the final drive fulfils another purpose; this is

..........................................................................................................

..........................................................................................................

The two gears forming the final drive are named:

1. ...................................... 2. ......................................

**Investigation**

Examine a rear axle and complete the drawings below to show how the final drive gears are positioned relative to each other to give the desired motion.

Front of vehicle

This or This

Complete the table below for the axle you examine.

| Number of teeth on crown wheel | Number of teeth on pinion | Final drive gear ratio |
|---|---|---|
| | | |

**Investigation**

(a) Three types of final drive gear are, STRAIGHT BEVEL, SPIRAL BEVEL and HYPOID. Examine each of these and indicate below the type illustrated.

(b) List alongside each drawing the advantages of the particular gear design.

| Gear type | Advantages |
|---|---|
| Type 1<br>*Straight bevel* | .......................................... |
| Type 2<br>.............................. | .......................................... |
| Type 3<br>.............................. | .......................................... |

# THE DIFFERENTIAL

When a vehicle is cornering the inner driven wheel is rotating slower than the outer driven wheel. It is the *differential* which allows this difference in speed to take place whilst at the same time transmitting an equal driving torque to the road wheels.

Why does this difference in speed between inner and outer road wheels need to occur?

..........................................................................................

..........................................................................................

..........................................................................................

The differential is normally an assembly of bevel gears housed in a casing (or cage) which is attached to the crown wheel. The essential parts of a differential are:

1. Planet Wheels  3. ..............................
2. ..............................  4. ..............................

The differential could be described as a *torque equaliser.* Why is this?

..........................................................................................

..........................................................................................

..........................................................................................

..........................................................................................

During cornering the inner driven wheel is rotating at 100 rev/min and the outer driven wheel is rotating at 200 rev/min. The torque in the half shafts would be:

(a) double in the outer

(b) the same in each

(c) double in the inner

Answer ( )

**Investigation**

Examine a final drive and differential assembly and complete the drawing below by adding the main components of the differential; clearly label each component.

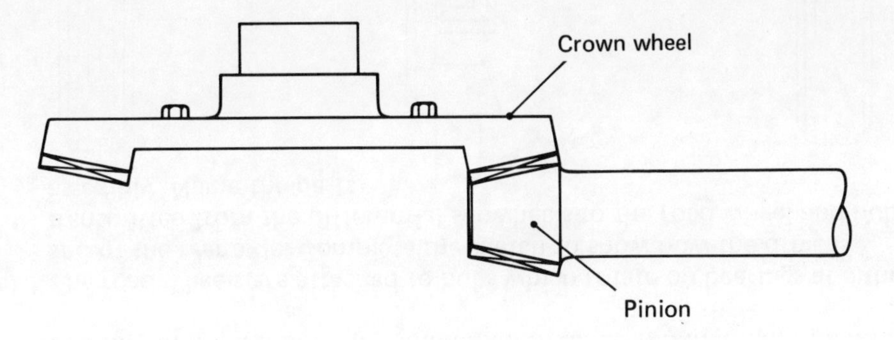


Which gearwheels transmit the drive to the axle shafts?

..........................................................................................

Power is transmitted from the final drive pinion to the axle shafts via the components listed below. Rearrange the list in the correct sequence in accordance with the power flow through the differential.

| Components | Power flow |
|---|---|
| Cross pin | 1. .............................. |
| Sunwheels | 2. .............................. |
| Crown wheel | 3. .............................. |
| Planet wheels | 4. .............................. |
| Axle shafts | 5. .............................. |
| Pinion | 6. .............................. |
| Differential cage | 7. .............................. |

# OPERATION OF THE DIFFERENTIAL

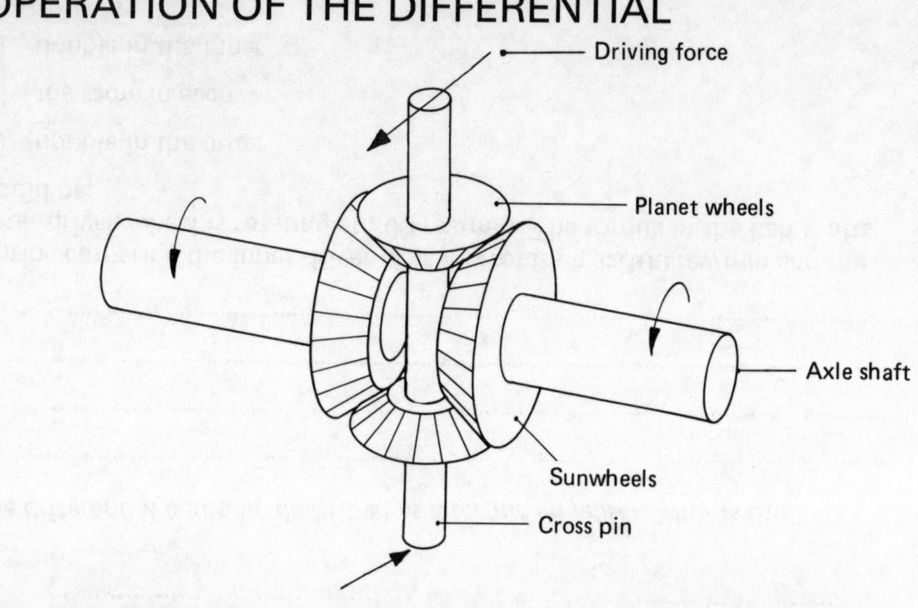


It can be seen from the drawing above that the planet wheels are pulled round by the cross pin. If the resistance to rotation at each axle shaft is equal, the sunwheels will rotate at the same speed as the cross pin, that is there is no relative rotation between planet wheels and sunwheels.
Under what conditions would this occur?

..............................................................................................

**Investigation**

Observe the action of a differential by rotating the sunwheels at different speeds to each other and describe the action of the planet wheels.

..............................................................................................

..............................................................................................

..............................................................................................

By the action of the planet wheels rotating on the cross pin the sunwheels must rotate at different speeds (cornering), while still receiving equal driving torque from the planet wheels.

# REAR AXLE

One type of rear axle casing is shown below. In this arrangement the 'bolt on' housing contains the final drive and differential with the tubular section carrying the axle shafts, hubs and brake assemblies.

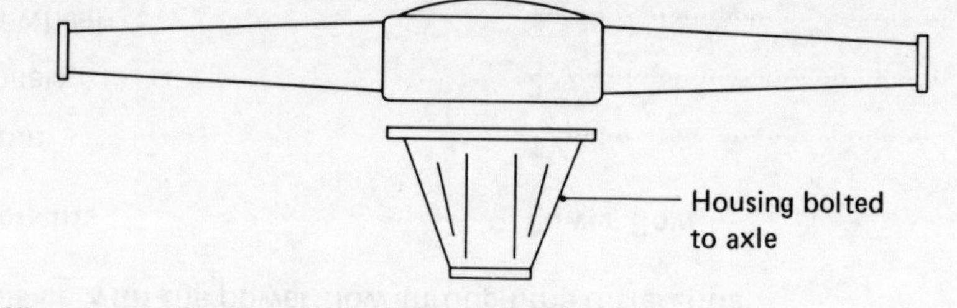


(a) What type of axle construction is this?

..............................................................................................

(b) What other purposes on the vehicle does the rear axle as a whole fulfil?

..............................................................................................

..............................................................................................

..............................................................................................

(c) The road wheels are attached to hubs which rotate on bearings at either end of the rear axle. Complete the sketch to show how the drive is transmitted from the differential sunwheels to the road wheel and hub assembly. Name the parts.

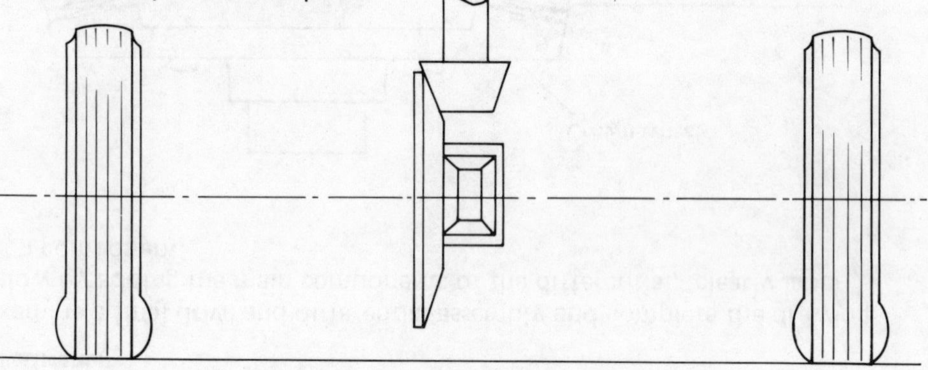

# REAR AXLE HUB CONSTRUCTION

Three types of hub construction are illustrated by the *very much simplified* drawings. The single, most important, factor when considering the differences in construction is the bearing arrangement. Name the type of construction in each case and complete the labelling on the drawings.

Type 1 ....................................

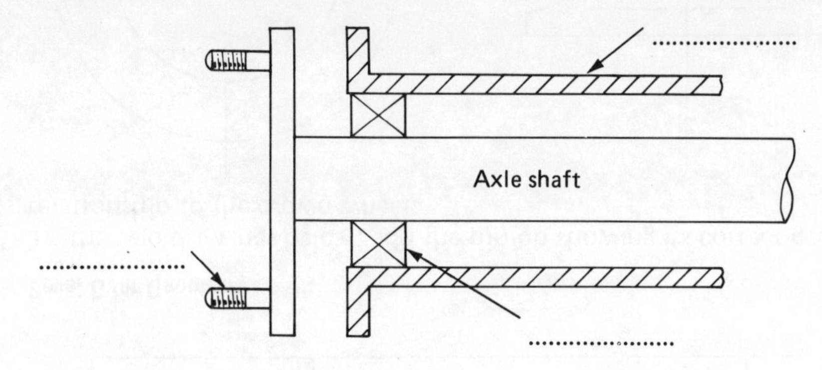


Type 2 ....................................

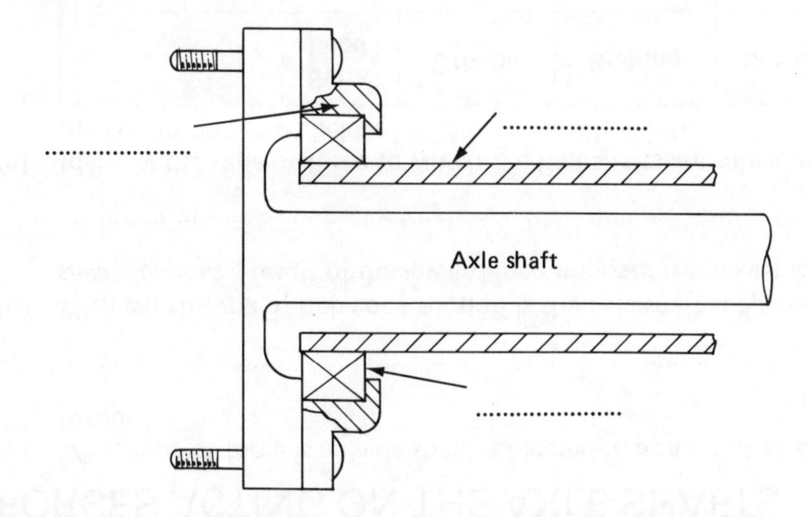


Type 3 ....................................................................

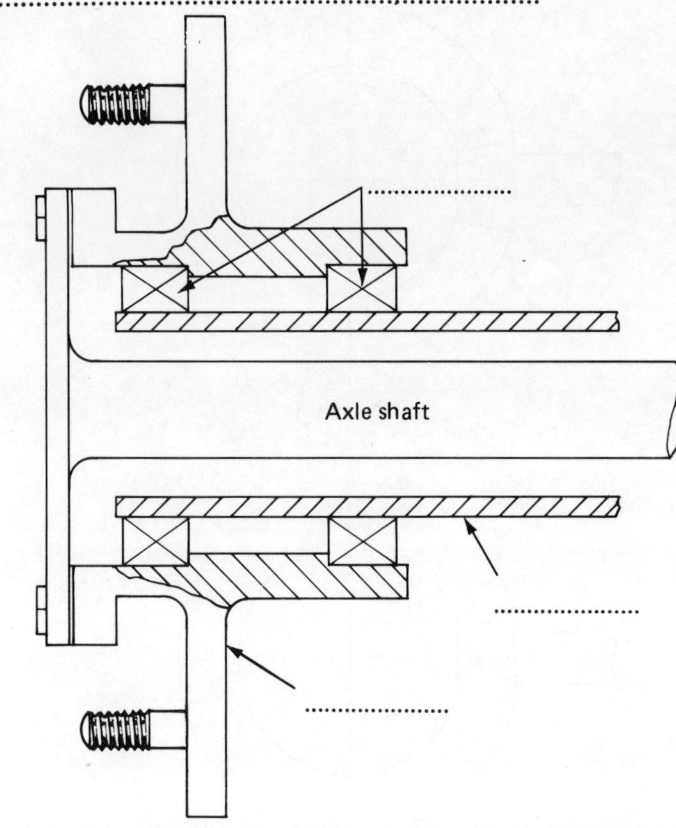


(a) Give examples of vehicle types in which the hub arrangements shown are used.

Type 1. ..........................................................................................

Type 2. ..........................................................................................

Type 3. ..........................................................................................

(b) In the event of an axle shaft breakage, which of the three types could allow the vehicle to be towed safely?

..........................................................................................................

B4: 14,15,17

# FORCES ACTING ON THE AXLE SHAFTS

(a) What type of force is an axle shaft subjected to as a result of driving torque?

...................................................................................................

(b) With which type of hub construction is the axle shaft subjected to a *shear force* as a result of downward load imposed by the vehicle weight?

...................................................................................................

(c) Identify the type of force to which the half shafts are subjected under the conditions listed below for semi- and fully floating hubs.

| | **Static Load** | **Driving** | **Braking** | **Cornering** |
|---|---|---|---|---|
| Semi-floating | | | | |
| Fully floating | | | | |

**Bevel Gear Geometry**

To the two drawings below, add the pinion showing its correct geometrical relationship to the crown wheel.

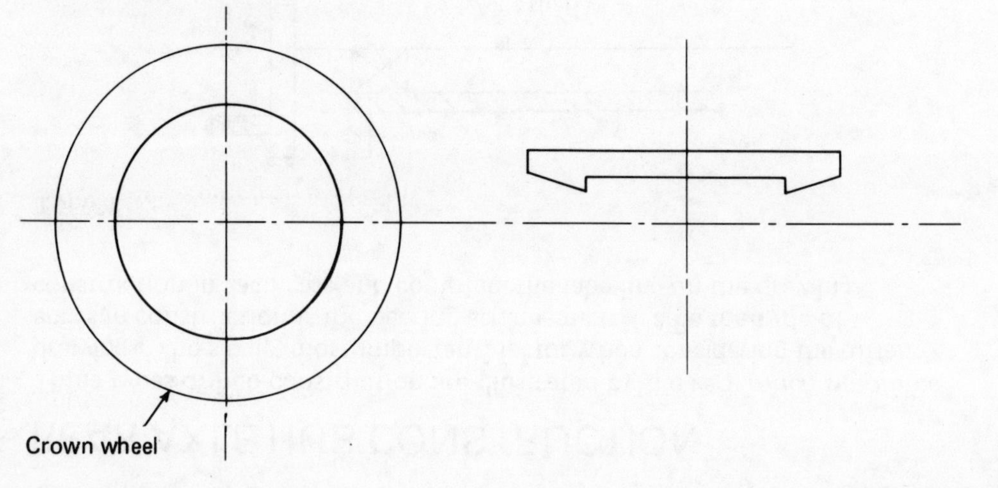


**Forces acting on the pinion (Spiral Bevel Gears)**

Certain forces act on the final drive pinion as a result of transmitting a driving force, for example the *axial* thrust on the pinion. This occurs when drive is transmitted or the vehicle is on over-run (as when using the engine as a brake).

Add arrows to the drawings below to show the direction of force due to this 'axial' thrust at the pinion. Show the general shape of the gear teeth.

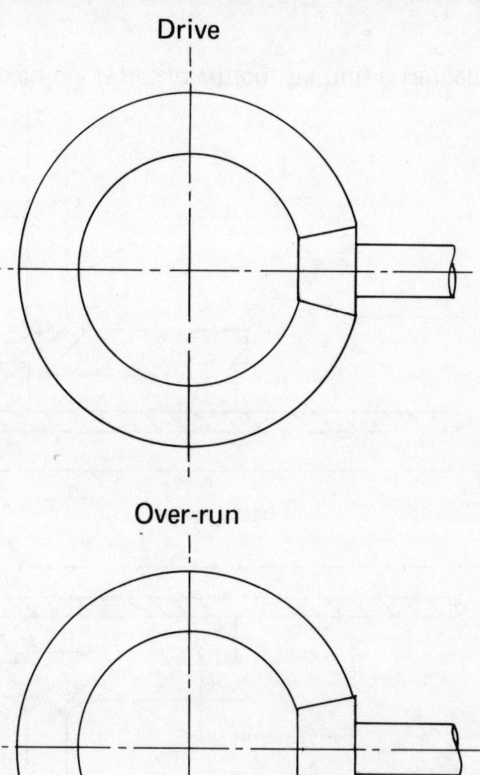

## TORQUE REACTION

When the drive is being transmitted the pinion exerts a force on the crown wheel teeth thus producing a 'driving torque' on the half shafts.

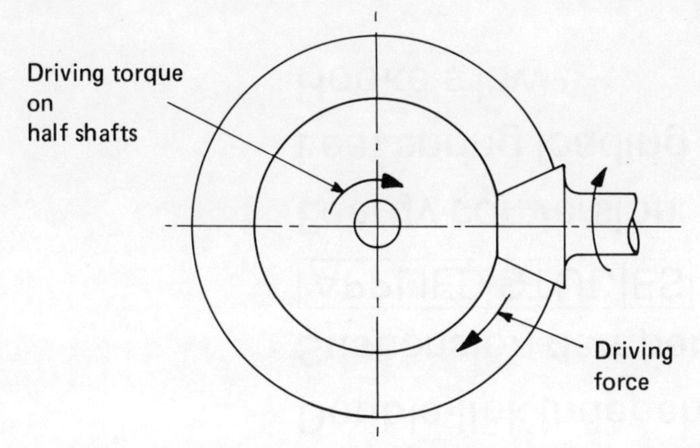


When a force is exerted an 'equal and opposite' force is established. In this case it acts on the pinion resulting in an effect known as torque reaction. Show by an arrow on the drawing below the direction in which the pinion *tends* to move when it turns the crown wheel clockwise.

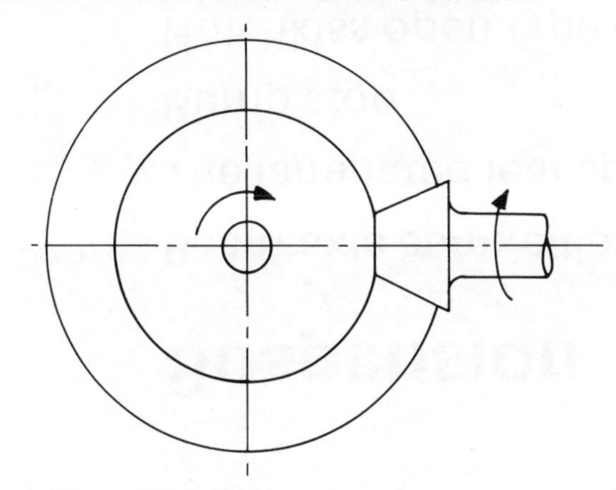

From this, the important conclusions to note are:

1. The *driving torque* is transmitted to the *axle shafts.*

2. The *torque reaction* is transmitted to the ..................................................

## EFFECT OF DRIVE TORQUE REACTION

(a) The effect of drive torque reaction is to twist the axle out of its normal operating position. Complete the second sketch to show this.

*Position before take up of drive*

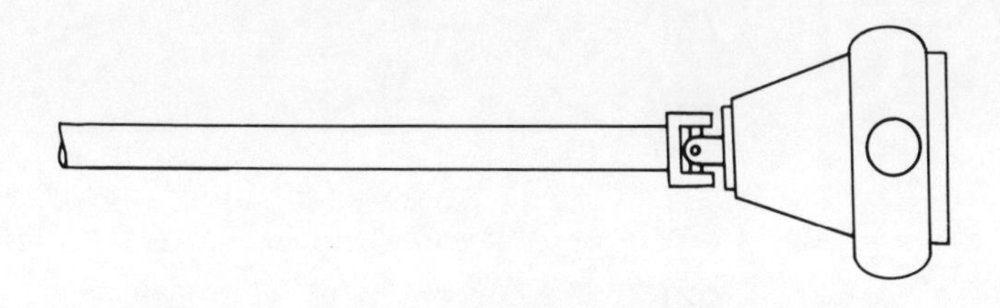

*Position during take up of drive*

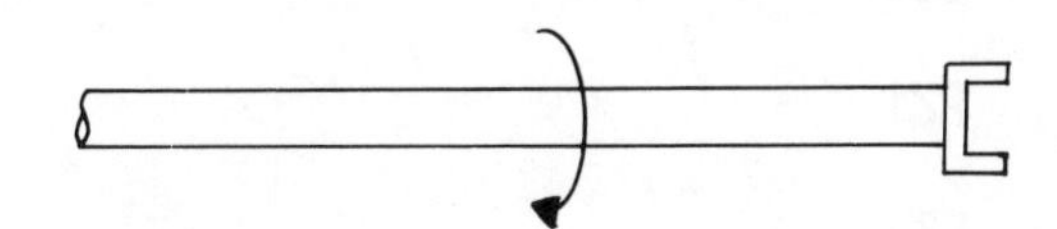

(b) Under which operating conditions are the forces on the driving axle at a maximum due to drive torque reaction?

..........................................................................................................

..........................................................................................................

..........................................................................................................

..........................................................................................................

..........................................................................................................

..........................................................................................................

..........................................................................................................

# B5.

# Suspension

B5: 1,3,5

The suspension on a vehicle performs two functions:

1. It insulates the vehicle body, hence the passengers or load, from shocks as the vehicle travels over irregularities in the road surface.
2. It assists in keeping the tyres in close contact with the road surface to ensure adequate adhesion for accelerating, braking and cornering.

One of the simplest and most widely used forms of suspension is the *beam axle semi-elliptic leaf spring* arrangement. This system is used at the rear of many cars and at both the front and rear of most

.................................................................................................

# BEAM AXLE SEMI-ELLIPTIC LEAF SPRING SUSPENSION

(a) Complete the labelling on the drawing:

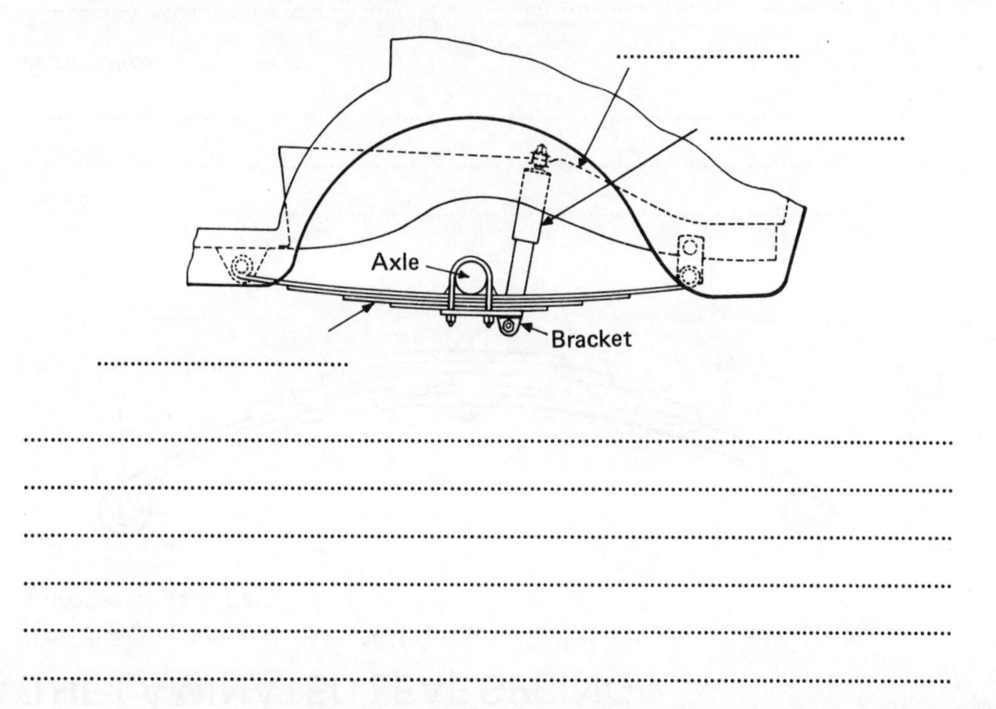


.................................................................................................

.................................................................................................

.................................................................................................

.................................................................................................

.................................................................................................

.................................................................................................

(b) Name and briefly describe the four suspension conditions illustrated below

.................................................................................................

.................................................................................................

.................................................................................................

.................................................................................................

B5: 2,4,6,8

# THE LAMINATED LEAF SPRING

The drawing below shows a leaf spring. Label the drawing and state the purpose of each part.

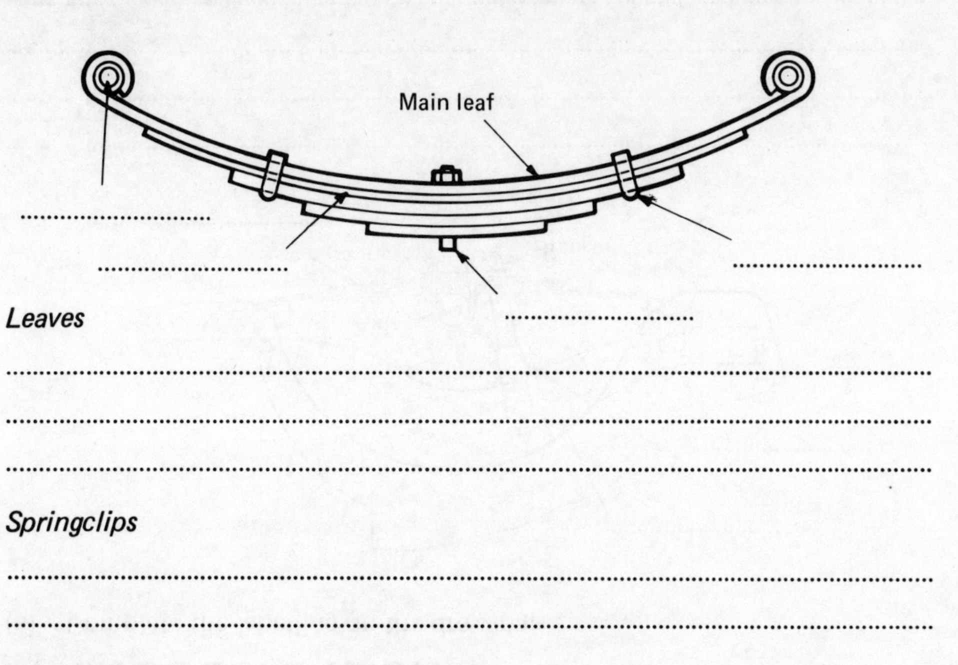


*Leaves*

*Springclips*

*Centre bolt*

*Spring eye bushes*

Why is this type of spring said to be semi-elliptical?

The simplified sketch (a) below shows how the leaf spring is attached to the chassis.

State the purpose of the swinging shackle and complete sketch (b) to show the action of the shackle as the spring is deflected.

Swinging shackle

(a) (b)

**Investigation**

(a) Examine a leaf spring and axle assembly (car type) and make a sketch to show how the spring is secured and located on the axle.

(b) Sketch and label the spring eye bush.

B5: 7,9,10

## BUMP STOP

(a) What is the purpose of a *bump stop* in a suspension system?

..............................................................................................................

..............................................................................................................

**Investigation**

(a) Examine a car with a leaf spring arrangement at the rear and make a sketch to show how the spring movement is limited.

(b) On certain vehicles a flexible strap connects the axle to the chassis. Why is this?

..............................................................................................................

## HOTCHKISS OPEN TYPE DRIVE

The drawing at the top opposite is of a Hotchkiss 'open type' drive arrangement. The driving force or 'tractive effort', produced at the point where the tyre contacts the road surface, results in a driving thrust on the vehicle frame. Add arrows to the drawing to show how the driving thrust is transmitted to the chassis.

..............................................................................................................

..............................................................................................................

..............................................................................................................

..............................................................................................................

..............................................................................................................

..............................................................................................................

(c) Why is this drive arrangement known as the 'open type'?

..............................................................................................................

..............................................................................................................

..............................................................................................................

## TORQUE REACTION

'Drive torque reaction' rotates the axle casing and when the brakes are applied the 'brake torque reaction' rotates the casing in the opposite direction. In the suspension arrangement shown above the leaf spring resists this torque.

Complete the drawing on the right below to show the effects of brake torque reaction on the spring.

*Drive torque reaction* *Brake torque reaction*

# HELICAL SPRINGS

(a) State the advantages of a helical or coil spring over a laminated leaf spring.

**Advantages**

1. ........................................................
2. ........................................................
3. ........................................................
4. ........................................................
5. ........................................................

As the term implies 'independent suspension' describes a suspension system in which the suspension at one wheel operates completely independently of the opposite wheel on the other side of the vehicle. This is not the case with a beam axle suspension when, if one wheel rises over a bump, the other wheel on the same axle is also affected.

Complete the sketch below to show how the other wheel is affected as one wheel rises over a bump with beam axle suspension.

*View of axle from front*

# DOUBLE-LINK INDEPENDENT SUSPENSION

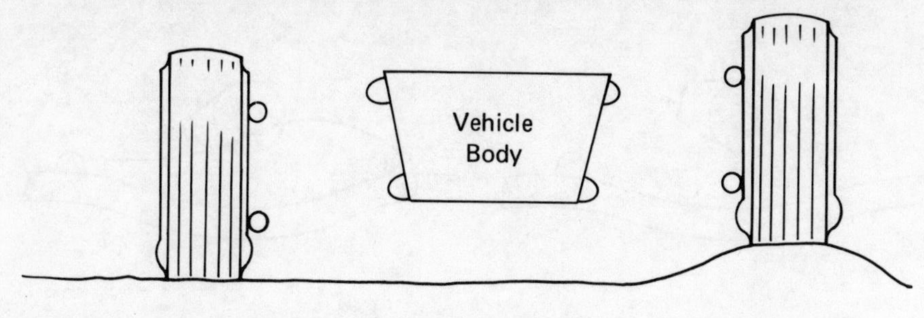


The drawing above is a simplified representation of a double-link independent suspension system. Complete the drawing to show the springs and the suspension as one wheel rises over a bump.

**Investigation**

Examine a vehicle fitted with a double-link independent front suspension which uses a helical spring and complete the drawing below to show one side. Label all major components.

Vehicle make/model ............................................ Year ..............................

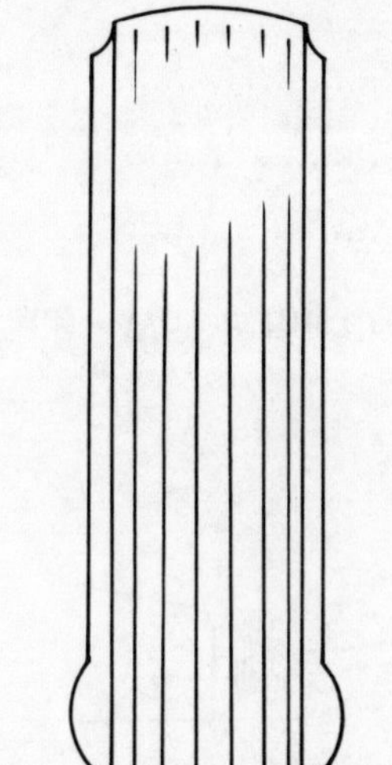

B5: 2,3,14,15,16

(a) State the meaning of the terms i.f.s. and i.r.s.

i.f.s. ..............................................................................................

i.r.s. ..............................................................................................

(b) State the advantages of independent suspension over beam-axle suspension.

1 ..............................................................................................

2 ..............................................................................................

3 ..............................................................................................

4 ..............................................................................................

5 ..............................................................................................

The main disadvantages of independent suspension are that it is usually more complicated and costly and the tyres tend to wear unevenly.

(c) In the suspension arrangement shown below 's' is the spring. Complete the labelling on the drawing and name this type of spring.

..........................................spring.

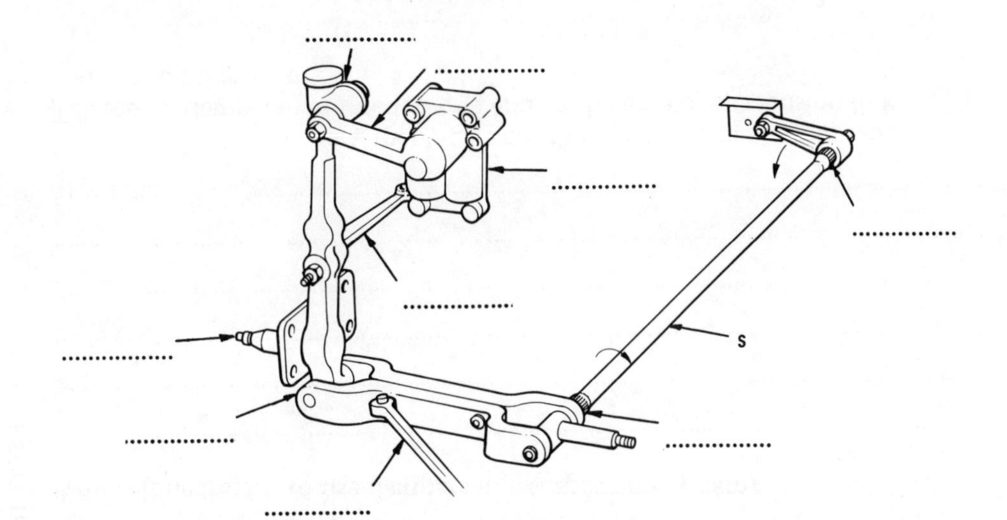


(d) Name the type of spring in each of the suspension arrangements shown below.

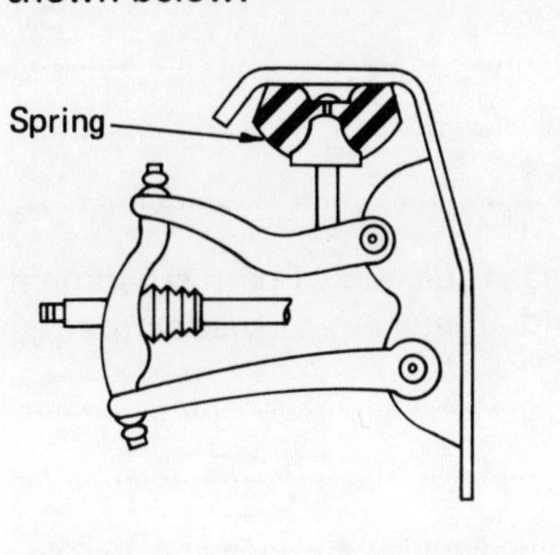


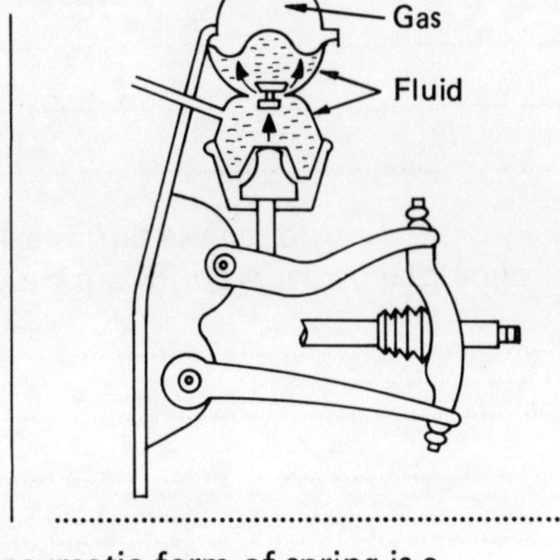


.............................................. ..............................................

(e) The suspension shown with the pneumatic form of spring is a 'hydro-pneumatic' suspension. Why is it so called?

..............................................................................................

..............................................................................................

..............................................................................................

(f) In the hydro-pneumatic suspension system the individual suspension units are interconnected. How are they interconnected?

..............................................................................................

(g) Give examples of modern vehicles which use the types of suspension springs illustrated on this page.

| Vehicle | Type of spring |
|---|---|
| | |
| | |
| | |

# SUSPENSION DAMPERS

Why is it necessary to use dampers in a suspension system?

....................................................................................................

....................................................................................................

....................................................................................................

....................................................................................................

....................................................................................................

The dampers used on very many cars are the hydraulic telescopic type. Telescopic dampers are fixed at one end to the axle or suspension link and at the other to the

....................................................................................................

**Principle of operation**

Piston Rod

Fluid Seal

Reservoir

Complete the simplified drawing of the telescopic damper shown and briefly describe its operation.

....................................................................................................

....................................................................................................

....................................................................................................

....................................................................................................

....................................................................................................

....................................................................................................

....................................................................................................

....................................................................................................

....................................................................................................

....................................................................................................

....................................................................................................

## APPLIED STUDIES

# ENERGY CONVERSION

When a spring is defected for example

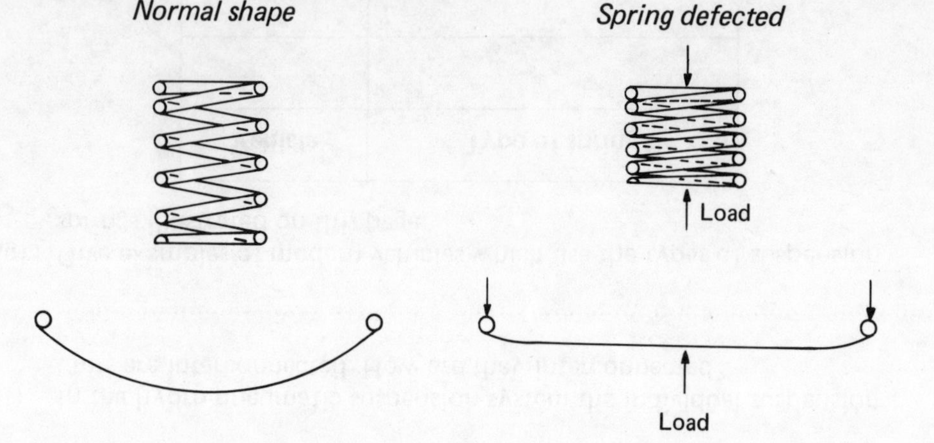


*Mechanical energy* creates the deflection.

(a) What happens to the energy in an 'undamped' spring?

....................................................................................................

....................................................................................................

....................................................................................................

....................................................................................................

....................................................................................................

(b) What happens to the energy put into the spring when an hydraulic damper is used to prevent excessive spring oscillation?

....................................................................................................

....................................................................................................

....................................................................................................

....................................................................................................

....................................................................................................

# APPLIED STUDIES (SUSPENSION)

B5: 19–22

It has already been established that drive and brake torque reaction rotates the axle casing and that in certain suspension arrangements the leaf springs resist the movement.

(a) What effect do the forces due to torque reaction have on a leaf spring?

..............................................................................................................

..............................................................................................................

From the main leaf the leaves of a laminated spring are progressively shorter in length. This obviously makes the spring deeper in section towards the centre or axle mounting.

(b) Add an arrow to the drawing below to indicate the point on the spring where the greatest load is imposed.

..............................................................................................................

..............................................................................................................

..............................................................................................................

..............................................................................................................

..............................................................................................................

..............................................................................................................

..............................................................................................................

(c) Why are the spring leaves of different length?

..............................................................................................................

..............................................................................................................

..............................................................................................................

..............................................................................................................

..............................................................................................................

..............................................................................................................

..............................................................................................................

..............................................................................................................

**Inter-leaf friction**

When a laminated leaf spring flexes the individual leaves slide over each other. Friction due to this action can be an advantage or a disadvantage.

(d) Give examples of the advantages and disadvantages of inter-leaf friction.

Advantages:

..............................................................................................................

Disadvantages:

..............................................................................................................

..............................................................................................................

(e) How can inter-leaf friction be reduced?

..............................................................................................................

..............................................................................................................

..............................................................................................................

..............................................................................................................

..............................................................................................................

..............................................................................................................

..............................................................................................................

**Load-deflection characteristics**

The amount of spring deflection for a given load depends on a number of factors. With a leaf spring these include:

1 ....................................................................................................

2 ....................................................................................................

3 ....................................................................................................

4 ....................................................................................................

(a) The softness of the ride in a vehicle is, to a large extent, controlled by the *spring rate.* What is meant by this term?

....................................................................................................

....................................................................................................

....................................................................................................

....................................................................................................

*high rate* springs will give a ........................................ride, and

*low rate* springs will give a ........................................ride.

(b) How does the length of a leaf spring affect the spring rate?

....................................................................................................

....................................................................................................

*Hooke's Law*

Hooke's law, related to springs, is concerned with the LOAD and the DEFLECTION of a spring.

(c) State Hooke's Law.

....................................................................................................

....................................................................................................

....................................................................................................

**Experiment**

Conduct a simple experiment to verify Hooke's Law. Sketch the apparatus used and enter the results in the table below.

Apparatus:

Results:

Original spring length ....................................mm

| Load (N) | Extension (mm) |
|---|---|
| | |
| | |
| | |
| | |

(d) To what 'law' does the relationship of load and extension conform?

....................................................................................................

....................................................................................................

B6.

# Wheels And Tyres

# TYPES OF ROAD WHEEL

Various designs of road wheels are in use on both cars and goods vehicles. On cars the pressed steel type of wheel has been used more than any other. Name two other types of road wheel in use on cars.

1. ................................................ 2. ................................................

**Investigation**

Remove a wheel from a hub and complete the drawing below (with labels) to show how the wheel is secured and located.

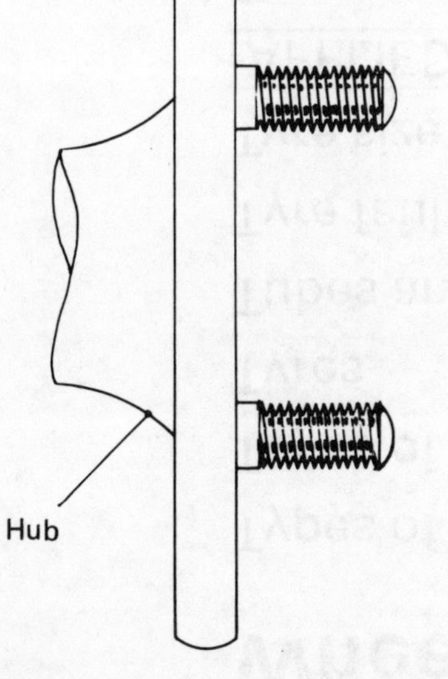


What is the purpose of the taper on the wheel nuts?

..............................................................................................................

Three types of car road wheels are shown opposite. Name the types and list the advantages and disadvantages of each.

..............................................

Advantages

..............................................

..............................................

..............................................

Disadvantages

..............................................

..............................................

..............................................

..............................................

Advantages

..............................................

..............................................

..............................................

Disadvantages

..............................................

..............................................

..............................................

..............................................

Advantages

..............................................

..............................................

..............................................

Disadvantages

..............................................

..............................................

..............................................

B6: 2,3,7

# TYPES OF WHEEL RIM

Three types of wheel rim design are shown on this page. The *well base rim* shown below is used on cars and light goods vehicles.

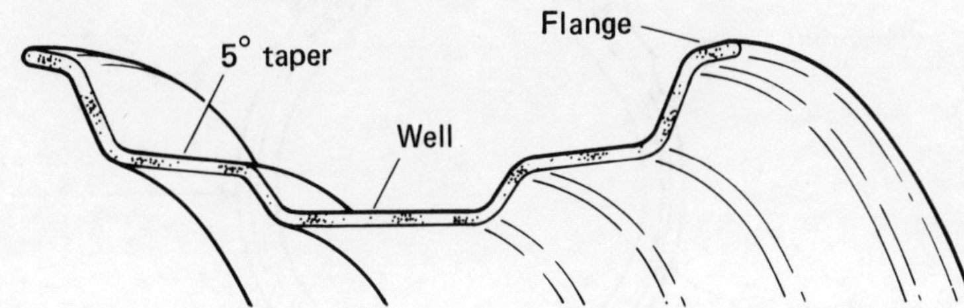


State the purpose of the well in the rim above.

..................................................................................

..................................................................................

..................................................................................

..................................................................................

..................................................................................

List four safety precautions to be observed when fitting or inflating tyres on the rims shown.

..................................................................................

..................................................................................

..................................................................................

..................................................................................

..................................................................................

..................................................................................

..................................................................................

..................................................................................

..................................................................................

..................................................................................

..................................................................................

(c) Name the types of wheel rim shown below.

1. ..................................................................................

Detachable flange

Flat base

This type of rim is used on certain goods vehicles. Removal of the flange allows large tyres, which have a stiff bead structure to be fitted easily on to the rim.

2. ..................................................................................

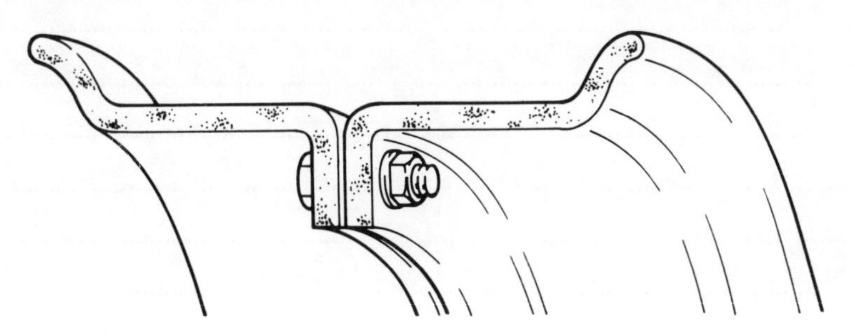

On which type of vehicle is the 'split rim' used and why is the rim split?

..................................................................................

..................................................................................

..................................................................................

..................................................................................

..................................................................................

..................................................................................

..................................................................................

# TYRES

The pneumatic tyre was originally developed for use on vehicles by J. B. Dunlop in the year 1888. Its main advantages over the solid tyres, in use at that time, were that it provided a cushion for the vehicle against road shocks and it rolled with greater ease.

However, pneumatic tyres also fulfil a number of other functions:

1. ..................................................
2. ..................................................
3. ..................................................
4. ..................................................
5. ..................................................

**Tyre Construction**

The tyre is a flexible rubber casing which is reinforced or supported by other materials, for example Rayon, Cotton, Nylon, Steel.

Label the main parts on the tyre section shown below.

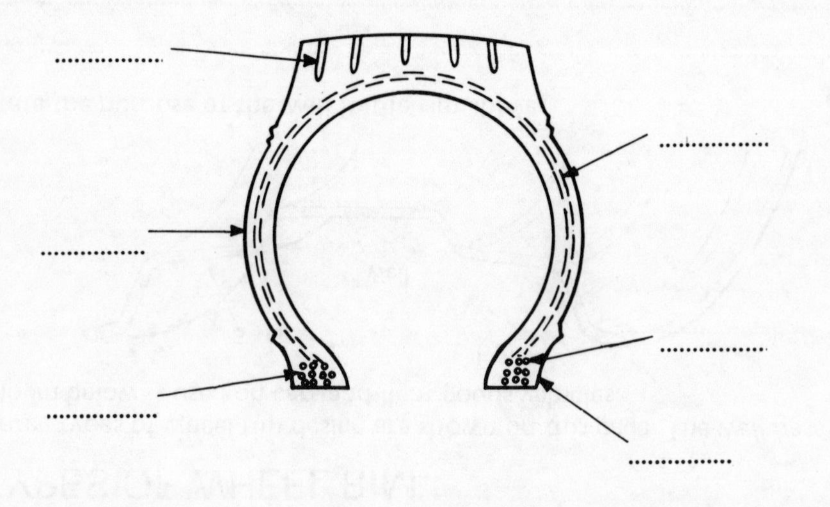

# TUBED AND TUBELESS TYRES

Tubeless tyres have now largely superceded tubed tyres on cars. Outline the essential differences between the two designs.

Tubed tyre

..................................................

..................................................

..................................................

Tubeless tyres

..................................................

..................................................

..................................................

..................................................

..................................................

..................................................

The drawings below show tubed and tubeless tyre valves. Label the parts of the sectioned valve.

*Tubed valve*

Valve stem

Slots

Wheel

Tube

*Tubeless valve*

Wheel

(c) What is the purpose of the slots in the outer stem of the tubed valve?

..................................................

..................................................

B6: 5.8

State three advantages of tubeless tyres over tubed tyres.

......................................................................................................................

......................................................................................................................

......................................................................................................................

......................................................................................................................

......................................................................................................................

......................................................................................................................

......................................................................................................................

......................................................................................................................

**Types of tyre construction**

The two principal types of tyre construction used on road vehicles are:

1. ......................................................................................................

2. ......................................................................................................

A tyre casing consists of *plies* which are layers of material looped around the beads to form a case. The basic difference in structure between radial and diagonal ply tyres is in the arrangement of the casing plies.

With diagonal ply construction the ply 'cords' form an angle of approximately ......................................to the tyre bead, radial ply cords form an angle of ......................................to the tyre bead.

Radial ply tyres are in use on most cars and on many goods vehicles.

Add lines to the two outlines at the top opposite to show the position of the cords in relation to the tyre bead.

*Radial ply* *Diagonal ply*

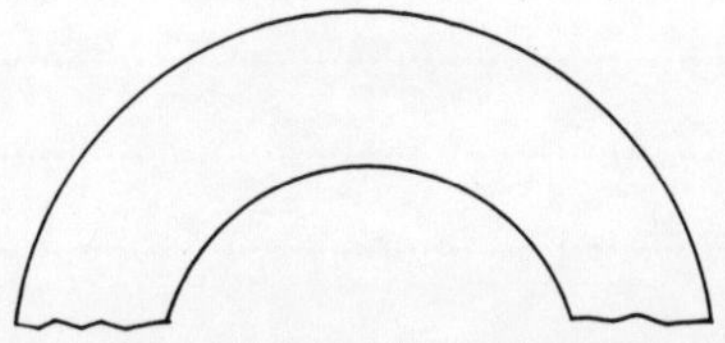

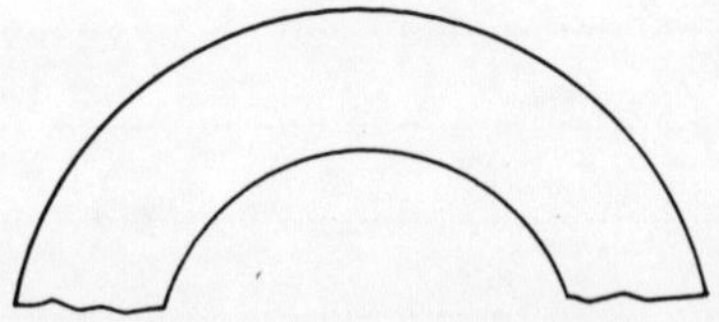

Label the tyre sections illustrated below.

......................................................................................................................

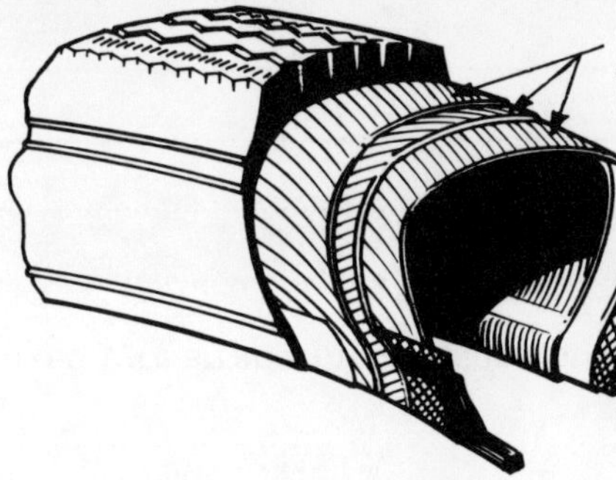

..................................

......................................................................................................................

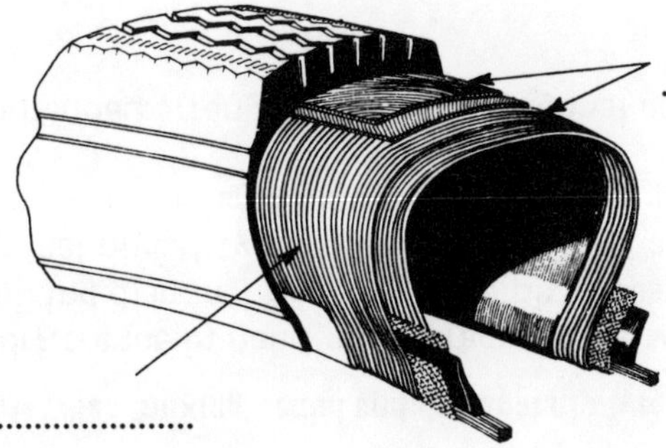

..................................

..................................

One feature of the radial ply tyre is that the walls are more flexible than the diagonal ply tyre. Why is this?

......................................................................................................................

......................................................................................................................

......................................................................................................................

List the advantages of radial ply construction over diagonal ply construction.

Advantages

*Radial ply construction*

..........................................................................................................

..........................................................................................................

..........................................................................................................

..........................................................................................................

..........................................................................................................

..........................................................................................................

..........................................................................................................

..........................................................................................................

..........................................................................................................

List the advantages of diagonal ply construction over radial ply construction.

Advantages

*Diagonal or Cross Ply construction*

..........................................................................................................

..........................................................................................................

..........................................................................................................

..........................................................................................................

..........................................................................................................

..........................................................................................................

Note: The radial ply tyre has virtually replaced the diagonal ply tyre for car applications.

Why does a radial ply tyre normally give longer tread life than a diagonal ply tyre?

..........................................................................................................

..........................................................................................................

..........................................................................................................

**Safety requirements when 'mixing' radial and diagonal ply tyres**

Because of the difference in handling characteristics, vehicle instability can be created by mixing diagonal ply and radial ply tyres. It is best to use all radial or all diagonal ply. If tyres are to be mixed on a vehicle the arrangement must conform to the legal requirement regarding tyre fitment.

State the recommended arrangement when diagonal and radial ply tyres are mixed.

..........................................................................................................

..........................................................................................................

..........................................................................................................

Why are some mixed tyre arrangements dangerous?

..........................................................................................................

..........................................................................................................

..........................................................................................................

..........................................................................................................

..........................................................................................................

..........................................................................................................

..........................................................................................................

..........................................................................................................

..........................................................................................................

..........................................................................................................

..........................................................................................................

# TYRE FAULTS

Certain tyre defects make it illegal to use a vehicle on a public road. Outline the main legal requirements with regard to the tyre faults listed below.

*Tread wear*

........................................................................................................................

........................................................................................................................

........................................................................................................................

........................................................................................................................

*Cuts*

........................................................................................................................

........................................................................................................................

........................................................................................................................

........................................................................................................................

........................................................................................................................

*Lumps and bulges*

........................................................................................................................

........................................................................................................................

........................................................................................................................

**Investigation**

Examine the tyres on a vehicle and complete the table below.

| Position | Tread depth | | Pressure | Other defects | Serviceability |
|---|---|---|---|---|---|
| | Maximum | Minimum | | | |
| Front O/S | | | | | |
| Rear O/S | | | | | |
| Front N/S | | | | | |
| Rear N/S | | | | | |
| Spare | | | | | |

# TYRE SIZE MARKINGS

The size of a tyre is indicated by two dimensions on the sidewall, for example

5.20 – 13 or 145 – 13

Identify the part to which each tyre size refers by adding these dimensions to the diagrams below.

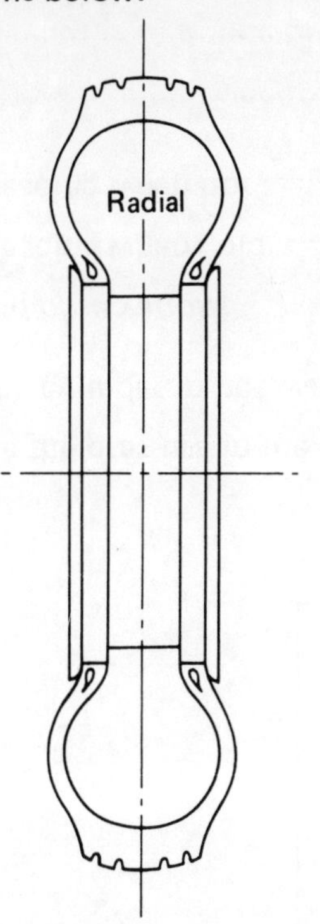


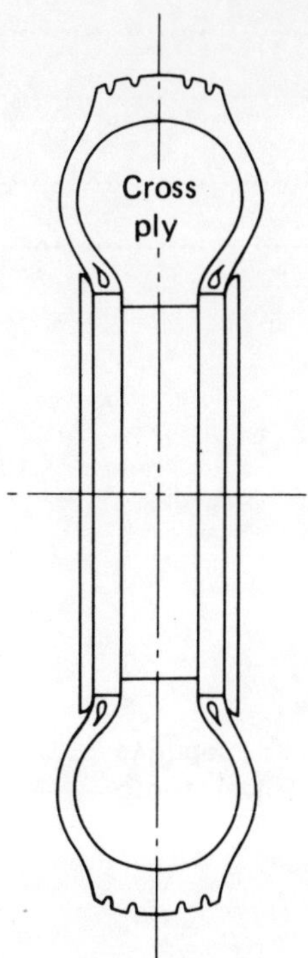

# APPLIED STUDIES

**Tyre Pressures**

The inflation pressure of a tyre depends upon the size and type of tyre and the loan to be carried. For the average family saloon car, tyre pressures are usually in the region of

..............................................................................................................

At what intervals is it advisable to check the tyre pressures on a vehicle?

..............................................................................................................

State three effects of 'under inflation'.

1. ..........................................................................................................
2. ..........................................................................................................
3. ..........................................................................................................

State two effects of 'over inflation'.

1. ..........................................................................................................
2. ..........................................................................................................

**Relationship between pressure and temperature**

The air pressure in a tyre varies with temperature change. After a long fast run the air temperature in a tyre will increase. How does this affect the tyre pressure?

..............................................................................................................

What is a typical tyre pressure change after a long run?

..............................................................................................................

..............................................................................................................

..............................................................................................................

..............................................................................................................

**Change of Pressure with temperature**

An experiment to show the change in pressure of air, when its temperature is raised, can be performed using the type of equipment shown below. Note: volume remains constant.

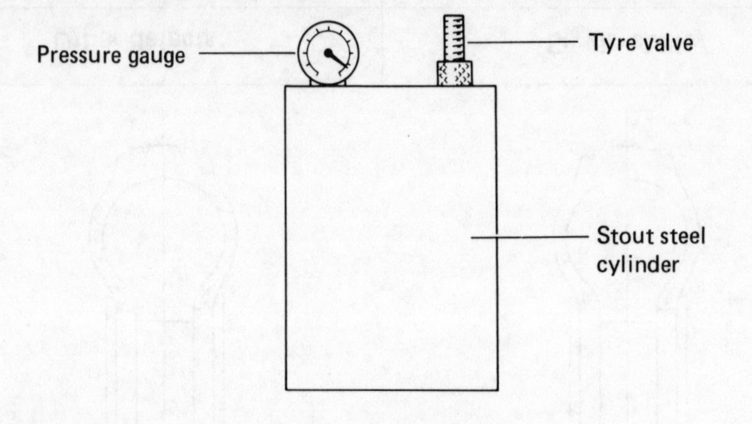


1. Increase the pressure in the cylinder to 30 p.s.i.
2. Place the cylinder in hot water.

*Results and observations*

Pressure reading when cold ..............................................

Pressure reading when hot ..............................................

..............................................................................................................

..............................................................................................................

..............................................................................................................

Considering the relationship between pressure and temperature, should tyre pressures be checked after a long run when hot or before when cold?

..............................................................................................................

..............................................................................................................

# B7.

# Brakes

B7: 1,13,33

# THE BRAKING SYSTEM

The braking system provides the driver of a vehicle with a means of safely slowing down (or retarding) the vehicle and bringing it to a halt. When the brakes are applied ......................... is generated which converts the energy of movement, .............................. energy into .............................. energy.

**Simple Mechanically Operated Drum Brake**

The drawing on the left below shows a simple 'cam' operated drum brake in the 'off' position. Complete the drawing on the right to show the brake in the applied position.

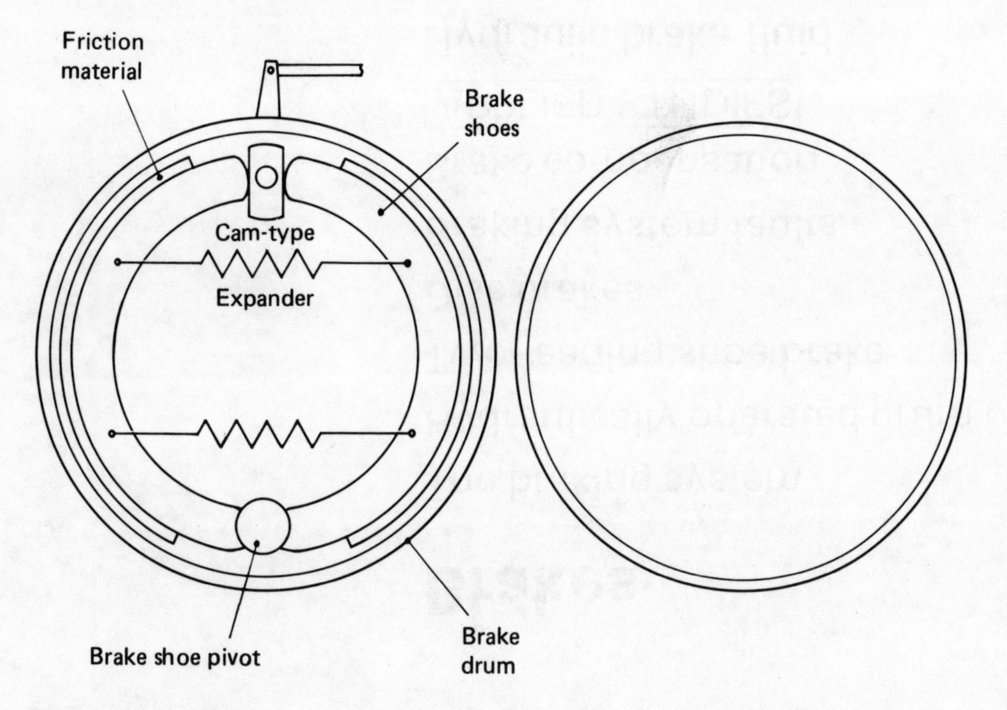


Which two methods are used to secure the friction material to the brake shoes?

..............................................................................................................

The simplified braking system shown below is a

.............................................................. system.

Cables

Brake Pedal

Comment on the use of mechanically operated brakes on cars.

..............................................................................................................

..............................................................................................................

..............................................................................................................

..............................................................................................................

..............................................................................................................

..............................................................................................................

What is the most common friction material used for brake linings?

..............................................................................................................

What health hazards are associated with the dust from this friction material?

..............................................................................................................

..............................................................................................................

..............................................................................................................

..............................................................................................................

B7: 2,3,4,5,13,14

# HYDRAULICALLY OPERATED DRUM BRAKES

Most modern car braking systems and many light commercial vehicle braking systems are operated hydraulically. Label the parts on the single-line hydraulic drum brake layout below.

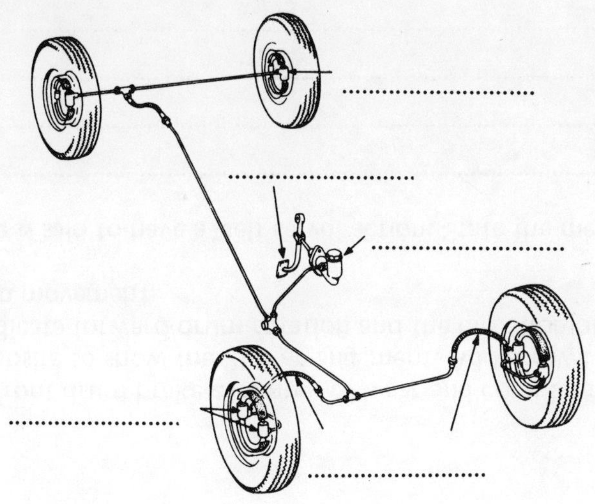

*Operation*

Which vehicles usually use drum brakes at each wheel?

What is the reason for using flexible pipes in parts of the hydraulic system?

Name the parts in the drum brake assembly below

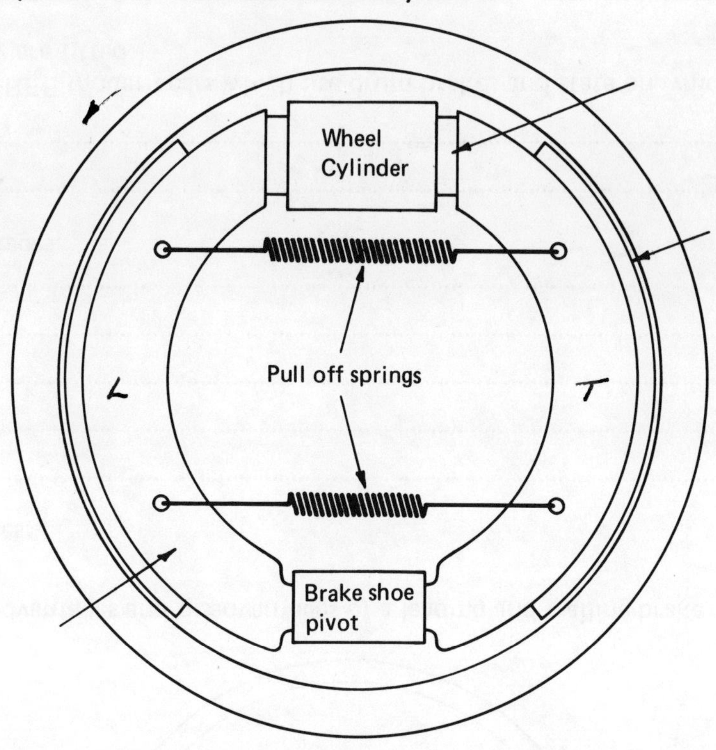


The drawing above shows a 'double-piston wheel cylinder' acting on a *leading brake shoe* and a *trailing brake shoe.* The leading shoe is pressed harder against the drum by drum rotation whereas the trailing shoe tends to be forced away by drum rotation. A much greater braking effect is therefore obtained from a leading shoe.

Indicate drum rotation on the above drawing and show which is the leading and which is the trailing shoe.

Why does the leading shoe wear at a greater rate than the trailing shoe?

# TWO-LEADING SHOE BRAKE

Front drum brakes are normally two-leading shoe arrangements. What is the reason for this?

..............................................................................................................

..............................................................................................................

..............................................................................................................

..............................................................................................................

..............................................................................................................

..............................................................................................................

..............................................................................................................

..............................................................................................................

..............................................................................................................

..............................................................................................................

**Investigation**

Examine the front drum brake assembly of a car and complete the drawing at the top opposite to show the 2LS arrangement. Add arrows to the drawing to indicate forward drum rotation and the direction of wheel cylinder piston movement.

A leading shoe is said to have a 'self servo' action. State the meaning of this.

..............................................................................................................

..............................................................................................................

..............................................................................................................

..............................................................................................................

..............................................................................................................

On what do the brakes shoes in a 2LS assembly pivot?

..............................................................................................................

*Front drum brake assembly (2LS)*

List the advantages and disadvantages of a leading and trailing brake assembly.

Advantages:

1. ..........................................................................................

   ..........................................................................................

2. ..........................................................................................

3. ..........................................................................................

   ..........................................................................................

Disadvantages:

1. ..........................................................................................

2. ..........................................................................................

Name THREE modern cars which use drum brakes and state on which axles they are fitted.

..............................................................................................................

B7: 9–12

# DISC BRAKES

A disadvantage with drum brakes is that repeated brake applications at high speeds, for example fast driving along winding roads or during long downhill descents, causes a gradual build-up in temperature of the brake assemblies particularly the linings and drums. Too great an increase in temperature reduces the efficiency of the brakes making it more difficult to stop the vehicle. In effect the brakes may become temporarily useless.

This fall-off in brake performance is known as

..........................................................................................................

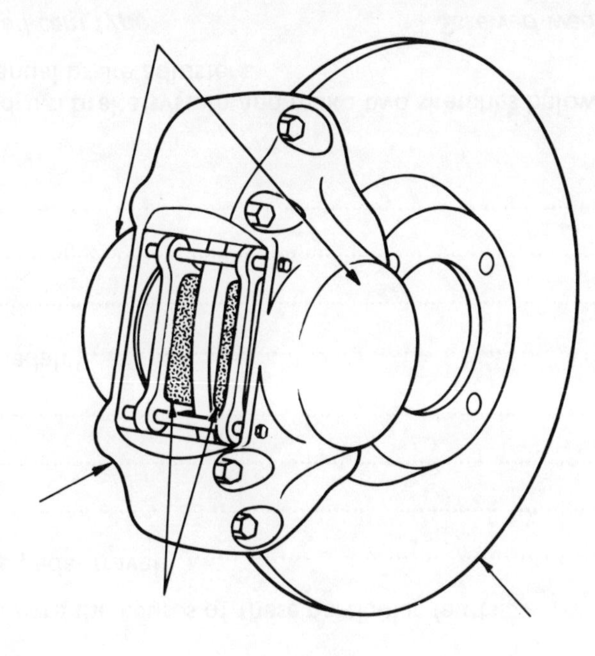

**Investigation**

Examine a front disc brake assembly and name the component to which the brake caliper is attached.

..........................................................................................................

Disc brakes are now in use on most car front brakes and at both front and rear on many of the larger and faster cars. The disc brake, shown opposite operates rather like a bicycle brake, that is friction pads are clamped on to a rotating disc by a caliper mechanism.

(a) Label the parts on the simplified disc brake shown opposite.

(b) List the advantages and disadvantages of the disc brake when compared with the drum brake.

Advantages:

..........................................................................................................

..........................................................................................................

..........................................................................................................

..........................................................................................................

..........................................................................................................

..........................................................................................................

Disadvantages:

..........................................................................................................

..........................................................................................................

..........................................................................................................

..........................................................................................................

..........................................................................................................

A vacuum servo is part of the braking system on many modern cars, in particular vehicles with disc brakes. Why is the servo used?

..........................................................................................................

..........................................................................................................

..........................................................................................................

..........................................................................................................

..........................................................................................................

..........................................................................................................

B7: 15,16,19

# BRAKING SYSTEM FAULTS

Many faults can occur in a braking system, two of the most common being;

1. Excessive footbrake pedal travel.
2. A 'spongy' feel when the footbrake pedal is depressed.

What usually are the causes of these particular faults.

1. Excessive pedal travel: ....................................................

..............................................................................

..............................................................................

..............................................................................

2. Spongy pedal: ..............................................................

..............................................................................

..............................................................................

..............................................................................

**Investigation**

Examine a drum brake system and make two sketches below to show two types of manual brake adjusters.

*Snail cam type* *Screwed wedge type*

Why does the presence of air in an hydraulic system give a spongy feel when the footbrake pedal is operated?

..............................................................................

..............................................................................

..............................................................................

..............................................................................

Illustrate the effect of air in the system by completing the drawing on the right below.

*Pedal released* *Pedal depressed*

Air bubble in pipe

**Bleeding Brakes**

'Bleeding brakes' is a method by which air is removed from a hydraulic braking system. The method of bleeding varies slightly according to the type of braking system. Describe one method of bleeding brakes.

..............................................................................

..............................................................................

..............................................................................

..............................................................................

..............................................................................

..............................................................................

..............................................................................

..............................................................................

..............................................................................

..............................................................................

# BRAKE COMPENSATION

An hydraulic braking system is said to be 'self-compensating'. What is meant by brake compensation and why are hydraulically operated brakes self-compensating?

........................................................................................................................

........................................................................................................................

........................................................................................................................

........................................................................................................................

........................................................................................................................

........................................................................................................................

........................................................................................................................

........................................................................................................................

With a mechanically operated parking brake a 'brake compensator' is usually incorporated in the linkage to ensure that both brake units receive the same applying force.

**Investigation**

One type of handbrake compensator is shown below. Examine a vehicle fitted with this type and label the drawing.

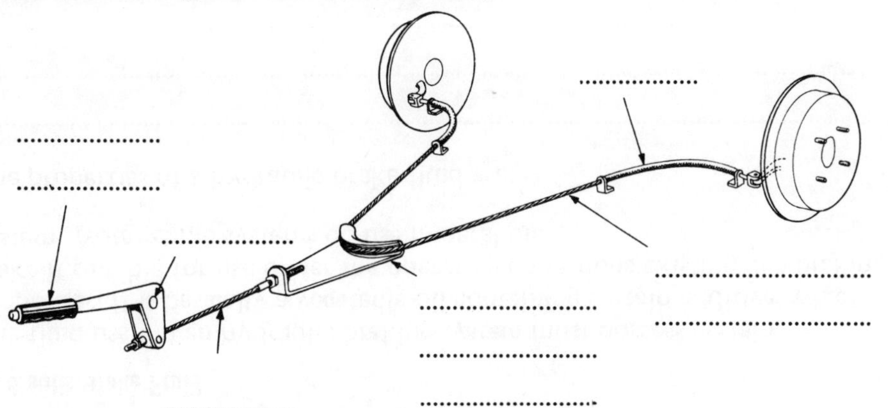

Examine a vehicle fitted with an alternative type of handbrake compensator and make a sketch below to illustrate this.

Name the type of braking system shown diagramatically below.

........................................................................................................................

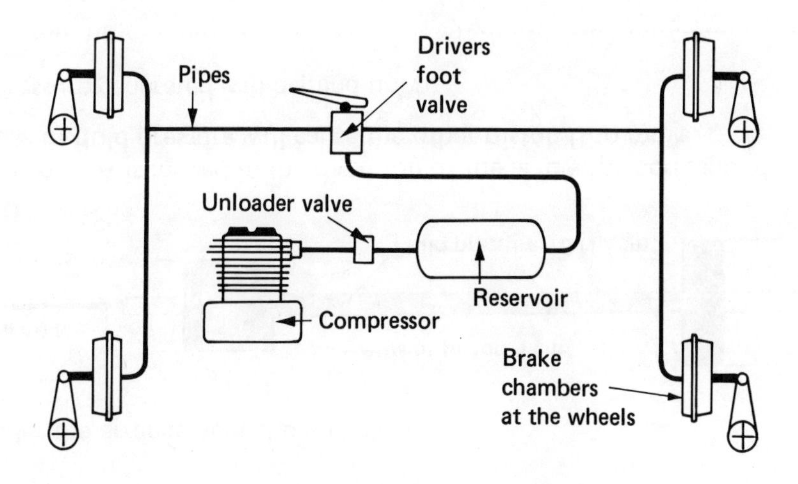


On which type of vehicle is this system normally found.

........................................................................................................................

# APPLIED STUDIES

**Hydraulic Brake Fluid**

The fluid used in an hydraulic braking system must possess certain properties. It is basically a vegetable oil containing certain additives which make it suitable for use under the operating conditions existing in a braking system. *Note:* some systems do use mineral oil.

The properties of a hydraulic brake fluid are:

1 ..........................................................................................

..........................................................................................

2 ..........................................................................................

3 ..........................................................................................

4 ..........................................................................................

How does heat affect brake fluid and what provision is made for this in the braking system?

..........................................................................................

..........................................................................................

..........................................................................................

At what intervals should the brake fluid be changed on a vehicle and why is this necessary?

..........................................................................................

..........................................................................................

..........................................................................................

..........................................................................................

State one important precaution when handling brake fluid in close proximity to a vehicle.

..........................................................................................

..........................................................................................

**Principal of Operation** (Hydraulic brakes)

For all practical purposes brake fluid is incompressible. Pressure applied anywhere in the fluid is transmitted equally throughout it.

Consider the arrangement shown below:

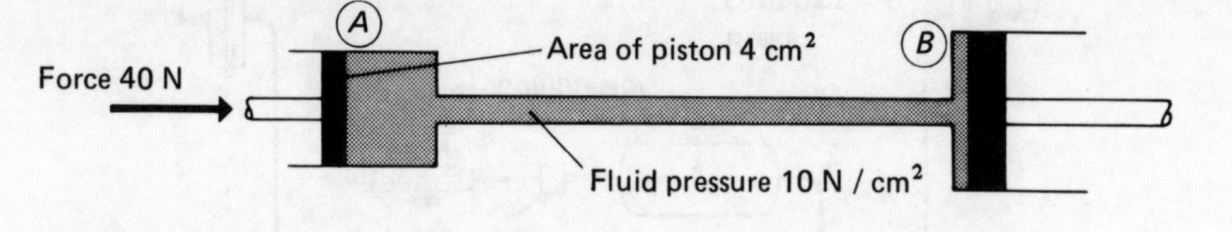


If the piston A is moved in the direction of the arrow the corresponding increase in fluid pressure will cause the other piston B to move.

The pressure generated will depend upon:

..........................................................................................

State the formula used to calculate the pressure.

Pressure =

What will be the force on piston B above, if its area is 8 cm$^2$ ?

Force = ..........................................................................

The 'force ratio' is therefore ..........................................................

How will the movement of piston A compare with the movement of piston B?

..........................................................................................

Why is this?

..........................................................................................

..........................................................................................

..........................................................................................

..........................................................................................

# CALCULATIONS

(a) When the footbrake is applied the force exerted on the brake shoe by a rear wheel cylinder piston is 900 N. If a 600 N force is applied to the master cylinder piston of cross sectional area 500 mm², calculate:

1. the force ratio.

2. the cross-sectional area of the wheel cylinder piston.

(b) If the force ratio of a braking system is 3 : 1 for the master cylinder and front caliper pistons, calculate the area of the master cylinder piston if the caliper pistons have an area of 12 cm².

(c) Complete the table below:

| CSA M/Cyl.(mm²) | CSA W/Cyl.(mm²) | Force at M/Cyl. (N) | Force at W/Cyl. (N) | Force ratio |
|---|---|---|---|---|
| 450 | 675 | 300 | | |
| 800 | | | 350 | 1.75 : 1 |
| | 950 | 400 | | 1.25 : 1 |
| 600 | | | 700 | 1.4 : 1 |
| 1000 | 1200 | 750 | | |

(d) (Hydraulic braking system)

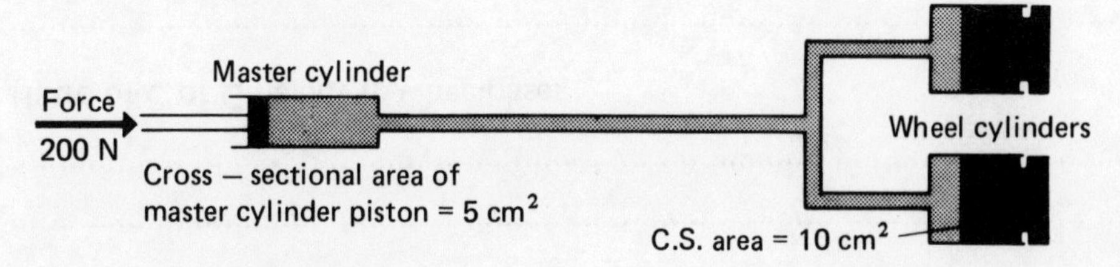


Study the sketch above and state:

1. Force at wheel cylinders ...................................... (neglecting friction)

2. The movement of the wheel cylinder pistons for 40 mm movement of the master cylinder piston.

   ..........................................................................................................

3. Line pressure ..........................................................................................

4. Movement ratio =

(e)

1. If the area of the master cylinder piston is 5 cm² and the area of a rear wheel cylinder piston is 7 cm², calculate the force ratio. (Neglect friction.)

2. What force would be required at the master cylinder pedal rod to generate a force of 600 N at the wheel cylinder piston?

# CENTRE OF GRAVITY AND LOAD TRANSFER

On the vehicle shown below the cross marks the *'centre of gravity'*. With a front engine, front wheel drive vehicle the C of G would be nearer to the front. However, with a rear engine, rear wheel drive vehicle the C of G would be nearer to the rear of the vehicle.

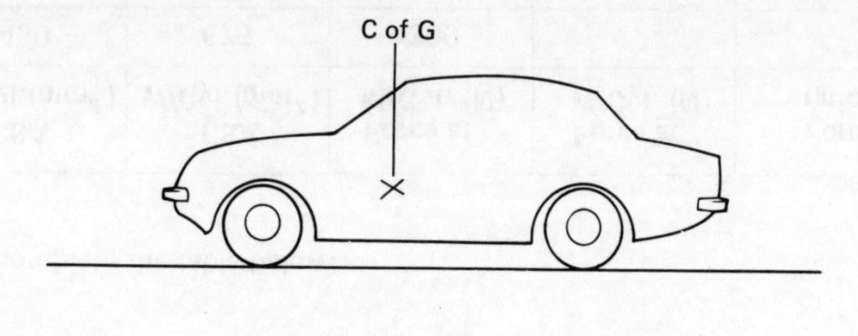


Briefly describe what is meant by the term 'centre of gravity'

................................................................................................................

................................................................................................................

................................................................................................................

................................................................................................................

................................................................................................................

................................................................................................................

The stability of a vehicle when cornering or braking is greatly affected by the actual position of the vehicles C of G.

Give examples of vehicle types which have:

1. Low C of G. ................................................................................

2. High C of G. ................................................................................

Consider the vehicle shown below. During braking the force 'F' acting at the C of G tends to tilt the vehicle about the front wheels, thus putting more load on to the front wheels, and reducing the load on the rear wheels. 'Load transfer' takes place.

C of G

F

Wheelbase

The degree of load transfer is dependent upon a number of factors. How do the following affect load transfer during braking?

1. Height of centre of gravity:

................................................................................................................

................................................................................................................

2. Wheelbase:

................................................................................................................

................................................................................................................

3. Rate of retardation:

................................................................................................................

................................................................................................................

4. Ratio of C of G height to wheelbase:

................................................................................................................

................................................................................................................

# STOPPING DISTANCE

The stopping distance for a particular vehicle is dependent upon a number of factors other than the design and condition of the vehicle's braking system.

List FIVE factors, external to the vehicle, which can affect stopping distance.

1..........

2..........

3..........

4..........

5..........

Maximum retardation of a vehicle is achieved just before wheel lock (skidding) occurs. This is due to the fact that when sliding or skidding of the tyres on the road surface occurs friction is reduced. This is known as *kinetic* or *sliding* friction.

Why is the braking force higher if the wheels continue to roll?

..........

..........

..........

..........

..........

# WORK DONE

When a vehicle is brought to a halt the 'work done' by the braking system is a product of:

1..........

2..........

The formula used to calculate work done is:

The retarding force produced by the brakes when stopping a vehicle is 5000 N. If this force is applied over a distance of 25 m calculate the work done by the brakes.

If the work done by the brakes in stopping a vehicle is 200 KJ, calculate the retarding force if the distance travelled during brake application is 40 m.

The work done by the brakes in stopping a vehicle is 600 KJ. If the retarding force produced by the brakes is 20 KN, the distance travelled by the vehicle during braking is:

(a) 3 m

(b) 30 m

(c) 60 m

(d) 90 m

Answer ( )

# HEAT ENERGY

When the brakes are applied friction generates ....................................

energy; and energy is a form of work done.

Energy = force x distance.

Heat energy is measured in ....................................................................

Calculate the heat energy generated in stopping a vehicle if a retarding force of 7 kN is applied through a distance of 30 m.

A vehicle travels through a distance of 20 m during braking. If the retarding force produced by the brakes is 4.5 kN the heat energy generated is:

(a) 4.5 kJ, (b) 24.5 Nm, (c) 90 kJ, (d) 900 kN m.

Answer ( )

Calculate the distance travelled by a vehicle during braking if the heat generated is 60000 J and the brake retarding force is 4 kN.

# HEAT DISSIPATION

When heat is dissipated it is transferred from the heat source, usually to the atmosphere, by various means.

Three methods by which heat is transferred are:

1. From the hotter to the colder part of a material by travelling within the actual material; this is known as ....................................................

2. Through the atmosphere by means of rays; this is known as

....................................................................................................

3. By the movement of liquids or gases. This is known as

....................................................................................................

In many instances heat is dissipated from the heat source by more than one method at a time.

How is the heat dissipated from the friction surfaces in a drum brake assembly?

....................................................................................................

....................................................................................................

Two factors which determine the rate at which heat is transferred by radiation are:

1. ....................................................................................................

....................................................................................................

....................................................................................................

2. ....................................................................................................

....................................................................................................

Give examples of brake component materials which are:

1. Good conductors of heat ....................................................................

2. Poor conductors of heat ....................................................................

# B8.

## Steering

B8: 2,3

The front wheels on a normal vehicle rotate on stub axles which swivel or pivot about what is known as the 'swivel axis'. This provides a means of steering the vehicle. To make the stub axles pivot a control gear, operated by the driver via the steering wheel, and a linkage to the stub axles is necessary.

One of the simplest steering arrangements is that used with a beam axle system. Complete the beam axle steering layout below and label each part.

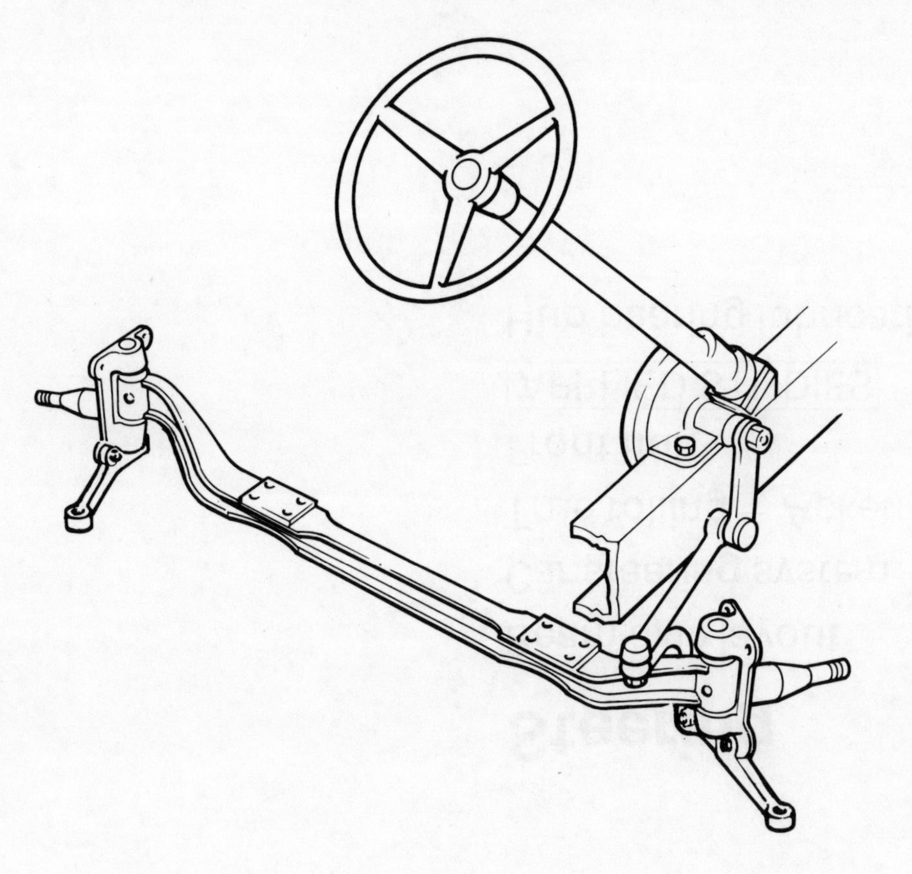

On what type of vehicle is the system shown above normally found?

..........................................................................................

State the purpose of each of the following steering components:

*Steering gearbox*

..........................................................................................

..........................................................................................

..........................................................................................

..........................................................................................

*Drop arm*

..........................................................................................

..........................................................................................

*Draglink*

..........................................................................................

..........................................................................................

*Steering arms*

..........................................................................................

..........................................................................................

*Track rod*

..........................................................................................

..........................................................................................

*Ball joints*

..........................................................................................

..........................................................................................

..........................................................................................

The *steering swivel axis* in the arrangement shown opposite is formed by 'king pins' and 'bushes'. That is, the stub axles pivot on hardened steel king pins which are held firmly in the beam axle; bushes in the stub axles provide the necessary bearing surfaces.

**Investigation**

Examine a beam axle steering system and complete the drawing below by adding the *king pin bushes* and the *king pin thrust bearing*.

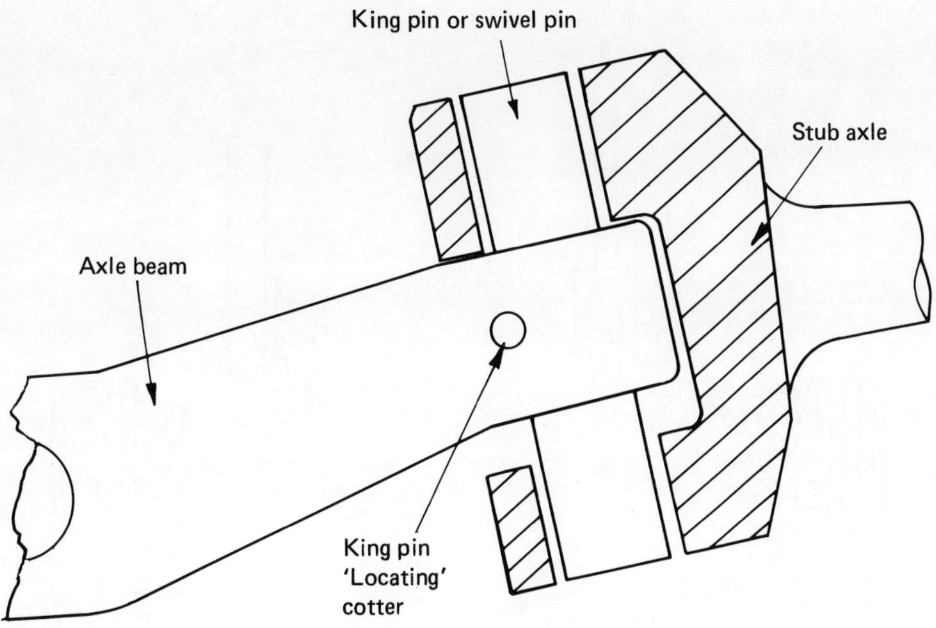


From what material are the king pin bushes made?

..........................................................................................

How are the bushes lubricated?

..........................................................................................

..........................................................................................

How is the king pin held firmly in the axle beam?

..........................................................................................

..........................................................................................

What is the purpose of the king-pin thrust bearing?

..........................................................................................

..........................................................................................

..........................................................................................

Complete the drawing below to show the construction of a steering linkage ball joint and the method used to attach the ball joint to the steering arm.

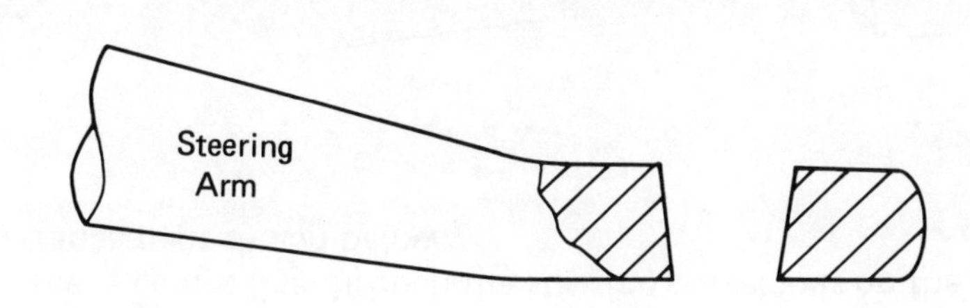


Why is the steering system used for a beam axle arrangement unsuitable for use on a vehicle with independent front suspension?

..........................................................................................

..........................................................................................

..........................................................................................

..........................................................................................

What effect would a worn linkage ball joint have on a steering?

..........................................................................................

..........................................................................................

..........................................................................................

# CAR STEERING SYSTEM

Most cars have independent front suspension (i.f.s.), and the steering linkage must therefore be designed to accommodate the up and down movement of a steered wheel without affecting the other steered wheel. In most systems two short track rods which pivot in a similar arc to the suspension links, are connected to the stub axles.

One system in use on cars can be described as; a steering gearbox with 'idler' and three track rod layout.

Complete the drawing of such a system shown below by adding the linkage and labelling the parts.

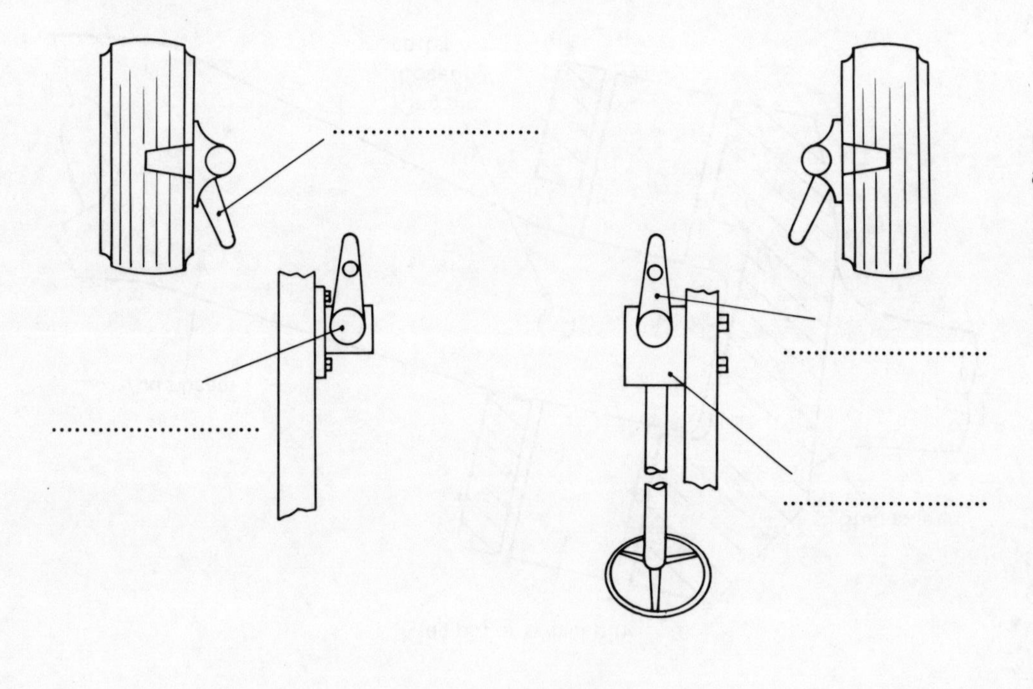

What are two main disadvantages of this layout?

...................................................................................................................................

**Investigation**

Examine a vehicle fitted with a 'rack-and-pinion' steering system and complete the drawing below to illustrate this; label all the parts.

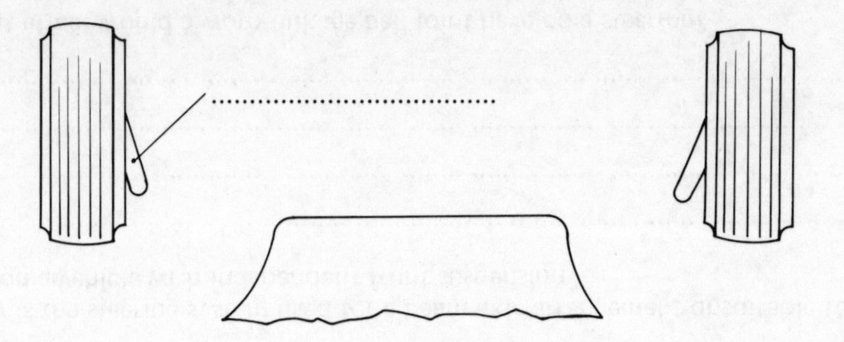

Draw a centre line through the steering swivel axis on the stub axle arrangement shown below.

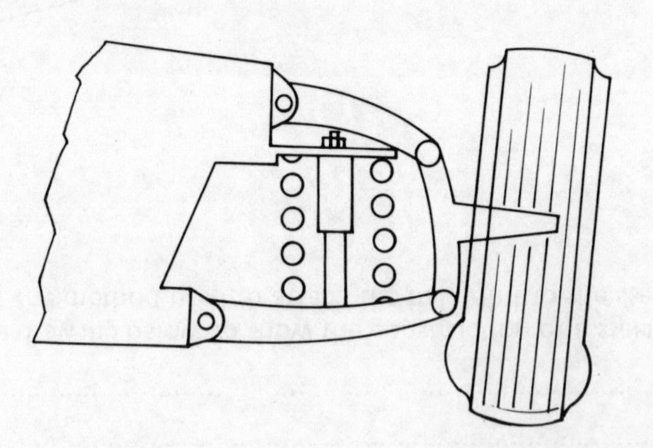

What provides the steering swivel action on this arrangement?

...................................................................................................................................

# TRUE ROLLING

When a vehicle tracels on a curved path during cornering, true rolling is obtained only when the wheels roll on arcs which have a 'common centre' or common axis. Show the common centre on the drawing below.

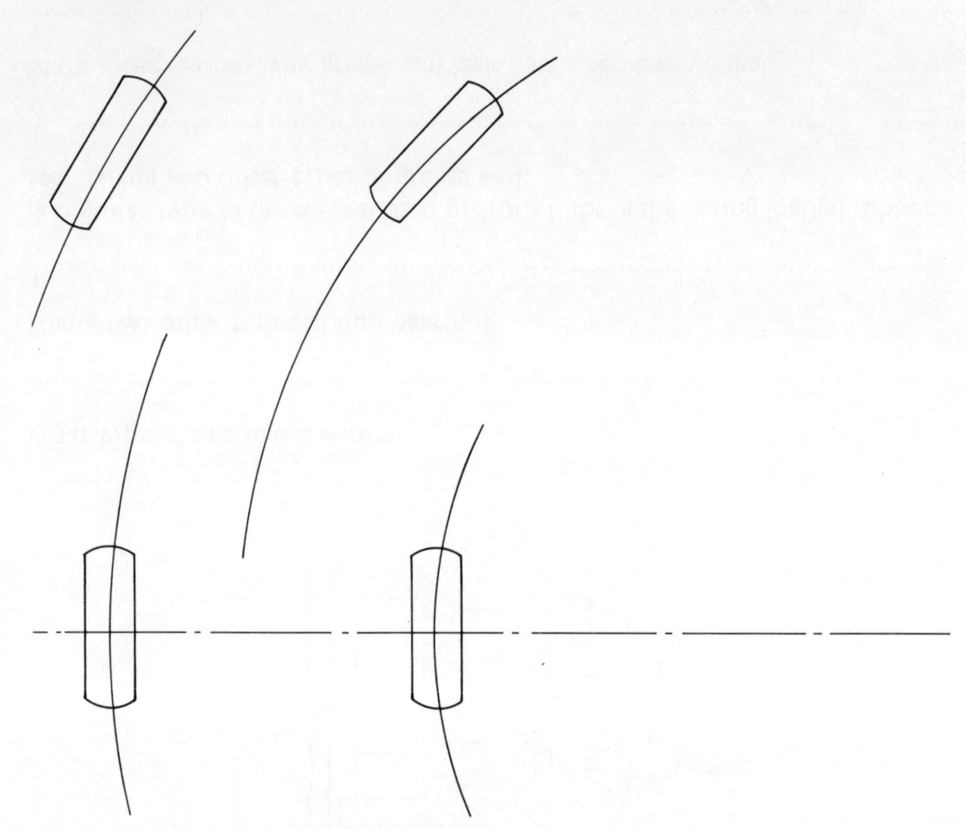

Why is true rolling of the wheels necessary?

.....................................................................................................................

.....................................................................................................................

To achieve true rolling while cornering the wheels are steered through different angles, that is they are not parallel; the inner wheel on a turn is turned through a ..........................................angle than the outer wheel.

**Ackerman System**

The difference in steering lock angles to give true rolling of the wheels while cornering can be achieved by making the track rod shorter than the distance between the king pin centres, that is the steering arms are usually inclined inwards. If the track rod is in front of the axle, as on many cars, then it is longer than the distance between the king pin centres and the steering arms must be inclined outwards.

Add a track rod and steering arms to the drawing below and extend lines through the steering arms to show the point of intersection on the vehicle centre line if the linkage is to satisfy conditions for true rolling.

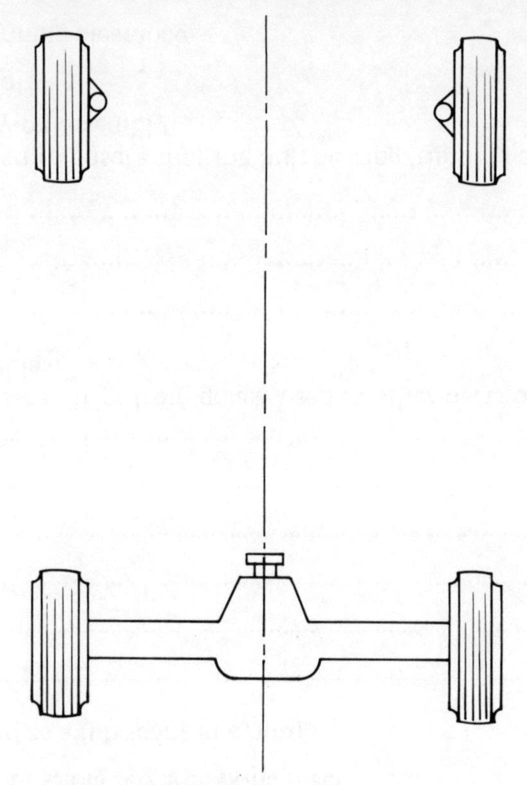

This type of steering linkage is known as:

.....................................................................................................................

# FRONT HUB

**Investigation**

Examine a front hub and complete the drawing below to include bearings and grease seal. Label all parts.

Stub axle

What type of bearings are used?

..........................................................................................

Name two other types of hub bearing?

1.......................................... 2. ..........................................

A popular type of grease seal used in front hubs is the spring loaded rubber seal. Name two other types of grease seal.

1. .......................................... 2. ..........................................

State three reasons why grease can leak past a serviceable seal.

1..........................................................................................

2..........................................................................................

3..........................................................................................

## APPLIED STUDIES

Lubrication of the hub bearings is necessary to minimise friction and prevent wear and possible seizure taking place.

Why is grease used as a lubricant in a hub?

1..........................................................................................

..........................................................................................

2..........................................................................................

..........................................................................................

3..........................................................................................

..........................................................................................

How does hub crease differ from grease used in other parts of the vehicle, for example brake cables?

..........................................................................................

..........................................................................................

..........................................................................................

Care must be taken to ensure that the hub bearing 'running clearance' is adjusted correctly on assembly.

State the effects of:

1. Insufficient running clearance.

..........................................................................................

2. Excessive running clearance

..........................................................................................

..........................................................................................

In the hub arrangement shown opposite, the hub nut is a 'slotted nut' and it is locked by a split pin. Describe one other method of locking a hub nut.

..........................................................................................

..........................................................................................

B9.

# Chassis Layout and Vehicle Body

# TYPES OF VEHICLE BODY

A vehicle body is designed according to the purpose for which the vehicle is intended. One of the most popular types of vehicle body is that shown below.

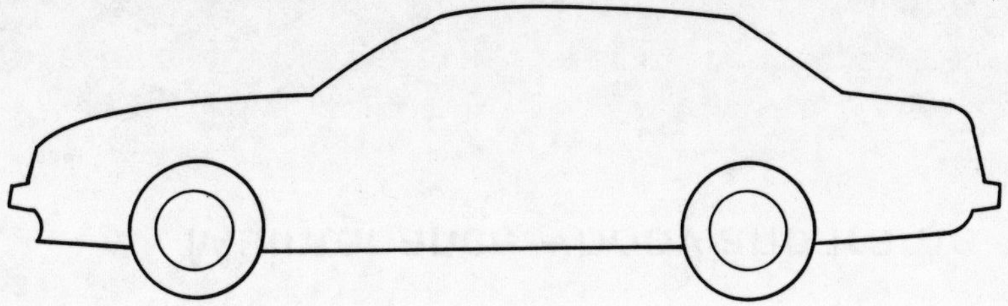

Body type........................................................................................

Name the type of body illustrated above and make simple sketches opposite to show the three body types named.

State below examples of current vehicle makes and models which are of the types listed.

| Type | Make | Model |
|---|---|---|
| Saloon | .............................. | .................................... |
| Convertible | .............................. | .................................... |
| Estate | .............................. | .................................... |
| Pick-up | .............................. | .................................... |
| Coupe | .............................. | .................................... |
| Sports | .............................. | .................................... |
| Grand Tourer | .............................. | .................................... |

..........................................................................................................

..........................................................................................................

..........................................................................................................

..........................................................................................................

..........................................................................................................

*Coupē*

*Convertible*

*Estate or Pick-up*

# VEHICLE LAYOUT

The 'layout' of the motor vehicle is concerned with the arrangement of the main mechanical components.

List the names of the main components.

1. ............................................ 2. ............................................
3. ............................................ 4. ............................................
5. ............................................

Two popular layouts (A and B) are shown opposite: Give a name to each layout and label the drawings.

State TWO advantages of layout A.

1. ...........................................................................................
2. ...........................................................................................

State TWO advantages of layout B.

1. ...........................................................................................
2. ...........................................................................................

Engines can be mounted longtitudinally or transversely.

State TWO disadvantages of a transversely mounted engine over a longtitudinally mounted engine.

1. ...........................................................................................
2. ...........................................................................................

Show an alternative vehicle layout by completing drawing C opposite. Label the parts you add. Give a name to the layout and state two advantages of the layout.

1. ...........................................................................................
2. ...........................................................................................
...........................................................................................

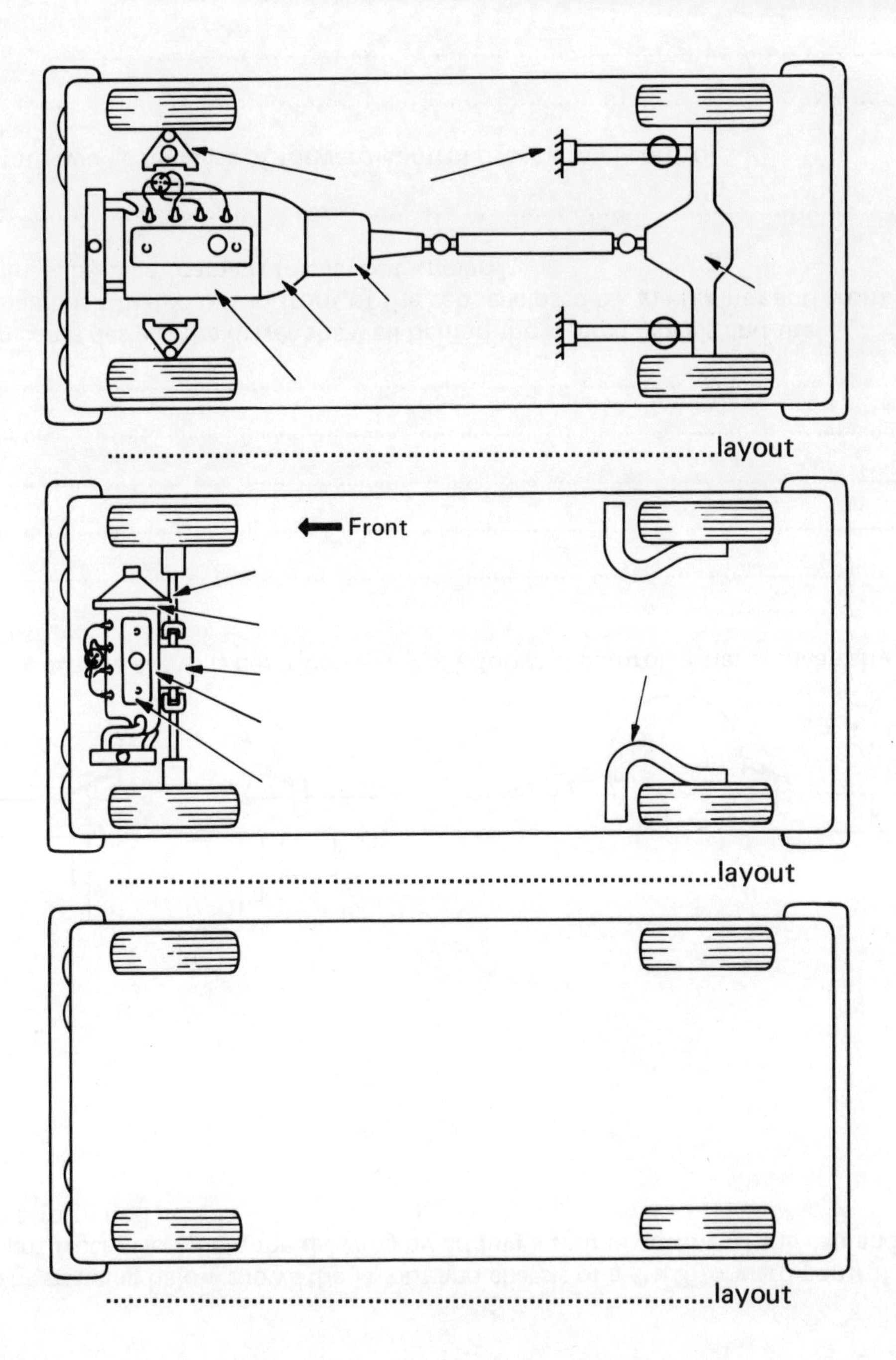

# CONSTRUCTIONAL DIFFERENCES VEHICLE TYPES

Many cars have a van or pick-up derivative, that is apart from the vehicle having a van or pick-up type of body, it is almost identical mechanically to the saloon version. However, certain differences do exist between many cars and their van derivatives.

Briefly outline the constructional differences between a car and a van derivative in relation to transmission and suspension components and give examples of these.

Transmission:

........................................................................................................

........................................................................................................

........................................................................................................

........................................................................................................

Suspension:

........................................................................................................

........................................................................................................

........................................................................................................

........................................................................................................

........................................................................................................

**Heavy goods vehicles**

Indicate the constructional differences between cars and heavy goods vehicles for the HGV items listed.

Chassis ........................................................................................

Number of axles ..........................................................................

Suspension ...................................................................................

Engine ..........................................................................................

The drawing below shows the layout and chassis of a 4 x 2 forward control light truck. Complete the drawing by adding a simple outline of the cab and platform body.

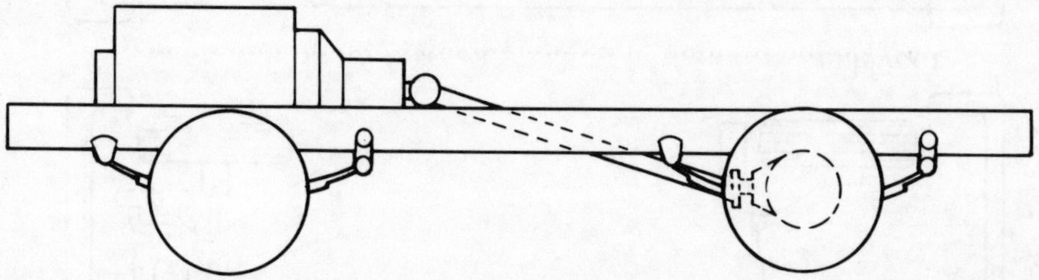

The vehicle above is described as a 4 x 2 forward control. What is meant by this?

........................................................................................................

........................................................................................................

........................................................................................................

........................................................................................................

........................................................................................................

In some designs the driver sits well behind the steered wheels and the engine is situated out in front of the cab, enclosed by the bonnet and front wings. By what name is this layout known?

........................................................................................................

State two advantages of forward control over normal control.

1. ....................................................................................................

2. ....................................................................................................

B9: 5,7

6 x 4, 6 x 2 and 8 x 4 are steered and driven axle arrangements for certain vehicles. Add the road wheels to the drawings below to illustrate these arrangements.

Mark the wheels 'S' for steered and 'D' for driven.

6 X 4

6 X 2

8 X 4

Why is it necessary to use more than two axles?

..............................................................................................................

..............................................................................................................

..............................................................................................................

..............................................................................................................

..............................................................................................................

Complete the drawing below to show a six-wheel arrangement with a 'dead' axle.

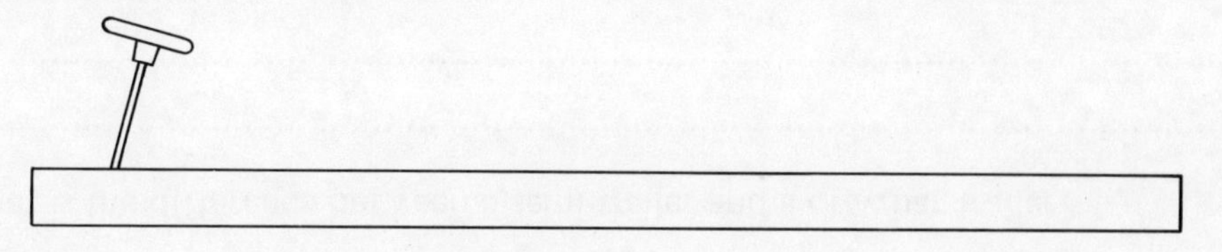

**Public Service Vehicles (PSVs)**

Public service vehicles have certain constructional features which distinguish them from heavy goods vehicles. Apart from the body, which is designed to carry passengers in comfort and safety, the chassis and arrangement of the main components is usually quite different.

Complete the drawing below to show the chassis and engine arrangement for a public service vehicle.

..............................................................................................................

..............................................................................................................

..............................................................................................................

..............................................................................................................

..............................................................................................................

..............................................................................................................

..............................................................................................................

## Articulated Vehicles

The vehicles considered on the previous page were of the 'rigid' type, that is all the main components, cab and body are mounted on a single rigid chassis. The articulated vehicle is a short wheelbase rigid (commonly known as a tractive or tractor unit) with a semi-trailer so attached that part of its load is imposed on the drawing vehicle.

Complete the drawing above to show a 4 x 2 tractive unit with a single axle semi-trailer.

State three advantages of articulated over rigid vehicles.

1. ..............................

2. ..............................

..............................

..............................

3. ..............................

What are the major disadvantages of an articulated vehicle compared with rigid vehicle?

1. ..............................

..............................

..............................

2. ..............................

..............................

The layout of one type of tractive unit is shown below. Label the component shown dotted and state its purpose on the vehicle.

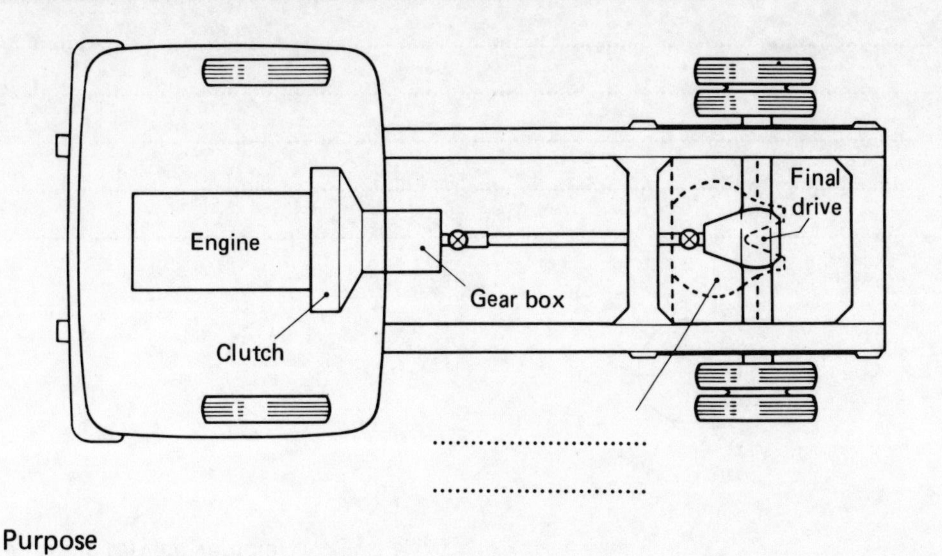


..............................

..............................

Purpose

..............................

..............................

..............................

The tractive unit shown is of the forward control type. One disadvantage of forward control was the inaccessibility of the engine since it is inside the cab. How has this problem been overcome?

..............................

..............................

What is the difference between a semi-trailer and a drawbar trailer?

..............................

..............................

..............................

..............................

# CHASSIS FRAMES

The chassis frame is that part of the vehicle to which the main mechanical components are attached. Heavy goods vehicles, light trucks and many vans have a separate chassis frame on to which the vehicle body is mounted. Most cars, however, do not have a separate chassis frame.

Label the parts of the light and heavy vehicle chassis frames shown opposite.

The shape of the chassis section most widely used is the *channel* section. Examine various chassis members and make sketches to illustrate these below.

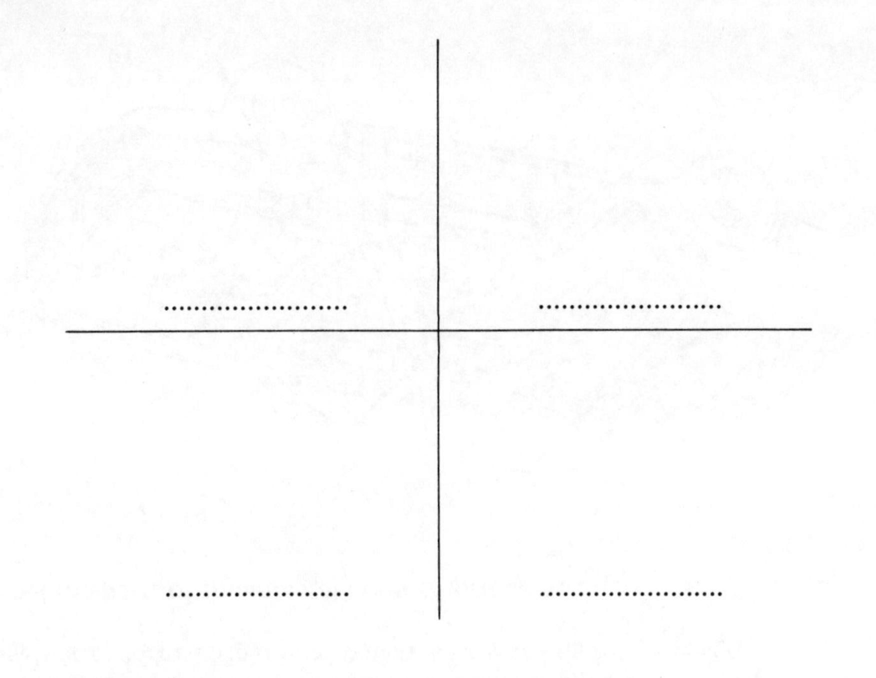

On which type of vehicle is the tubular section popular?

..............................................................................................

Which cars still retain a separate chassis frame?

..............................................................................................

*Light vehicle chassis frame*

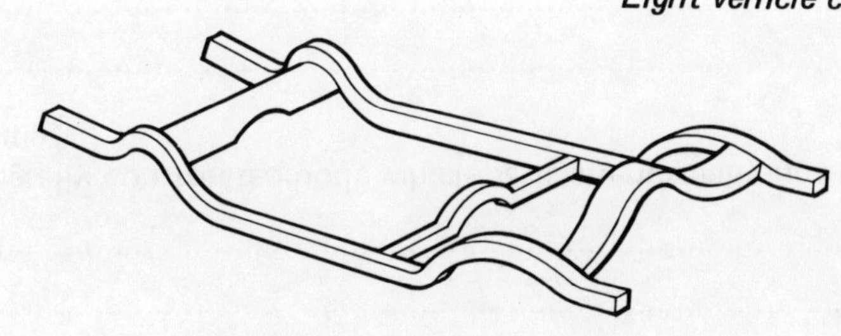

*Heavy vehicle chassis frame*

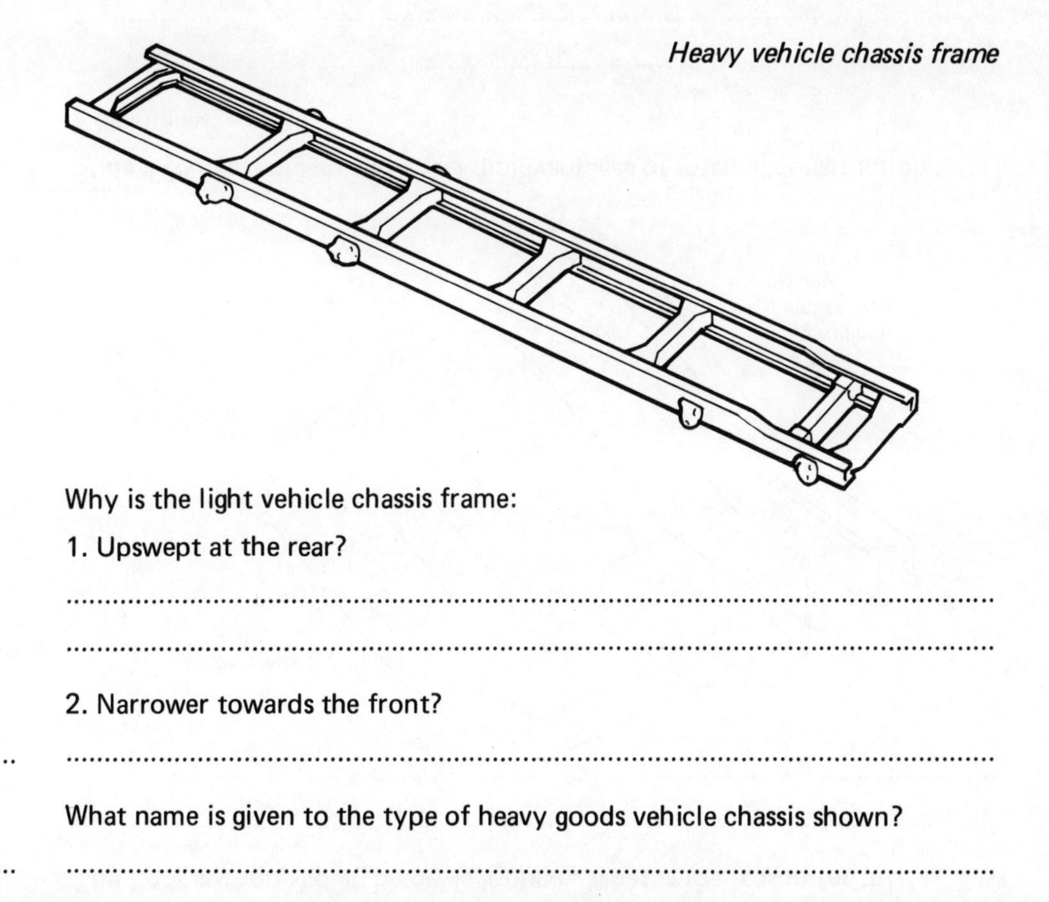

Why is the light vehicle chassis frame:

1. Upswept at the rear?

..............................................................................................

..............................................................................................

2. Narrower towards the front?

..............................................................................................

What name is given to the type of heavy goods vehicle chassis shown?

..............................................................................................

# INTEGRAL CONSTRUCTION

Most modern cars are constructed in this way. That is to say the main structural load-bearing members are built into the body shell; the body and chassis are, therefore, not separate units.

The integral structure is made up of specially shaped steel pressings welded together to form a 'rigid box' which is very strong for its weight.

Label the parts of the integral body shown below.

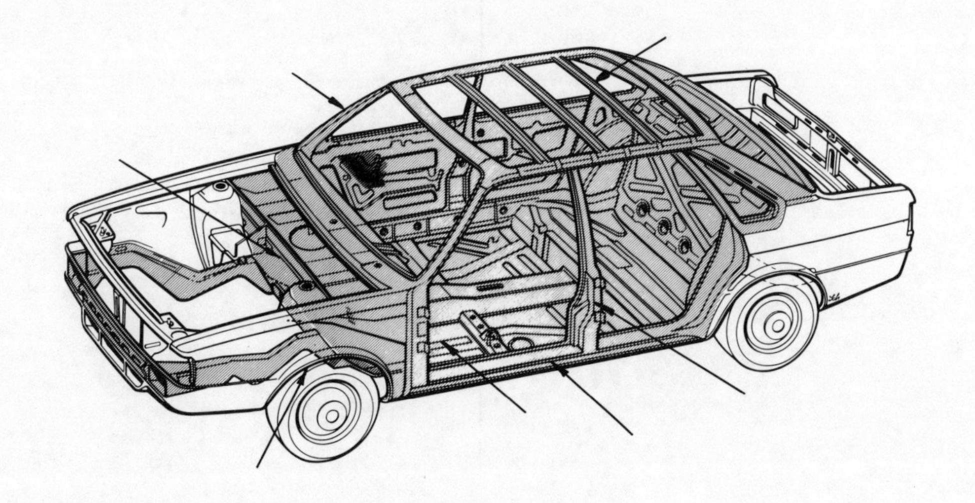

'Subframes' are very often used in conjunction with integral construction type vehicles. What are these and why are they used?

..............................................................................................

..............................................................................................

..............................................................................................

..............................................................................................

..............................................................................................

..............................................................................................

The floor section shown below is 'ribbed'. What is the reason for this?

..............................................................................................

..............................................................................................

Floor section ribbed

Longitudinal member welded to floor

State TWO advantages and TWO disadvantages of integral construction.

Advantages:

1. ..........................................................................................

2. ..........................................................................................

Disadvantages:

1. ..........................................................................................

2. ..........................................................................................

On an integrally constructed body which parts are normally not load-carrying?

..............................................................................................

..............................................................................................

B9: 11,16,17

# FLEXIBLE MOUNTINGS

Where main components are attached to the vehicle chassis, flexible mountings are normally positioned between such attached units and the chassis frame. Two flexible mountings are shown below. Indicate on the dotted lines under the drawings a typical location for the type shown.

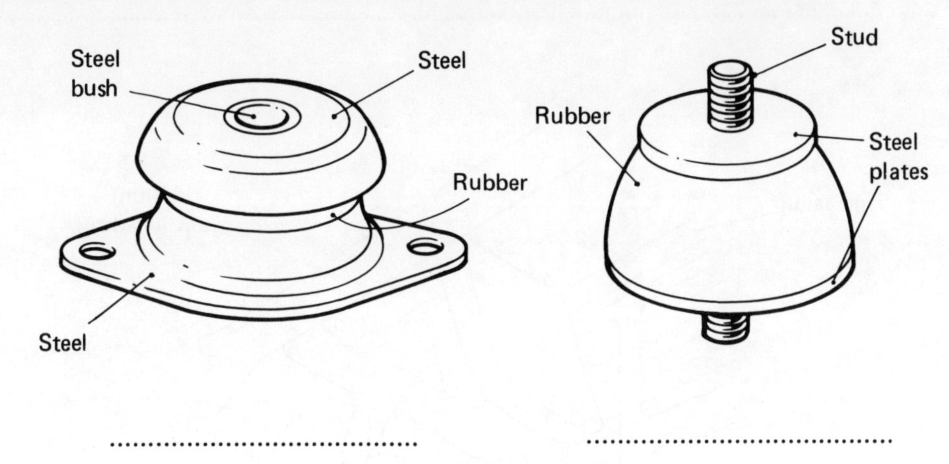


.................................... ....................................

State TWO reasons why flexible mountings are used.

1. ..........................................................................................

2. ..........................................................................................

..........................................................................................

# JACKING POINTS

The jacking points are the places on a vehicle body at which the jack is applied in order to lift a wheel (or wheels) clear of the ground. The body structure at the jacking points is made sufficiently strong to withstand the concentrated load imposed when the vehicle is jacked up.

How many jacking points are usually built into the vehicle body?

..........................................................................................

..........................................................................................

**Investigation**

Examine a vehicle and complete the drawing below to show the vehicle body outline. Indicate on the drawing the location of the jacking points and show by simple line outlines the position of the engine and transmission.

Make .................................... Model ....................................

Give two reasons why a vehicle's own jacking points are not normally used during servicing by a garage.

1. ..........................................................................................

..........................................................................................

..........................................................................................

2. ..........................................................................................

..........................................................................................

Measure the *track* and *wheelbase* on a vehicle and add these dimensions to the outline below.

Make .................................... Model ....................................

# SEAT BELTS

The law requires that safety belts must be fitted to protect the driver and front passenger on all private cars and dual purpose vehicles first registered on or after 1st January 1965.

The restraining force required to prevent car occupants from being thrown forward when a collision occurs is extremely high. Seat belt anchorage points on the vehicle body must therefore be sufficiently strong to withstand the loads involved.

**Investigation**

Examine a vehicle and complete the sketch below to show the seat belt arrangement. Show clearly the exact location of the belt anchorage points.

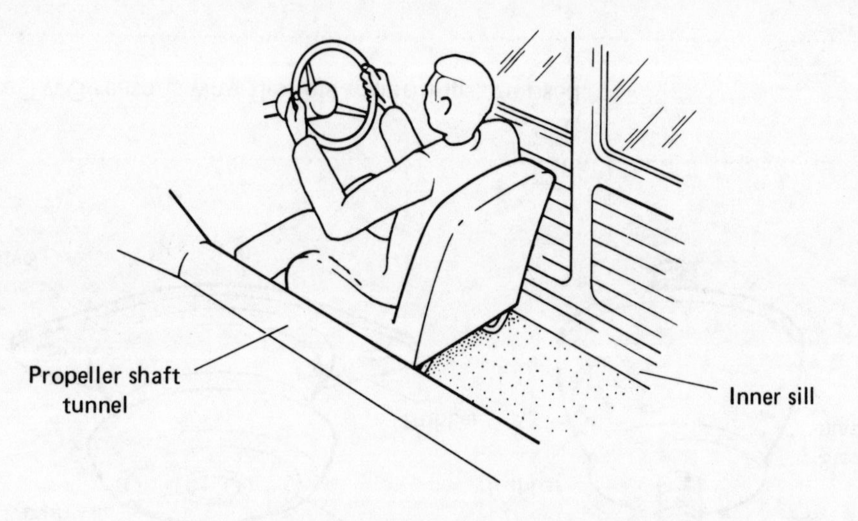


..............................................................................................................

..............................................................................................................

..............................................................................................................

..............................................................................................................

..............................................................................................................

# MAINTENANCE – BODY AND FRAME

Regular routine maintenance of the car body and frame is an extremely important part of the overall maintenance requirement for the vehicle.

Give three reasons why such maintenance is necessary.

1. ..............................................................................................................

..............................................................................................................

2. ..............................................................................................................

..............................................................................................................

3. ..............................................................................................................

..............................................................................................................

..............................................................................................................

List the main items of body and frame maintenance.

..............................................................................................................

..............................................................................................................

..............................................................................................................

..............................................................................................................

..............................................................................................................

..............................................................................................................

..............................................................................................................

..............................................................................................................

..............................................................................................................

..............................................................................................................

..............................................................................................................

..............................................................................................................

..............................................................................................................

..............................................................................................................

..............................................................................................................

B9: 22,23

# CHASSIS FRAME

The strength of a chassis frame member with regard to bending and twisting is dependent on a number of factors. For a frame member of a certain length, state FOUR factors which determine its strength.

1. ............................................................................................................
2. ............................................................................................................
3. ............................................................................................................
4. ............................................................................................................

**Investigation**

Three frame sections are illustrated below. Examine samples of each type shown which vary in *length* and *depth* (preferably the sample sections should be simple tinplate fabrications) and select the shape of frame section which provides the best 'all round' rigidity with regard to bending and twisting.

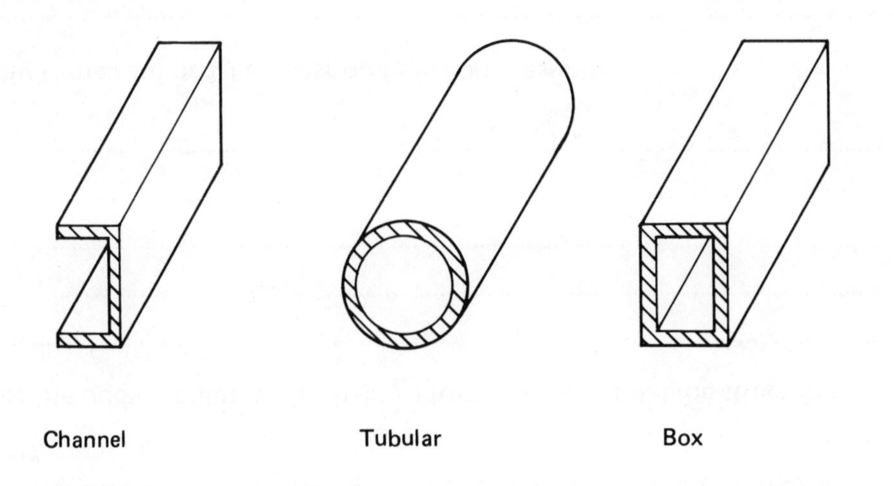


List the shapes shown above in order of strength.

............................................................................................................

Consider the loaded beam shown below. The material forming the upper surface is subjected to *compression* and the material forming the lower surface is in *tension.*

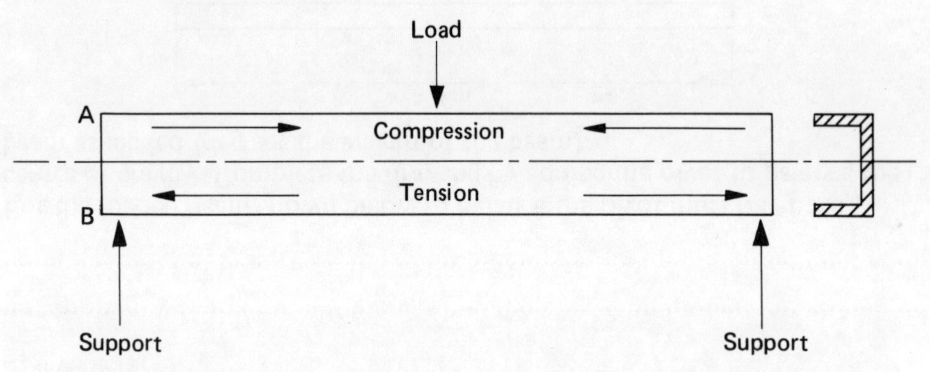


Along the centre line of the beam is the 'neutral axis'. The material along this axis is at minimum stress, that is the tensile and compressive forces progressively reduce from the outer surfaces to the neutral axis.

If the distance between A and B (that is the depth of the beam) is increased, how will its resistance to bending or deflection be affected?

............................................................................................................

............................................................................................................

It has already been stated that a ribbed sheet is stiffer and will not bend as easily as a flat sheet of the same material. Why is a ribbed sheet stronger than a flat sheet?

............................................................................................................

............................................................................................................

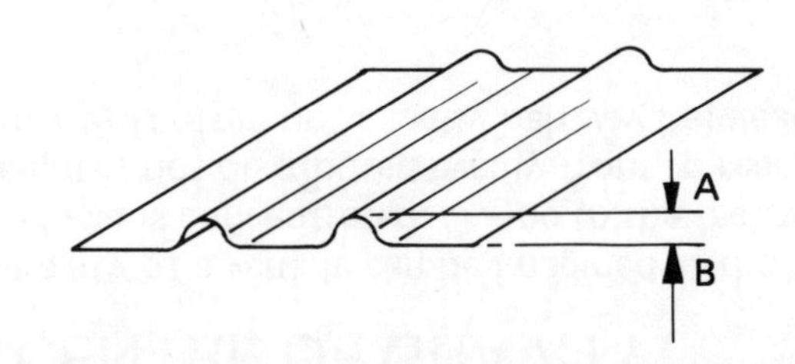

## PRINCIPLES (INTEGRAL CONSTRUCTION)

The relatively high strength to weight ratio of an integral car body when compared with the separate frame arrangement is due to a number of factors. One important factor is the 'box' formed by certain parts of the body.

List the body sections which help to form the rigid box-type structure.

1. ..........
2. ..........
3. ..........
4. ..........
5. ..........

Why is the roof panel of a car body in compression?

..........

..........

..........

..........

Two ways in which a car body structure is stiffened are therefore

1. ..........
2. ..........

State one other method used to stiffen body construction.

..........

..........

..........

..........

..........

## VEHICLE CENTRE OF GRAVITY

The centre of gravity of a vehicle can be imagined as the point at which the weight of the vehicle is concentrated. Owing to the fact that on most vehicles the weight is not distributed evenly front to rear, the position of the centre of gravity is often not exactly halfway between the front and rear wheels.

How does the position of the centre of gravity affect the loading on the wheels?

..........

..........

..........

..........

..........

By applying the 'principle of moments' it is possible to determine the position of the centre of gravity of a vehicle, provided certain relevant facts are known. What information is required to calculate the centre of gravity of a vehicle?

..........

..........

For the loaded beam shown below to balance the pivot must be at the centre of gravity. Complete the drawing by adding the pivot to balance the beam as loaded (neglect the weight of the beam).

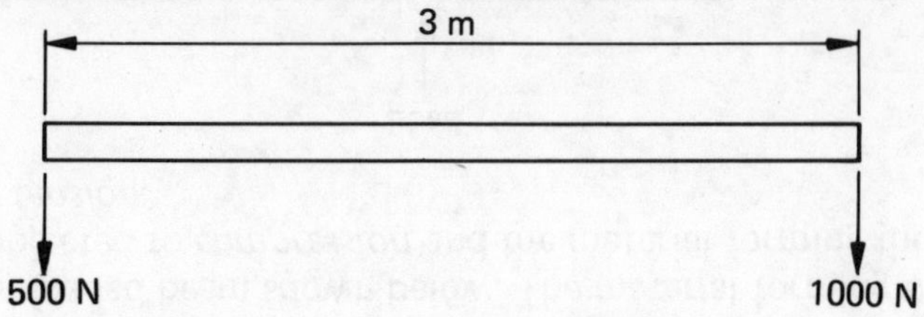

3 m

500 N    1000 N

# CALCULATIONS

**Centre of gravity**

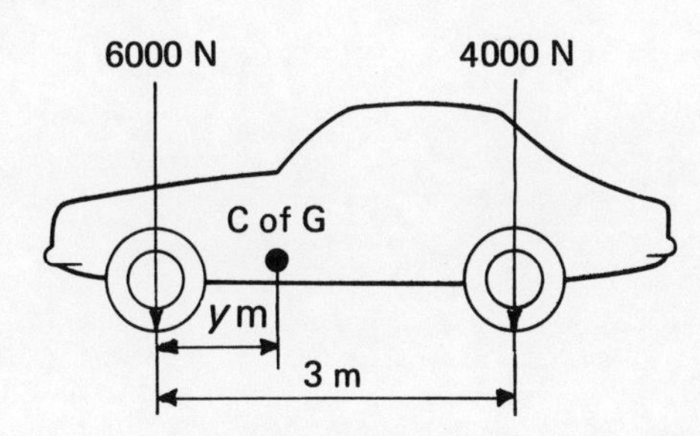


Theoretically the point of balance of the vehicle would be on a pivot at the C of G. To find the position of the C of G relative to the front wheels:

Take moments about the front wheels.

Clockwise moments = Anti-clockwise moments

$10\,000 \times y$ = $4000 \times 3$

Distance of C of G from front wheels =

Why is the distance $y$ multiplied by 10 000?

..........................................................................................................

..........................................................................................................

**Load on wheels**

Similarly, when the position of the centre of gravity, wheelbase and vehicle weight are known, the load on the wheels can be calculated, that is the load distribution.

Calculate the loads on the front and rear axles for the vehicle shown top opposite.

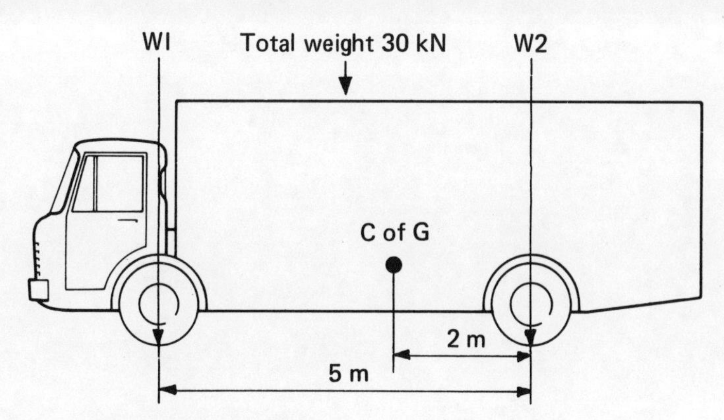


To calculate the load on front wheels:

Take moments about rear wheels

Clockwise moments = Anti-clockwise moments

A car has a wheelbase of 2.5 m. If the load on the front axle is 4500 N and the load on the rear axle is 3000 N calculate the distance of the C of G behind the front axle.

Let $y$ = distance of C of G from the front axle.

# FURTHER CALCULATIONS

(a) A car has a mass of 1200 kg and the load on the front wheels is 7000N. If the wheelbase is 3 m, find the position of the centre of gravity relative to the rear wheels.

(b) The position of the centre of gravity for a vehicle is 1 m behind the front wheel centres and the wheelbase is 2.5 m. Determine the loads on both the front and rear axles if the vehicle has a mass of 1000 kg.

(c) Calculate the distance of the centre of gravity from the centre of the trailer axle for the trailer shown below.

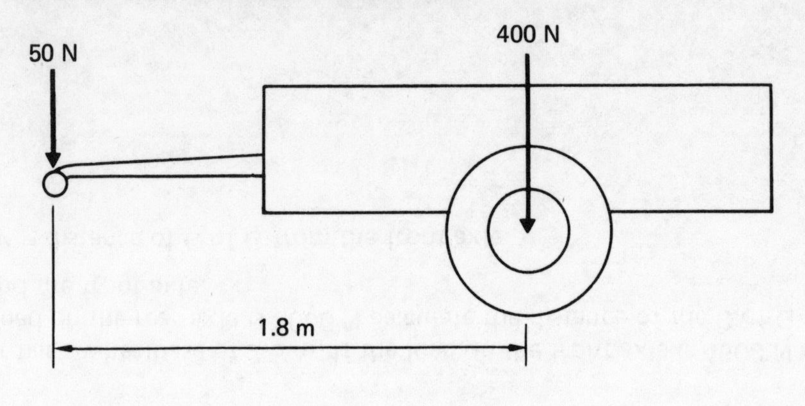


(d) A vehicle has a mass of 2000 kg. If the wheelbase is 4 m and the distance of the C of G from the front axle is 1.5 m, what upward force must a jack exert on the rear axle to raise the rear wheels off the ground.

# B10.

# Tools and Soldering

# TOOLS

Tools used for cutting metals are either:

1. Hand tools  or  2. Machine tools

Give THREE examples of such hand tools used in garage work

................................................................................................

................................................................................................

................................................................................................

Cutting action
Metal-removing tools work on the principle of forcing a *wedge* into the material to *shear* off the unwanted material (see opposite).

Tool materials
One basic requirement of a cutting tool is that it should be harder than the material being cut. State the materials used for the hand tools listed below.

| **Tool** | **Material** |
| --- | --- |
| Chisel | ................................................................ |
| File | ................................................................ |
| Hacksaw | ................................................................ |
| | ................................................................ |

Carbon steels used for hand tools normally have a carbon content of between 0.9 and 1.3%. Why are these steels not used for high-speed machining of metals?

................................................................................................

................................................................................................

*Chisels*

Cutting action
The drawing below shows the point of a chisel during cutting. Hammer blows cause the pointed 'wedge' to 'shear' through the metal. The depth of cut is maintained by holding the chisel at the correct angle (angle of inclination). Three other important factors that affect the efficiency of the cutting action are:

1. ................................ angle,  2. .................................... angle

and

3. .......................................... angle of the chisel.

Label the drawing.

..................

..................

.....................

Chisels with point angles in the region of 55–60° are used for cutting relatively hard materials and the tool point is quite strong. For cutting softer materials the point angle is reduced.

Sketch chisel points for the materials named below, and state the approximate point angle.

| *Mild steel* | *Aluminium* |
| --- | --- |
| | |

B10: 2

Examine chisels of the types named below, and in the spaces provided make sketches of each type.

Give examples of the use of each one.

*Flat chisel*

..................................................

..................................................

*Crosscut chisel*

..................................................

..................................................

*Diamond point chisel*

..................................................

..................................................

*Half round chisel*

..................................................

..................................................

*Hacksaws*

The individual teeth on a hacksaw blade form a pointed 'wedge' which digs into the metal and produces a 'shearing' action. The teeth on the blade are offset from one another. This offsetting is called the .................................... of the teeth.

Complete the sketch below to show a hacksaw blade in the sawcut. Indicate clearly the set on the teeth and state alongside the drawing, the purpose of the set.

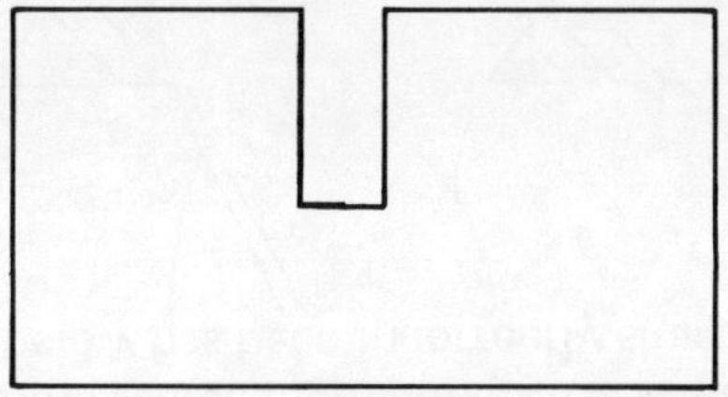

..................................................

..................................................

..................................................

..................................................

..................................................

Which way round should the blade be fitted into a hacksaw frame?

..................................................

On which stroke does the cutting action occur?

..................................................

Hacksaw blades are classified according to their length and number of teeth per centimetre. The choice of blade depends upon the shape and type of material being cut. Blades with teeth of 'fine pitch' are used for cutting.

..................................................

Saw blades with teeth of 'coarse pitch' are used for cutting,

..................................................

Give three causes of saw blade breakage.

1. ..................................................

2. ..................................................

3. ..................................................

*Files*

The cutting action of a file is similar to that of a chisel or hacksaw. Each tooth on a file is a tiny cutting blade. Files are classified according to: length, shape, grade of cut and type of cut.

**Investigation**

Examine a number of files and sketch the file section shapes named below.

*Flat* *Square* *Round*

*Half round* *Three square*

Complete the drawing below to show teeth on the files named. Indicate teeth angle in both cases.

*Single cut* *Double cut*

Files are graded according to the number of teeth per centimetre, that is their roughness or smoothness. Name four grades of file.

.................................................................................................................

*Twist drills*

Twist drills remove metal by using two cutting edges rotating about a centre point.

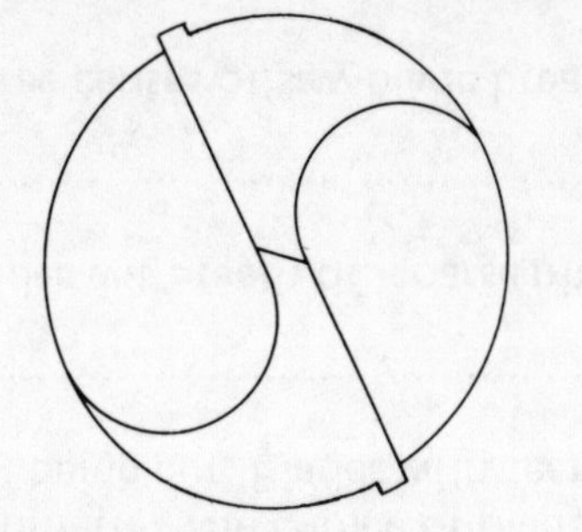

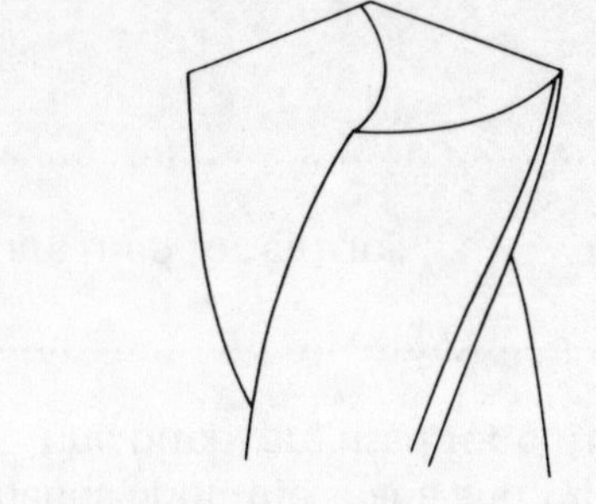

Indicate the cutting edges and lands. Indicate included (point) angle. Show the direction of rotation.

The point angle necessary for general purpose work is ..................................

State the purpose of the *land* on a twist drill.

.................................................................................................................

.................................................................................................................

When a drill is sharpened by grinding it is essential to keep the cutting edges (lips) the same length and at the same angle to the drill axis. State how each drill below has been incorrectly sharpened.

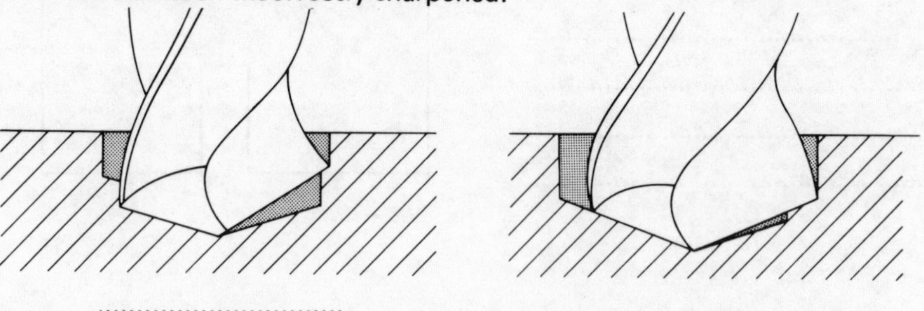

.............................. ..............................

How is the hole affected by the faults shown above?

.................................................................................................................

B10: 3,4

List the main causes of damage to or breakage of twist drills

..........................................................................................

..........................................................................................

..........................................................................................

..........................................................................................

*Drill speeds and feeds*

The *spindle speed* of a drill is the rotational speed at which the drill turns.

It is expressed in ..........................................................................

The *linear cutting speed* of a drill is the speed at which the cutting edges pass over the work. It is expressed in

..........................................................................................

What is meant by the *feed* on a drilling machine?

..........................................................................................

..........................................................................................

..........................................................................................

As a general guide the feed increases as the drill size increases.

The spindle speed of a drill is set according to:

1. ..........................................................................................

2. ..........................................................................................

State the linear cutting speed (using HSS drill) for:

1. Tool steel .................................. 2. Mild steel ..................................

3. Brass .......................................

..........................................................................................

..........................................................................................

..........................................................................................

..........................................................................................

..........................................................................................

It can be seen from the examples chosen that when cutting soft material the cutting speed is higher than that used for hard material. It is normal practice to refer to tables to obtain the correct spindle speed for a particular material and size of hole required.

However, the spindle speed can be calculated when given the cutting speed for a material and the drill diameter.

Example
A 10-mm hole is to be drilled in a mild-steel bracket. If the cutting speed is to be 30 m/min, calculate the spindle speed required.

$$\text{Spindle speed} \quad (N) = \frac{1000 \times S}{\pi \times d}$$

where $S$ = cutting speed (m/min)
and $d$ = drill diameter (mm)

$N$ =

Spindle speed =

Note: in practice spindle speed would be set to nearest convenient speed available.

Drill feed
A hole 25 mm is drilled in a time of 30 s. If the spindle speed of the drill is 500 rev/min, calculate the feed given to the drill.

$$\text{Feed} = \frac{\text{Depth of hole}}{\text{Revs Required}}$$

Revs required = Time x drill speed

=

Feed =

=

# CALCULATIONS

(a) When drilling to a depth of 12 mm a drill makes 48 revolutions. The feed on the drill is:

0.25 mm/rev, 0.48 mm/rev, 4 mm/rev or 25 mm/rev.

Answer ..........................................

(b) A hole is drilled through a 20 mm thick plate at a feed of 0.1 mm/rev. Calculate the time taken to drill the hole if the drill speed is 1600 rev/min.

(c) The time taken to drill a hole to a depth of 35 mm is 28 s. Calculate the feed on the drill if the spindle speed is 300 rev/min.

(d) Calculate the drill spindle speed required to drill a 5 mm hole in a piece of brass if the cutting speed is to be 50 m/min.

(c) The time taken to drill a 14 mm hole to a depth of 10 mm in a cast iron frame is 4.8 s. If the cutting speed is 22 m/min, calculate the drill spindle speed and feed.

# SOFT SOLDERING

B10: 8,9,10,14,16

Soft soldering is a low temperature metal-joining process used for joints which are relatively lightly loaded and not subjected to severe heating. It is also used for such as securing electrical cable connections and some pipe unions.

List FOUR metals that can be joined by soft soldering.

..............................................................................................................

Give THREE examples of the use of soft soldering in motor vehicle construction.

..............................................................................................................

..............................................................................................................

Soft soldering involves:

1. Preparing the surfaces to be joined.
2. Applying flux.
3. Applying sufficient heat for 'tinning' and running the molten solder into the joint.

How are the joint surfaces prepared?

1. ..............................................................................................................
2. ..............................................................................................................
3. ..............................................................................................................

Why is this preparation necessary?

..............................................................................................................

..............................................................................................................

..............................................................................................................

..............................................................................................................

..............................................................................................................

State the purpose of a soldering flux.

..............................................................................................................

..............................................................................................................

..............................................................................................................

..............................................................................................................

**Fluxes**

The type of flux must be chosen to suit the application. Two types of flux are in general use:

State materials for which the following fluxes are best suited.

| Corrosive | |
|---|---|
| Hydrochloric acid | |
| Zinc chloride (killed spirit) | |

| Non-corrosive | |
|---|---|
| Tallow | |
| Resin | |

*Corrosive* fluxes are ..................................fluxes which prevent oxidation taking place thereby protecting the joint surfaces during soldering. These fluxes also help to clean the joint surfaces.

*Non-corrosive* fluxes are .............................. fluxes which protect the 'cleaned' surface during the soldering process.

What precautions should be taken when using corrosive fluxes?

..............................................................................................................

..............................................................................................................

..............................................................................................................

..............................................................................................................

# SOLDER

Soft solders are *lead-tin* alloys which may contain a small percentage of *antimony*. The percentage of lead and tin in a solder is varied to suit the application. As the percentage of lead in the solder is increased, the melting temperature range between initial melting and fully molten becomes greater, that is the solder remains 'plastic' or 'pasty' over a wider temperature range. At what temperature does ordinary solder *begin* to melt?

..........................................................................................

Complete the table below.

| % Lead | % Tin | Temperature range while solder is in a plastic state | Typical use |
|---|---|---|---|
| 40 | 60 | | |
| 50 | 50 | | |
| 70 | 30 | | |

50/50 solder is commonly called ..........................................

40/60 lead-tin solder is commonly called ..........................................

70/30 lead-tin solder is commonly called ..........................................

State the advantage of 'tinmans' solder.

..........................................................................................

..........................................................................................

..........................................................................................

What benefit is to be gained by using a solder which has a prolonged 'pasty' stage when solidifying?

..........................................................................................

..........................................................................................

..........................................................................................

**Heat application**

State two methods of heat application during soldering.

1. ..........................................................................................

2. ..........................................................................................

What material is used for the 'bit' in a soldering iron and why?

..........................................................................................

..........................................................................................

The size of bit can vary considerably according to the type of work on which it is being used. What advantage is to be gained by using a large soldering bit?

..........................................................................................

..........................................................................................

..........................................................................................

Complete the drawing below to show a soldering iron being held to the work at approximately the correct angle.

B10: 11,12,15

State the purpose of 'tinning' a soldering iron.

..........................................................................................................

..........................................................................................................

..........................................................................................................

..........................................................................................................

**Investigation**

Investigate what occurs using a soldering iron that has been overheated causing all the solder to be removed from the bit.

Observe and record what happens when:

(a) The iron is heated and solder only is applied to the tip.

..........................................................................................................

..........................................................................................................

(b) The tip is cleaned with a fine file and, after reheating, again solder only is applied to the tip.

..........................................................................................................

..........................................................................................................

(c) The tip is cleaned with a file and, after reheating, flux and solder are applied.

..........................................................................................................

..........................................................................................................

Process (c) is called ........................................ the soldering bit.

How would a soldering operation be affected if the soldering bit chosen for the job was too small?

..........................................................................................................

..........................................................................................................

..........................................................................................................

..........................................................................................................



The joint shown above is a ..............................joint.

Outline the procedure for soldering this joint.

(a) ..........................................................................................................

(b) ..........................................................................................................

(c) ..........................................................................................................

This soldering process is known as ..........................................................

It may be necessary to apply a little solder at 'B'. If this is done the solder will flow into the joint formed between the faces; this is known as the

....................................................action of the solder.

Heat loss can be a problem when soldering. How can this be avoided.

..........................................................................................................

..........................................................................................................

Another problem associated with soldering is the damaging effect of heat flow to certain parts of a component being soldered. How can heat flow to special regions be limited during the soldering process?

..........................................................................................................

..........................................................................................................

..........................................................................................................

..........................................................................................................

..........................................................................................................

# B11.

# Vehicle Electrical Systems

B11: 1–4

# LEAD-ACID BATTERY

The lead-acid battery is of the secondary cell type and is used on most automobiles in either 12 or 24-V form. The 12 V is the most popular.

**Construction**

A 12-V battery container consists of six separate compartments. Each compartment contains a set of positive and negative plates; each set is fixed to a bar which rises to form the positive or negative terminal. The plates have a lattice-type framework into which is pressed the chemically-active material.

Between each plate is an insulating separator.

Name the parts on the sketch below.

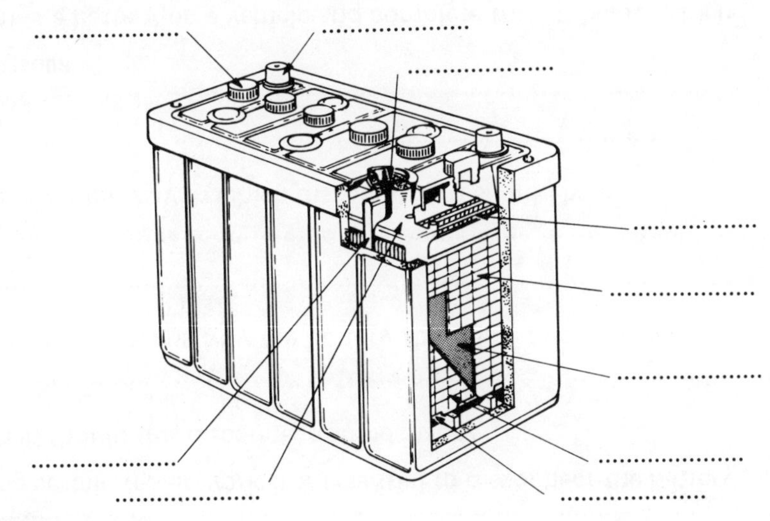

**Investigation**

Examine batteries suitable for dismantling. Dismantle a cell and state:

The colour of the active material:

(a) Positive plate ..........................

(b) Negative plate..........................

The number of plates in each cell:

(a) Positive ..................................

(b) Negative ..................................

**Investigation**

Examine batteries with different types of terminal posts and battery-lead connections.

Sketch the type of connectors that would be fitted to the terminal posts shown. Make the sketches as if the leads are fitted on to the terminals

Type ..............................................

The polarity of this type of terminal post may be determined by their relative size. The positive terminal is: ..................................... and the negative terminal is: ..................................................

Type ..............................................

The polarity of this shape of terminal post is often distinguished by coloured paint. What colours are used?

Positive ..........................................

Negative .........................................

Name a third type of connector ..........................................................................

What are the common battery polarity connections?

.............................................................................................................

Why is it important that the battery is connected correctly to the vehicle?

.............................................................................................................

.............................................................................................................

.............................................................................................................

.............................................................................................................

B11: 7,8

## TERMINALS AND CONNECTIONS

When a battery is in use on a vehicle the terminals are naturally prone to corrosion.

What is commonly done to resist this corrosion?

..............................................................................................................

..............................................................................................................

During certain repair work it is essential to disconnect the battery.

1. When should this disconnection be made?

   ..............................................................................................................

2. Give three reasons why the battery should be disconnected?

   ..............................................................................................................

   ..............................................................................................................

3. Describe the way in which disconnection should be made.

   ..............................................................................................................

   ..............................................................................................................

**Investigation**

Examine a battery on a vehicle and complete the list below which indicates possible faults that could lead to premature battery failure.

| Item | Check condition | Tick if correct |
|---|---|---|
| Casing | Cracks, corners missing or other casing damage | |
| Top | Cracks | |
| | Terminal posts secure | |
| | Clean and dry | |
| | Stoppers or lid | |
| Electrolyte | Level | |
| Connections | Tight | |
| | Clean and smeared with a protective coating | |
| | Insulation on starter cable | |
| Securing frame | Tight | |
| | Location correct | |
| | Free from corrosion | |

B11: 9,13

Battery plates are immersed in an electrolyte which is a mixture of

..............................................................................................................

How should these two solutions be mixed together?

..............................................................................................................

..............................................................................................................

What is the reason for this method of mixing?

..............................................................................................................

..............................................................................................................

## SAFETY PRECAUTIONS

The fact that the battery electrolyte contains acid and that during the charging process the chemical reaction produces a flammable gas makes the battery a safety hazzard.

List precautions to be taken:

(a) When fitting a bench-charged battery to the vehicle:

1 ..............................................................................................................

2. ..............................................................................................................

3. ..............................................................................................................

4. ..............................................................................................................

(b) With regard to personal safety:

1. ..............................................................................................................

2. ..............................................................................................................

3. ..............................................................................................................

4. ..............................................................................................................

What method should be used to neutralise contact with:

(a) Human skin ..............................................................................................

(b) Eyes ..............................................................................................................

(c) Clothing .......................................................................................................

(d) Vehicle .........................................................................................................

B11: 5,6,14,15

# BATTERY CONDITION

The two principal features indicating the condition of a battery are:

1. State of charge
2. Ability to supply a heavy current for a short period of time.

What can be tested using a hydrometer? ..............................................................

What does the test indicate? ..............................................................

The hydrometer readings of a battery electrolyte will vary between about

.........................and..............................

Name the main parts of the hydrometer shown

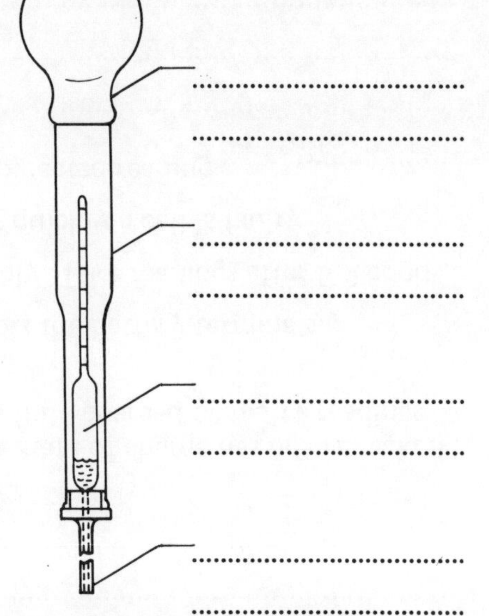

Complete the table below to show a specific gravity range for the conditions listed.

| State of charge | Specific gravity |
|---|---|
| Fully charged | |
| Half charged | |
| Discharged | |

Complete the drawings below to show the expected float level position.

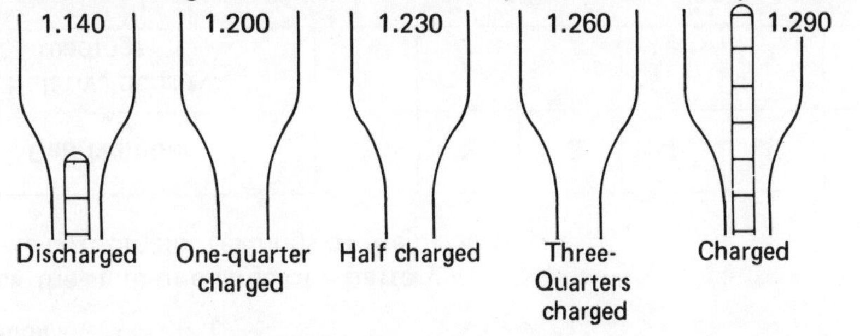


What is meant by relative density (or specific gravity)? ..............................................................

Why do the relative density values indicate the state of charge of a battery?

..............................................................

What can be checked by a high-rate discharge tester?

..............................................................

The high-rate discharge tester may be a hand-held unit that tests each individual cell, or tests all the cells by being connected to the two terminals. Alternatively, the tester may form part of a battery, starter, charging system test unit.

Show a sketch of the high-rate discharge tester available for use in the next investigation and name the main parts.

**Investigation**

To check the state of charge of a battery:
(a) Take hydrometer readings of the battery.

| Cell Number | 1 | 2 | 3 | 4 | 5 | 6 |
|---|---|---|---|---|---|---|
| Relative density readings | | | | | | |

General condition of battery ..........................................................

..........................................................................................

(b) Carry out a battery capacity test.

Note: This test must only be used after the state of charge has been checked. The battery must be at least three-quarters fully charged or faulty readings may be obtained

Connect the high-rate discharge tested across the battery terminals.

Use tester for approximately 10 seconds only. Take readings after 5 seconds.

The reading should hold steady. If it drops quickly a cell is faulty.

Actual reading .................................... Expected reading ..........................

Any other effects ..........................................................................

..........................................................................................

General condition of battery: ..........................................................

## B11: 16 RECTIFICATION

When bench-charging batteries from the mains supply; the supply is connected through a rectifier to the battery.

What is the purpose of the rectifier?

..........................................................................................

..........................................................................................

## B11: 17,18 CABLES

The selection of cable and type of insulation required for motor-vehicle use depend upon two main factors. These are:

1. ..........................................................................................

2. ..........................................................................................

Cables are often bunched together in a harness or loom. This simplifies fitting and ensures less chance of breakage or short circuits. Each cable within the harness is colour coded.

..........................................................................................

..........................................................................................

The main feed cable to a specific switch may have a single colour and past the switch the lead has the same main colour but with a different coloured trace line passing through it.

Typical main colours for circuits are:

Ignition .......................................... Headlamp.......................................

Sidelamp.......................................... Flasher..........................................

The amount of current a cable can pass is determined by its size. How are these classified? ..........................................................................

What does a cable having a size of 28/0.30 indicate?

..........................................................................................

What is a recognised safe current capacity for each strand of cable 0.30 mm thick? ..................................................

**Investigation**

Examine cables of various thickness obtained from or still held in a wiring harness.
From what material are the wires made? ..................................................

With the aid of the cables examined complete the table on the next page, that is count the number of strands and measure their diameter.

| Cable used | Cable size | Colour | Safe current supply (A) |
|---|---|---|---|
| Starter | | | |
| Main feed supply | | | |
| Headlamp | | | |
| A lightly loaded feed | | | |

B11: 19

# CABLE CONNECTORS

The connections between electrical units and cables must be mechanically positive and easy to connect but not liable to slacken under vibration.

Identify the following types of connectors:

Spade, grub screw, ferrule and eyelet

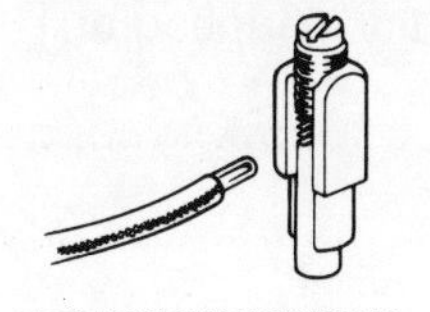

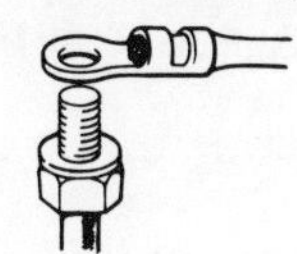

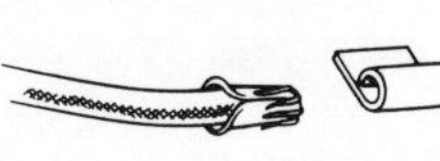

........................ ........................ ........................ ........................

The two types of modern snap connectors below are called:

1. ..............................................................................................

2. ..............................................................................................

Show the type of terminal each cable would have, to push into the connector below:

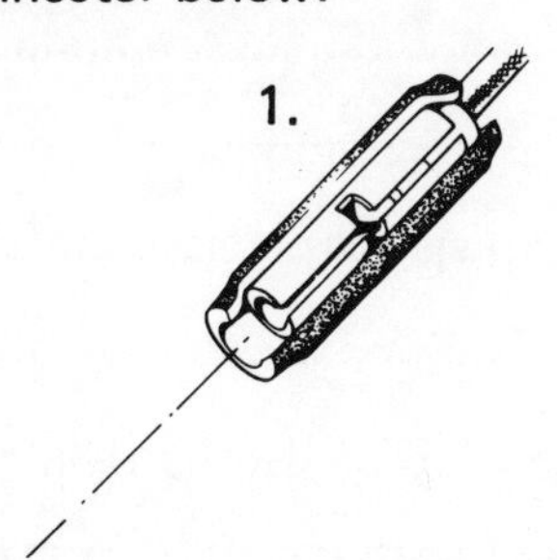


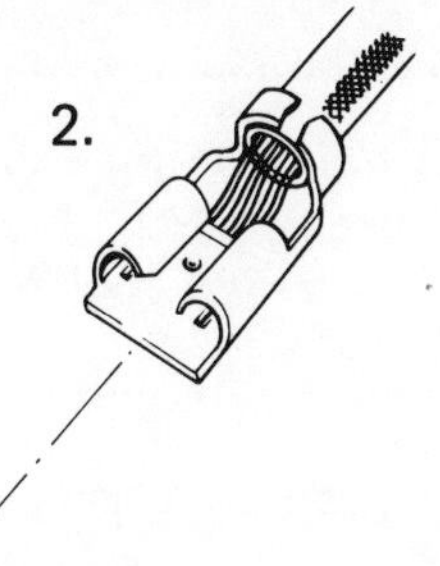


B11: 20,21

# FUSES

A fuse is intended to be the weakest part of any circuit.
Why is it designed in this way?

..............................................................................................

..............................................................................................

Sketch and name two types of fuse. Identify the materials used.

Certain circuits fit a fuse in the supply cable (radios, direction-indicator flashers). These are known as

..............................................................................................

The safe current capacity of cartridge fuses (Lucas) is given on a label inside the fuse. This label is colour coded.

The body of the ceramic type is also coloured depending on current capacity.

Give examples of:

Cartridge type: ..............................  Ceramic type: ..............................

..............................  ..............................

**Investigation**

Examine the wiring on a modern vehicle and state the number of fuses used in the fuse block. Identify the fuses and their rating.

Number of fuses in block ..............................

Complete the table below:

| Circuits protected | Colour of fuse | Fuse capacity |
|---|---|---|
| | | |
| | | |
| | | |
| | | |

# VEHICLE LIGHTING SYSTEMS

The lighting system of a car may be split into two basic circuits. These are

..........................................................................................

List the basic essentials that make up a lighting circuit.

..........................................................................................

..........................................................................................

..........................................................................................

When more than one lamp is used the circuit is usually wired in ....................

The side light circuit consists of two lamps at the front and at least two at the rear plus a lamp to illuminate the vehicle's rear registration plate.

..........................................................................................

..........................................................................................

..........................................................................................

The headlight circuit is basically two circuits, the main beam and dip beam.

..........................................................................................

..........................................................................................

..........................................................................................

Examine three vehicles of widely varying types, for example commercial vehicle, Land Rover, and a modern saloon. Observe the correct working of head, dip and sidelights. If lights operate correctly place tick in column. If inoperative state which light is faulty.

| Vehicle make | | | |
|---|---|---|---|
| Model | | | |
| Sidelights | | | |
| Tail lights | | | |
| No. plate light | | | |
| Headlight main beam | | | |
| Headlight dip beam | | | |

Complete the following diagrams using the earth return system.

Sidelight circuit

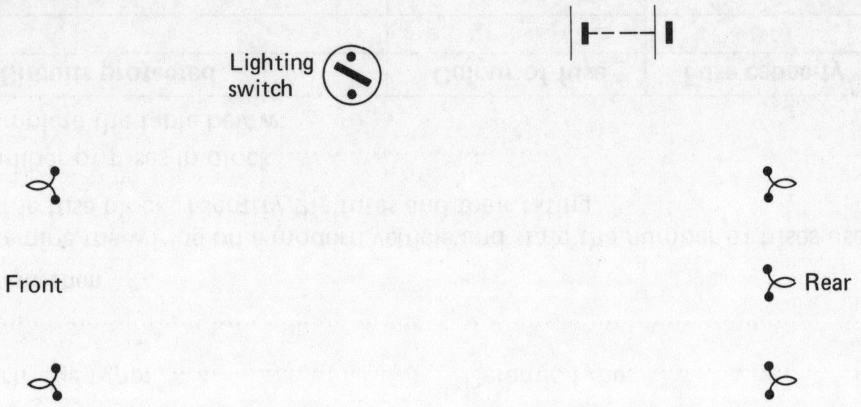

Lighting switch

Front

Rear

Headlight circuit

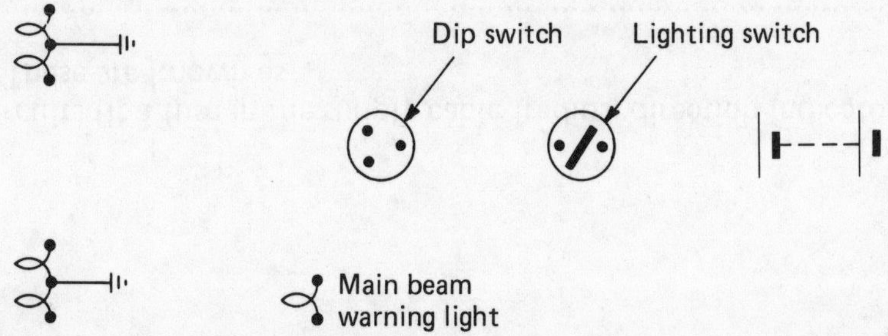

Dip switch

Lighting switch

Main beam warning light

Other circuits, which are sometimes considered as part of the basic lighting system but, which use lights for signalling purposes or for better visibility are the:

1. ..........................................................................................
2. ..........................................................................................
3. ..........................................................................................

# TYPES OF BULB

Examine light bulbs of different types.
Identify those shown and state where these may be fitted on a vehicle, in each case give a typical wattage rating.

Note: These sketches are not to scale.

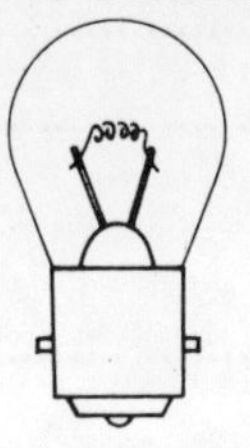

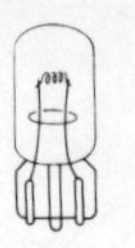

1. ..............................
2. ..............................
3. ..............................

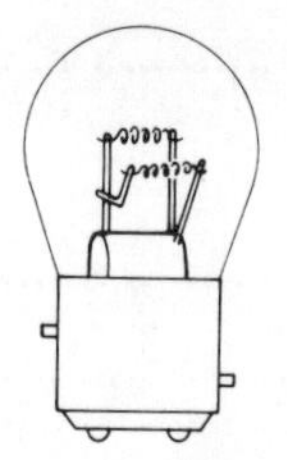

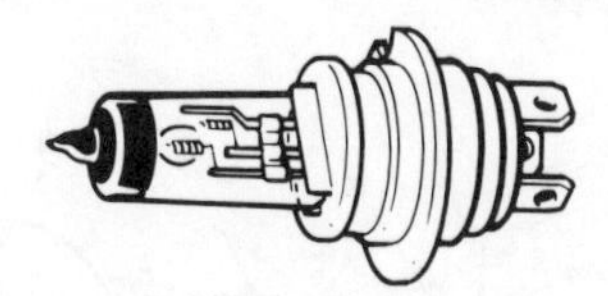

4. ..............................
5. ..............................

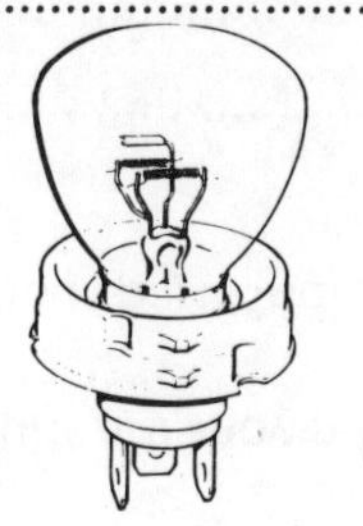

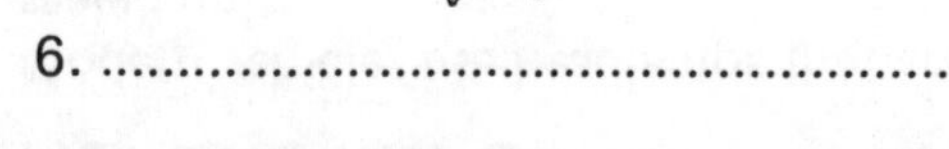

6. ..............................
7. ..............................

The inert gas used inside the bulb is usually ..............................

The resistance wire used for the filament is ..............................

The temperature reached by this wire is approximately ..............................

In what important way does bulb 3 differ from the other small bulbs?

..............................

Why does bulb 4 have a staggered pin fitment? ..............................

..............................

Bulbs 5 and 6 are known as pre-focus bulbs. What identifying feature gives them this name?

..............................

What does bulb 7 include within the bulb? ..............................

..............................

For the same wattage rating the quartz-halogen headlamp (5) will give off a much brighter light. How is this improvement achieved?

..............................

# HEADLAMPS

Modern vehicles use headlamps that are either sealed beam units or semi-sealed units.

Three such units are shown below and although similar have certain basic differences.

Name the various parts indicated.

Type A

1. ........................................
2. ........................................
3. ........................................
4. ........................................
5. ........................................
6. ........................................

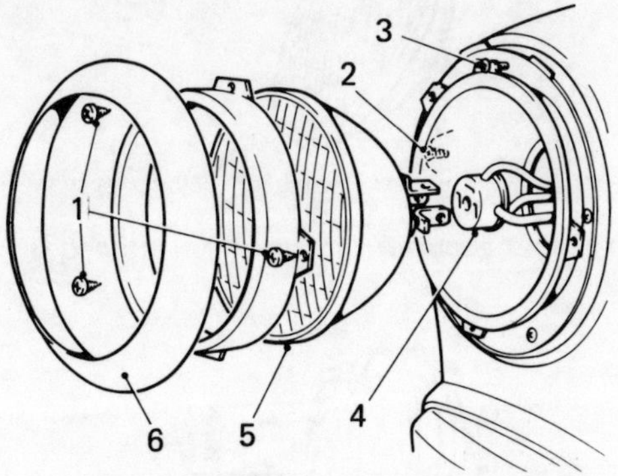

Type B

1. ........................................
2. ........................................
3. ........................................
4. ........................................
5. ........................................
6. ........................................

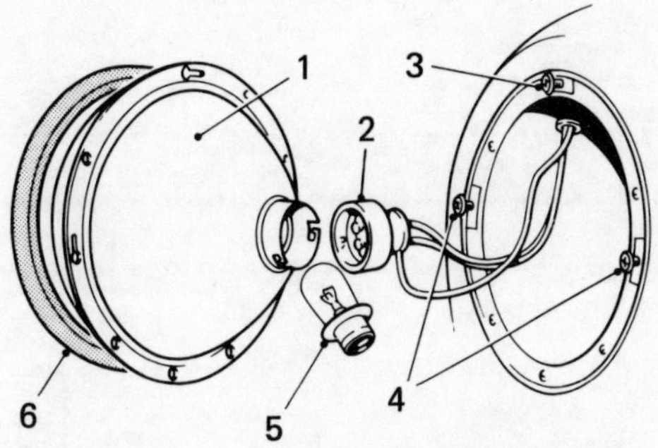

Type C

1. ........................................
2. ........................................
3. ........................................
4. ........................................
5. ........................................
6. ........................................

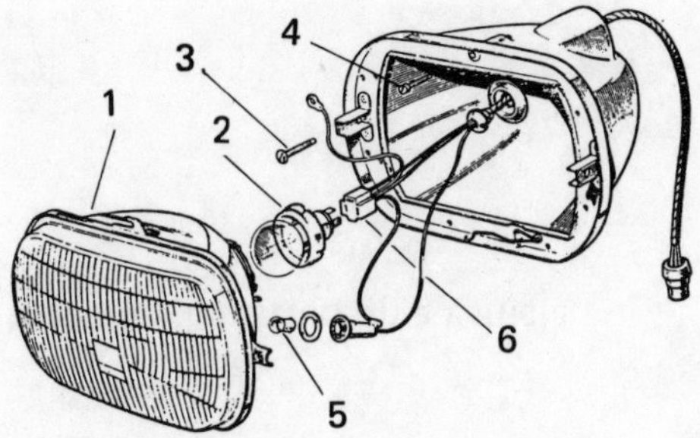

With reference to the sketches opposite:

Type A is a sealed beam unit

..............................................................................

Type B is a British pre-focus type bulb assembly

..............................................................................

Type C is a European pre-focus type bulb assembly

..............................................................................

State the purpose of the following parts:

Reflector..............................................................................

..............................................................................

Lens..............................................................................

..............................................................................

Vertical and horizontal screws..............................................................................

..............................................................................

State how, in each case, a new bulb would be fitted.

Type A..............................................................................

..............................................................................

..............................................................................

Type B..............................................................................

..............................................................................

..............................................................................

Type C..............................................................................

..............................................................................

..............................................................................

B11:27

# METHODS OF DIPPING THE BEAM

*Two-headlamp system*

When on main beam the light rays illuminate the road as far ahead as possible.

What occurs when the lights are dipped?

..................................................................................................

..................................................................................................

..................................................................................................

Show the position of the dipped beams.

*Four-headlamp system*

With some systems, when on main beam the outer lamps are on permanent dip while the inner lamps throw out brighter longer range beam along the road.

What occurs when the lights are dipped?

..................................................................................................

..................................................................................................

Show the position of the light beams when on main beam.

B11:28

# SIMPLE METHOD OF SETTING HEADLAMPS

Describe, with the aid of the diagram, how the headlamps should be set without the aid of special equipment.

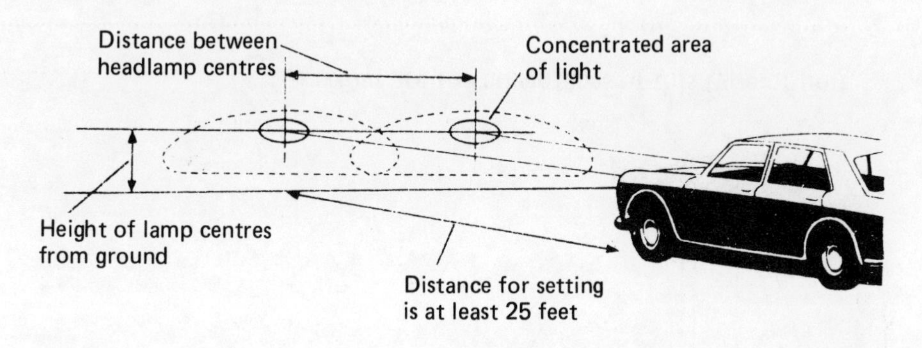


..................................................................................................

..................................................................................................

..................................................................................................

..................................................................................................

..................................................................................................

..................................................................................................

..................................................................................................

..................................................................................................

..................................................................................................

..................................................................................................

..................................................................................................

..................................................................................................

..................................................................................................

..................................................................................................

..................................................................................................

# METHOD OF REDUCING DAZZLE

1. Pre-focus, offset filament bulb

Name the arrowed parts.

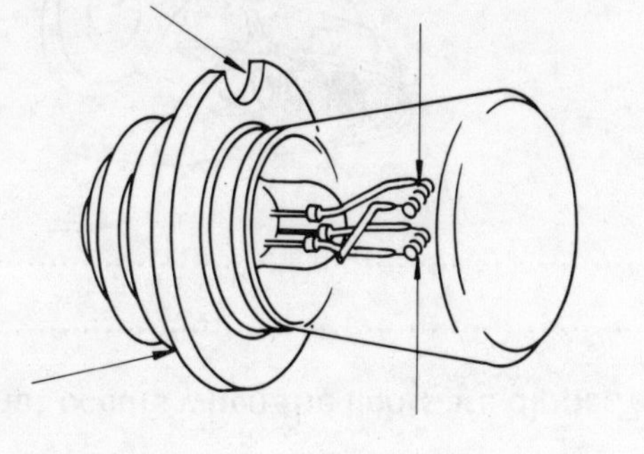

2. Pre-Focus, shielded filament bulb

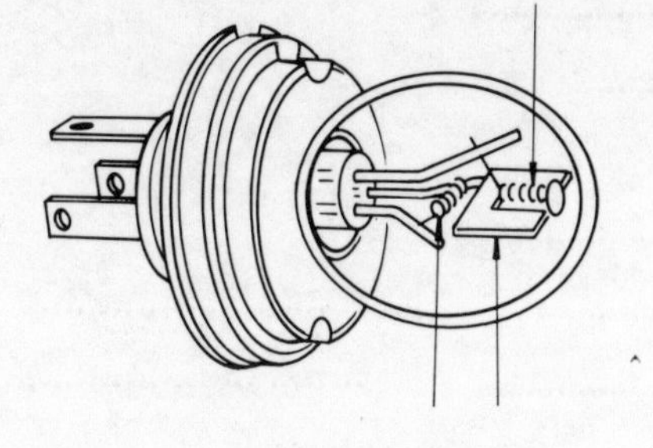

Main beam

The bulb filament is set on the focal point (focus) point of the reflector and the light rays are reflected parallel. Show these rays.

Parabolic reflector

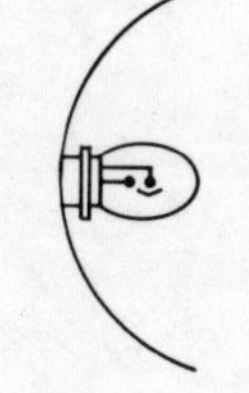

Dip beam

Show how the light rays are reflected when the dip filament is operated.

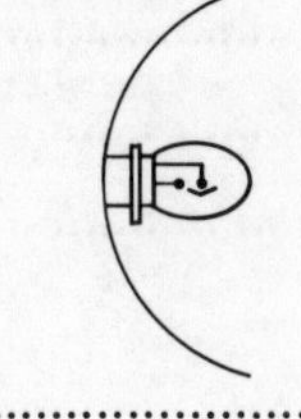

..............................................................................

..............................................................................

..............................................................................

..............................................................................

Sealed beam light unit

The sealed beam unit provides a shield in front of the dip filament and relies on the reflection and lens combination to deflect the light rays correctly.

Examine a sealed beam light unit. Identify the two filaments and complete the sketch below. Name the important parts.

*Lucas sealed-beam unit*

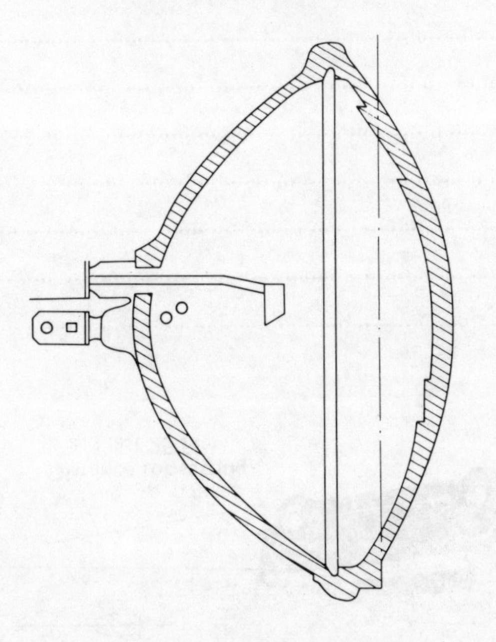

What are the advantages of this type of unit.

1. ..............................................................................

..............................................................................

2. ..............................................................................

..............................................................................

B11: 30,36

## THE BATTERY

The battery is a series of chemical cells. Each cell of a lead acid battery is capable of producing 2 V. The size and number of plates in the cell determine its capacity or output. It is of a secondary cell type.

What is the basic purpose of a battery?

................................................................................................................

What is a primary cell? Give an example.

................................................................................................................

................................................................................................................

The positive and negative plate active materials of the secondary cell, although of a similar base, have a different chemical composition and when submerged in a suitable electrolyte produce an electrical pressure difference which when connected to a circuit allows a current to flow. The chemical reaction then discharges the cell until the plates become chemically similar.

Why is the cell then capable of being recharged?

................................................................................................................

................................................................................................................

................................................................................................................

## 12-V BATTERY

Since each cell has a nominal electrical pressure of 2 V, to produce a 12-V battery six cells must be joined together in series.

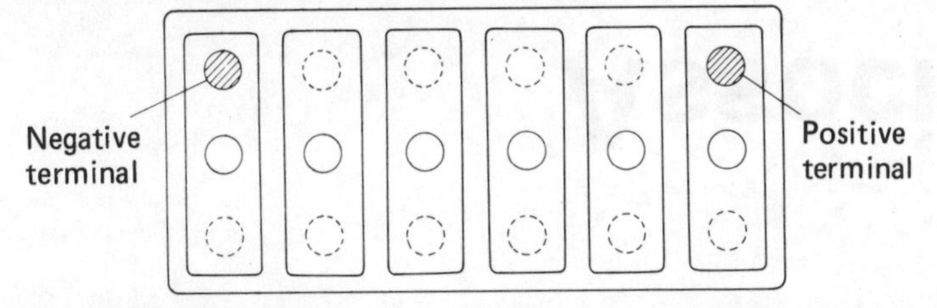


The cells are connected by buss bars (or links), not normally seen on modern batteries. Show where these would be connected in the diagram above and indicate the polarity of each cell by symbols.

## CHARGING

When the battery requires charging, the supply, be if from the vehicle's charging system or the mains supply, must be a direct current (d.c.). Why must only direct current be used?

................................................................................................................

................................................................................................................

Complete the table to show how the plate materials and electrolyte are affected during the charge and discharge cycle.

| Process | Positive plate | Electrolyte | Negative plate |
|---|---|---|---|
| Fully charged | | | |
| Discharged | | | |

Name the two gases given off from the cells when the battery is being recharged.

1. ............................................... 2. ...............................................

Which gas is flammable? ...........................................................................

**Investigation**

(1) Connect a battery to an external charging system.
What way (electrically) are the charger-to-battery connections made?

................................................................................................................

(2) Connect three 12 V batteries to a constant current charger. Show on the sketch how the batteries are connected to the charger.

The cells are connected in ..............

Constant current battery charger

− + − + − + − +

List the precautions required when charging batteries.

................................................................................................................

................................................................................................................

SECTION C

# Associated Studies

C1.

# Calculations

# FRACTIONS

*Addition*

$2\frac{3}{4} + 1\frac{5}{6}$ ← mixed number

$= 3\frac{9+10}{12}$ ← lowest common denominator

$= 3\frac{19}{12} = 4\frac{7}{12}$

Improper fraction

*Subtraction*

$3\frac{4}{5} - \frac{5}{9}$

$= 3\frac{36-25}{45}$ ← subtract; ← l.c.d.

$= 3\frac{11}{45}$

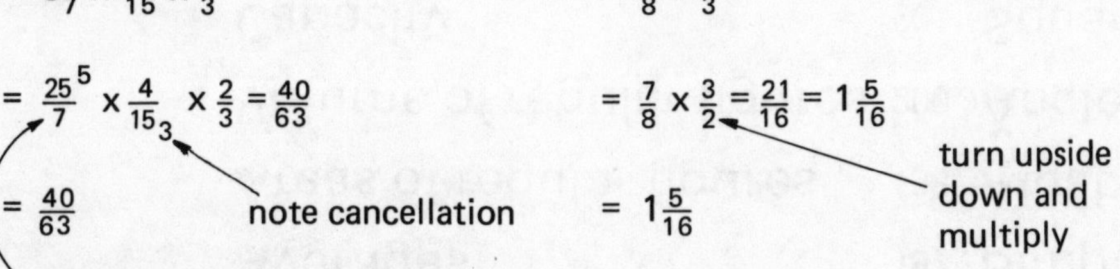

*Multiplication*

$3\frac{4}{7} \times \frac{4}{15} \times \frac{2}{3}$

$= \frac{25^{5}}{7} \times \frac{4}{15_{3}} \times \frac{2}{3} = \frac{40}{63}$ ← note cancellation

$= \frac{40}{63}$

converted to improper fraction

*Division*

$\frac{7}{8} \div \frac{2}{3}$

$= \frac{7}{8} \times \frac{3}{2} = \frac{21}{16} = 1\frac{5}{16}$ ← turn upside down and multiply

$= 1\frac{5}{16}$

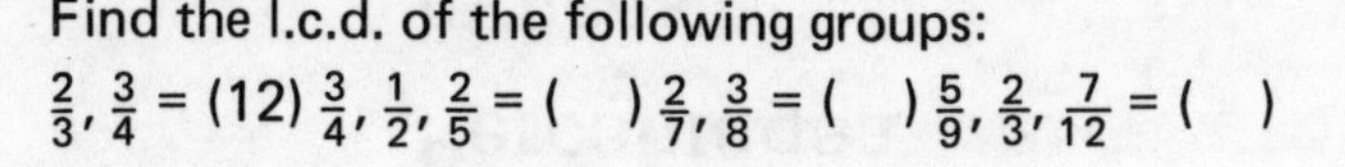

Find the l.c.d. of the following groups:

$\frac{2}{3}, \frac{3}{4} = (12)$ $\frac{3}{4}, \frac{1}{2}, \frac{2}{5} = (\quad)$ $\frac{2}{7}, \frac{3}{8} = (\quad)$ $\frac{5}{9}, \frac{2}{3}, \frac{7}{12} = (\quad)$

Reduce the following to their lowest terms:

$\frac{9}{24} = (\frac{3}{8})$ $\frac{12}{36} = (\quad)$ $\frac{22}{46} = (\quad)$ $\frac{15}{27} = (\quad)$ $\frac{63}{84} = (\quad)$

Convert the following to improper fractions:

$2\frac{5}{8} = (\frac{21}{8})$ $3\frac{3}{4} = (\quad)$ $8\frac{9}{16} = (\quad)$ $5\frac{4}{11} = (\quad)$ $3\frac{18}{23} = (\quad)$

..........................................................................

..........................................................................

..........................................................................

..........................................................................

..........................................................................

**Problems**

1. The oil capacity of an engine is $3\frac{3}{4}$ litre. When the oil level was checked $1\frac{1}{3}$ litres of oil was needed. How much oil did the engine contain?

..........................................

..........................................

..........................................

..........................................

2. If a vehicle weighs 912 kg and $\frac{5}{8}$ of the weight is on the rear wheels, what is the weight on the front wheels?

..........................................

..........................................

..........................................

..........................................

..........................................

3. A vehicle travels $11\frac{1}{2}$ km on 1 litre of fuel. If the fuel-tank capacity is 40 litres how far will the vehicle travel on a full tank of fuel?

..........................................

..........................................

..........................................

..........................................

..........................................

4. $\frac{1}{3}$ of a bar of steel is used on one day, $\frac{1}{6}$ on the next, and $\frac{1}{4}$ on the third day. How much is left?

..........................................

..........................................

..........................................

..........................................

..........................................

5. Work out the following:

$$4\frac{1}{6} - 1\frac{2}{5} + \frac{7}{15}$$

..........................................

..........................................

..........................................

..........................................

..........................................

6. Work out the following:

$$\frac{1\frac{5}{8} \times 3\frac{11}{13}}{2\frac{7}{9}} \times 5\frac{2}{3}$$

..........................................

..........................................

..........................................

..........................................

..........................................

C1:1, 2

# DECIMALS

*Addition*

```
   53.00
    4.85
    0.36
+   0.002
   58.212
```

Note
The decimal points must be under one another.

*Subtraction*

```
  47.97
 −35.60
  12.37
```

Note
The decimal points must be under one another

*Multiplication*

```
   67.89
x   8.56
  407.34
 3394.5
54312
581.1384
```

Four figures on the right of the point.

Therefore count four figures from the right in the answer.

Treat as whole numbers to multiply then position point as indicated

*Division*

276.56 ÷ 35.4

```
        7.8
354)2765.6
    2478
     2876
     2832
       44
```

This answer is correct to one decimal place.

The divisor is made into a whole number by moving the decimal point to the right. The point must also be moved the same number of places in the number being divided.

*Multiplying and dividing decimals by 10 and multiples of 10*

| Multiplying | | Dividing | |
|---|---|---|---|
| 56.42 x 10 | = 564.2 | 56.42 ÷ 100 | = 0.5642 |
| 56.42 x 1000 | = | 56.42 ÷ 10 | = |
| 56.42 x 10 000 | = | 56.42 ÷ 1000 | = |
| 56.42 x 100 | = | 56.42 ÷ 100 000 | = |

..................................................................................

..................................................................................

..................................................................................

**Problems**

Solve the following:

```
  36.96        287.6
+  3.7       +  58.67

  1.037        300.6
+ 0.36       +  28.683
```

Solve the following:

```
  80.26        356.1
− 33.1       − 253.23

  961.35       87.38
− 298.2      −  6.29
```

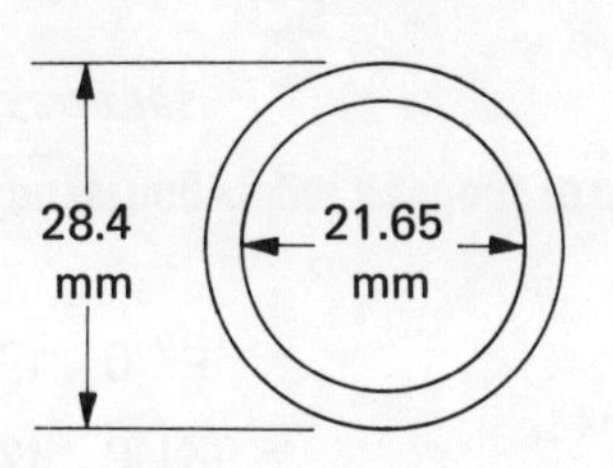


Find the thickness of metal in the pipe shown.

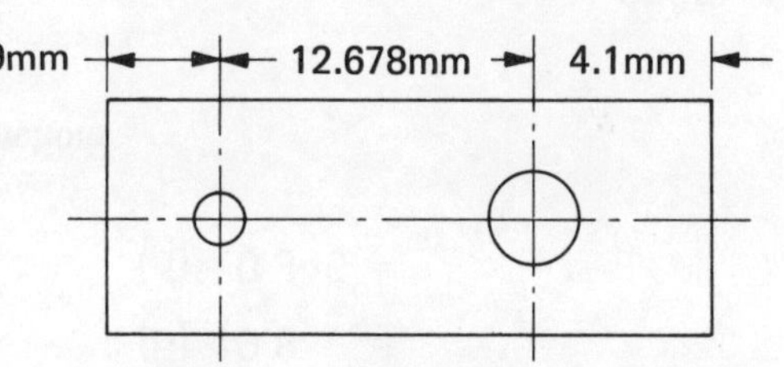


What is the overall length of the metal plate shown?

The circumference of a tyre is 1.25 m. How many revolutions will it make in travelling 20 m?

The stroke of an engine is 6.58 cm. calculate the linear distance travelled by the piston in 1 s when the engine speed is 1200 rev/min.

The answer to a problem may be correct to a number of decimal places, or correct to a number of significant figures, depending upon the accuracy required.

*Decimal places*

The following have been corrected to two decimal places.

(a) 21.632 is 21.63

(b) 184.676 is 184.68

(c) 3.5601 is 3.56

(d) 27.067 is 27.07

(e) 0.079 is 0.08

*Significant figures*

The following have been corrected to three significant figures.

(a) 23.518 is 23.5

(b) 336.8 is 337

(c) 19.18 is 19.2

(d) 0.007526 is 0.00753

(e) 0.03573 is 0.0357

State the following to the number of decimal places shown.

| Number | Decimal places | Answer |
|---|---|---|
| 35.78 | 1 | |
| 276.14 | 1 | |
| 2.0676 | 3 | |
| 896.073 | 2 | |
| 1.8725 | 1 | |

State the following to the number of significant figures shown.

| Number | Significant figures | Answer |
|---|---|---|
| 24.69 | 3 | |
| 349.2 | 3 | |
| 2.481 | 2 | |
| 0.0369 | 2 | |
| 0.0193 | 1 | |

Solve the following to two significant figures.

(1) 9.8 × 4 (2) 4.7 × 8 (3) 24.52 × 3 (4) 3.578 × 12

Solve the following to two decimal places.

(1) 69.7 ÷ 7.6 (2) 126.2 ÷ 7.1 (3) 23.6 ÷ 0.22 (4) 528.9 ÷ 32.6

**Converting decimal fractions to vulgar fractions**

*Examples*

(a) $0.25 = \frac{25}{100} = \frac{1}{4}$ (b) $0.6 = \frac{6}{10} = \frac{3}{5}$ (c) $0.325 = \frac{325}{1000} = \frac{13}{40}$

Convert the following decimals to fractions

(a) 0.125 = (b) 0.8 =

(c) 0.75 = (d) 0.345 =

**Converting vulgar fractions to decimal fractions**

*Examples*

(a) $\frac{1}{4}$ 4)10 = .25; 8; 20; 20; ..

(b) $\frac{13}{20}$ 20)130 = .65; 120; 100; 100; ...

(c) $\frac{1}{16}$ 16)100 = .0625; 96; 40; 32; 80; 80

C1:6, 8, 9

Convert the following fractions to decimals

(1) $\frac{1}{2}$ (2) $\frac{1}{8}$ (3) $\frac{2}{5}$

# PERCENTAGES

Per cent or percentage (usually denoted by %) refers to a part or fraction of some quantity expressed in hundredths.

To obtain the percentage, the fraction or the decimal is multiplied by 100.

Express the following as percentages:

(a) $\frac{3}{5} \times \frac{100}{1} = 60\%$ (b) $\frac{9}{64}$ (c) $\frac{23}{32}$

(d) 0.4 (e) 0.35 (f) 0.01

When commencing a workshop exercise, 15 students share equally a bar of mild steel 2 m in length. What percentage of the bar will each student receive?

Each will receive $\frac{1}{15}$ of the bar.

∴ The percentage will be:

$$\frac{1}{15} \times \frac{100}{1} = 6\tfrac{2}{3}\%$$

If the repair charge for a job is £120 and 27% of this is the cost of parts how much did the parts cost?

$$\text{Cost of } \frac{\text{Parts}}{£120} \times \frac{100}{1} = 27\%$$

$$\therefore \text{Cost of Parts} = \frac{27 \times 120}{100} = \frac{162}{5} = 32\tfrac{2}{5}$$

Cost of parts = £32.40

**Problems**

1. The rate for repair charges at a garage is £18.15 per hour. If 20% of this is profit, 60% is overheads and the rest is the mechanic's pay, at what hourly rate is the mechanic paid?

2. A stick of solder has a mass of 3 kg. If it is composed of 30% tin and 70% lead, what is the mass of lead?

3. An engine cylinder is to be rebored to give a 2% increase in diameter. If the original diameter is 60 mm, determine the diameter after reboring.

4. If the retail price for a brake master-cylinder is £30 and a mechanic is allowed $12\frac{1}{2}$% discount on this, how much would he pay for the master cylinder?

5. If a car reduces speed by 8% and is then travelling at 70 km/h, what was its former speed?

6. A mechanic sets the ignition timing on a vehicle to 9° b.t.d.c. If the correct setting is 5° b.t.d.c., calculate the percentage error.

# INDICES

3 x 3 can be written as $3^2$ (three squared or three to the 'power' of two).

Similarly 3 x 3 x 3 x 3 is $3^4$ (three raised to the power four). The figure placed above the 3 in the examples above is the

..................................................

When multiplying and dividing numbers which are the same their indices can be added or subtracted. The same rule applies to letters used instead of numbers. For example

$a^2 \times a^3$ becomes $a^{2+3} = a^5$

or

$a \times a \times a \times a \times a = a^5$

$\frac{a^6}{a^2}$ is $\frac{a \times a \times a \times a}{a \times a} \times a \times a = a^4$

When multiplying ........................the indices. When dividing ...................... the indices.

Simplify the following:

(a) $y^2 \times y^3 \times y^5$ =

(b) $\frac{a^2 \times a^4 \times a^7}{a^3 \times a^2}$ =

(c) $a^2 \times b^3 \times a^3 \times b^2$ =

When dealing with expressions like $ab^2$, only the $b$ is squared.

That is $ab^2 = a \times b \times b$

But $(ab)^2$ =

A value can be stated by using the base number 10 raised to a certain power. For example

$100 = 10^2$

Instead of writing 100 we write $10^2$, it has the same value. This method can be convenient when large numbers are involved or when fractions of 10 are involved.

(d) Express the following by using base 10 raised to a power.

1000 =

10000 =

100000 =

1000000 =

10000000 =

100 =

10 =

1 =

Fractions of 10

0.1 =

0.01 =

0.001 =

0.0001 =

0.00001 =

0.000001 =

When multiplying decimal fractions by the base 10 raised to a power, the decimal point is moved right or left according to the value of the index.

If the index is 'positive', the decimal point moves to the

..................................................

If the index is 'negative', the decimal point moves to the

..................................................

*Examples*

$12.47 \times 10^2$ =

$1003 \times 10^2$ =

$1.5684 \times 10^3$ =

$138.51 \times 10^5$ =

$5000.35 \times 10^1$ =

$542 \times 10^{-2}$ =

$368.76 \times 10^{-3}$ =

$15768.62 \times 10^{-6}$ =

Using the 'power ten' method numbers can be expressed in a shorter form. For example

10500 can be expressed as

$10.5 \times 10^3$

(e) Express the following numbers using this method. Express in powers $10^6$, $10^3$, $10^{-3}$, or $10^{-6}$

6575000 =

49500000 =

85650 =

0.0000013 =

0.001 =

0.000354 =

..................................................

..................................................

..................................................

..................................................

..................................................

..................................................

..................................................

# AVERAGES

The average (or mean value) of a set of numbers is equal to their sum divided by the number of them.

Find the average of: 3, 5, 9 and 11

$$\text{Average} = \frac{3 + 5 + 9 + 11}{4} = \frac{28}{4} = 7$$

During a 4 hour journey a man did 40 km in the first hour, 48 in the second, 44 in the third and 51 in the last hour. What was his average speed for the journey?

$$\text{Average speed} = \frac{40 + 48 + 44 + 51}{4}$$

$$= \frac{183}{4} = 45\tfrac{3}{4}$$

$$= 45\tfrac{3}{4} \text{ km/h}$$

**Problems**

1. A vehicle's fuel consumption during three different journeys was calculated as 10 km litre, 12.5 km/litre and 11.25 km/litre. The average fuel consumption figure for the vehicle during the three journeys is therefore:

(a) 10 km/*l* (b) 11.25 km/*l*

(c) 11. 75 km/*l* (d) 15 km/*l*

Answer ( )

2. During a check on four spark plugs, the 'gaps' were found to be 0.6mm, 0.55mm, 0.7mm, and 0.75 mm. The average gap was:

(a) 0.7 mm (b) 0.8 mm

(c) 0.6 mm (d) 0.65 mm

Answer ( )

3. If a car averages 62 km/h for $4\frac{1}{2}$ hours, the total distance covered will be:

(a) 93 km (b) 124 km

(c) 279 km (d) 379 km

Answer ( )

4. In five consecutive months the number of services done by a garage was 86, 90, 79, 74 and 81. The monthly average was:

(a) 88 (b) 44

(c) 80 (d) 82

Answer ( )

5. Four different oil measures have capacities of 4 litres, 2 litres, 1 litre and $\frac{1}{2}$ litre. The average capacity is:

(a) $1\frac{1}{2}$ (b) $2\frac{1}{2}$

(c) 3 (d) $1\frac{7}{8}$

Answer ( )

6. After a tyre inspection on a vehicle the tread depths were found to be 3.5 mm, 2.5 mm, 0.5 mm and 2 mm. What was the average tread depth?

........................................................

........................................................

........................................................

........................................................

7. If the average interval between four oil changes on a vehicle is 9000 km, and the intervals between the first two are 6000 km and 10 000 km, what is the interval between the third and fourth oil change?

........................................................

........................................................

........................................................

........................................................

8. If a roll of copper tubing 16 m in length costs £86.40 what is the average cost per metre?

........................................................

........................................................

........................................................

........................................................

........................................................

9. Six apprentices receive a wage of £40 each. If four other apprentices receive wages of £48 each, what is the average wage of all the apprentices?

........................................................

........................................................

........................................................

........................................................

10. If the times taken to fit water pumps to three cars of the same type are 2.5 hours, 2.8 hours and 2.4 hours, what is the average time for the job?

........................................................

........................................................

........................................................

........................................................

11. If the total number of crankshafts sold by the stores in one year is 276, what is the average monthly sales figure?

........................................................

........................................................

........................................................

........................................................

........................................................

# AREAS OF REGULAR FIGURES

The figure shown below is a square. That is length and breadth are equal.

The shading represents the area of the square.

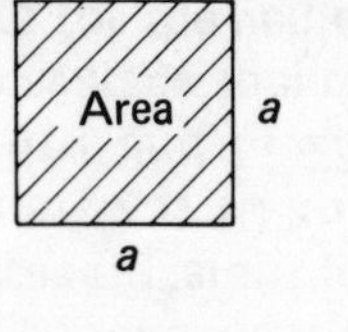


To calculate the area, we square the length of one side.

area = $a \times a = a^2$

**Rectangle**

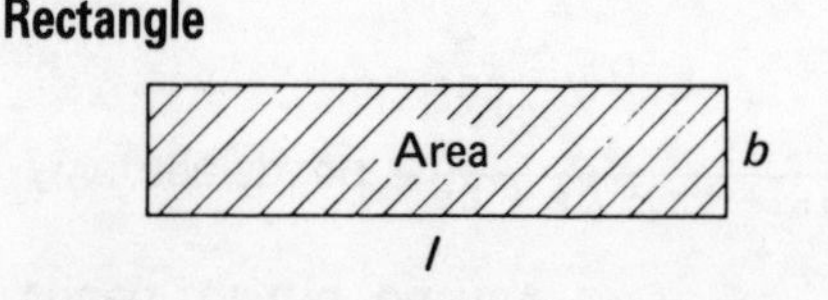


The area of a rectangle as shown above is found by multiplying the length and breadth.

area = $l \times b$

State the units used to express area.

................................................

................................................

Perimeter

How is the perimeter of a square rectangle calculated?

................................................

................................................

*Examples*

1. Calculate the area of a square whose sides are 3 m in length

   Area = 3 x 3 = 9 m$^2$

2. Calculate the area of the rectangle shown below.

   35 mm

   150 mm

   Area = 150 x 35 = 5250 mm$^2$

3. A workshop is 12 m square. The floor area is therefore:

   (a) 12 m$^2$ (b) 24 m$^2$

   (c) 144 m$^2$ (d) 240 m$^2$

   Answer ( )

4. A workshop has 4 work benches each measuring 1 m x $2\frac{1}{2}$ m. The floor area covered by the benches is therefore (a) 4 m$^2$ (b) 5 m$^2$ (c) $2\frac{1}{2}$ m$^2$ (d) 10 m$^2$

   Answer ( )

5. A motor-lorry platform measures 10 m x 2 m. How many boxes whose bases measure 0.5 m x 0.5 m would it take to cover the platform?

................................................

................................................

................................................

................................................

................................................

6. The figure shown below represents the workshop floor and pit area. Calculate:

   (a) the area of the pit, and

   (b) the area of the remaining floor space.

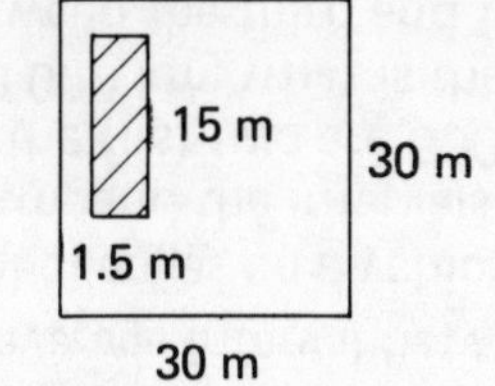


................................................

................................................

................................................

................................................

................................................

................................................

................................................

................................................

7. Determine the area and perimeter of the following shapes.

   (a)

   10 m
   9 m
   5 m
   13 m

   (b)

   5 m
   5 m
   3 m
   5 m
   15 m

8. Complete the following table, in respect of rectangles.

| Length | Breadth | Area |
|---|---|---|
| 4.5 m | 3 m | |
| 150 mm | 100 mm | |
| 8 m | | 16 m$^2$ |
| | 3.5 m | 21 m$^2$ |
| 25 mm | 200 mm | |

## Triangles

All triangles have an area which is half that of a rectangle whose length and breadth is equal to the base and perpendicular height of the triangle. For example

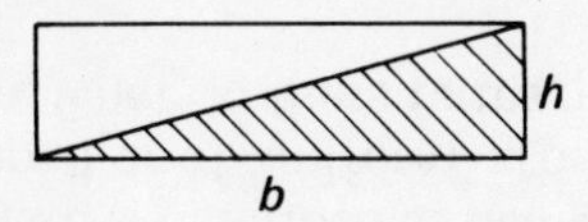


Therefore the area of a triangle would be:

$$\text{Area} = \frac{\text{base x perpendicular height}}{2}$$

This holds good for any triangle provided the height used is the perpendicular height

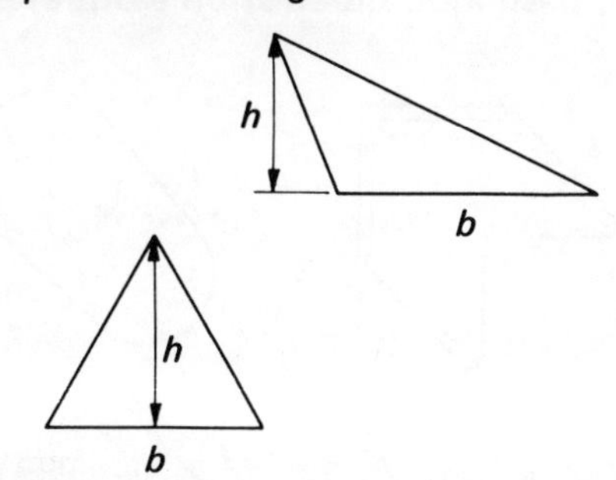


## Circle

To calculate the area of a circle the following formula can be used:

$$\text{Area} = \pi r^2 \text{ or } \frac{\pi d^2}{4}$$

Where:

$$\pi = \frac{22}{7} \text{ or } 3.142$$

$r$ = radius and $d$ = diameter

$\pi$(the greek letter pi) is the symbol for the ratio

$$\frac{\text{circumference}}{\text{Diameter}}$$

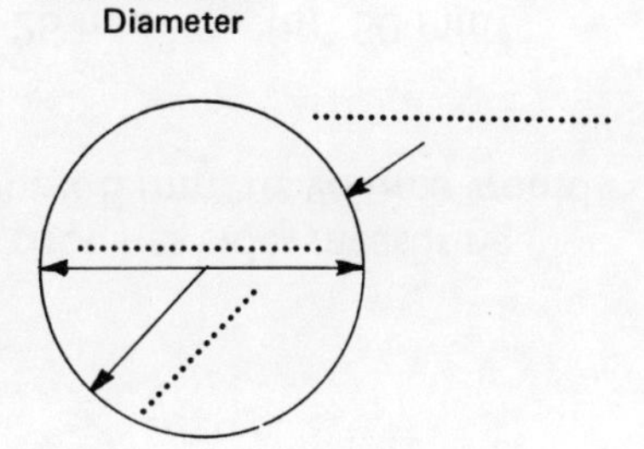

The 'perimeter' of a circle is the .......................... . State the formula to calculate the circumference of a circle.

*Examples*

1. Calculate the area of a circle which has a diameter of 40 mm.

   Area = $\pi r^2$

   Area = 3.142 x 20 x 20
   = 1256.8 $mm^2$

2. Calculate the area of the triangle shown below.

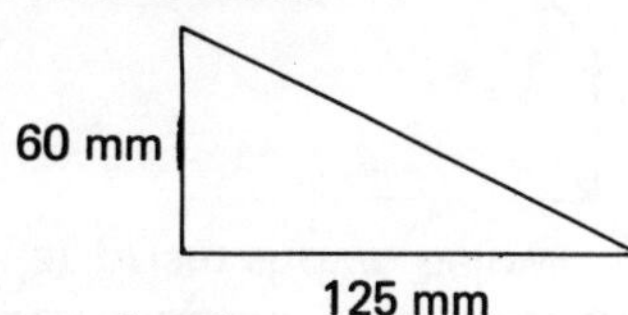


$$\text{Area} = \frac{h \times h}{2}$$

$$\text{Area} = \frac{125 \times 60}{2} = 3750 \text{ mm}^2$$

3. Calculate the area of a triangle which has a base of 0.2 m and a perpendicular height of 0.45 m.

4. A brake master-cylinder has a bore diameter of 25 mm. What is the area of the bore?

5. If the crank throw for a particular engine is 30 mm, calculate the distance travelled by the big end assembly during two strokes of the piston.

6. Determine the area and perimeter of the following shapes.

(a)

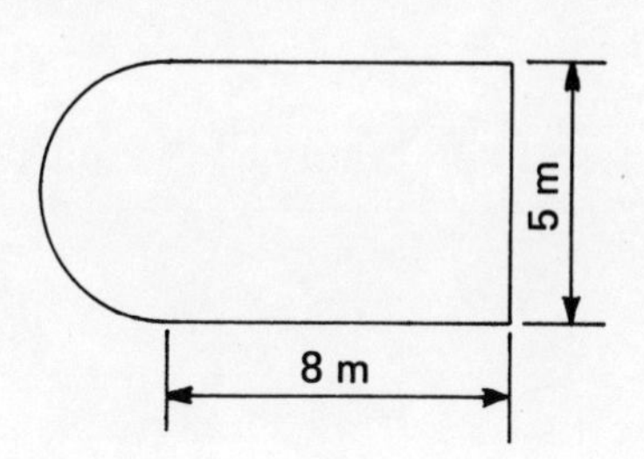


(b)

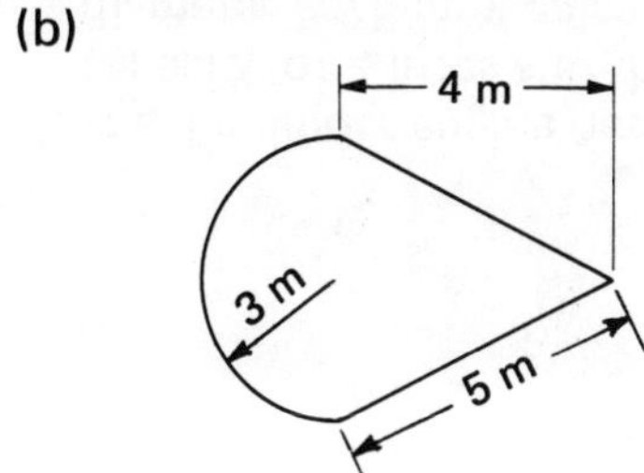

# VOLUME OF REGULAR FIGURES

The volume of any regular-shaped object can be found by multiplying the area of the end by the length. For example regular-shaped objects.

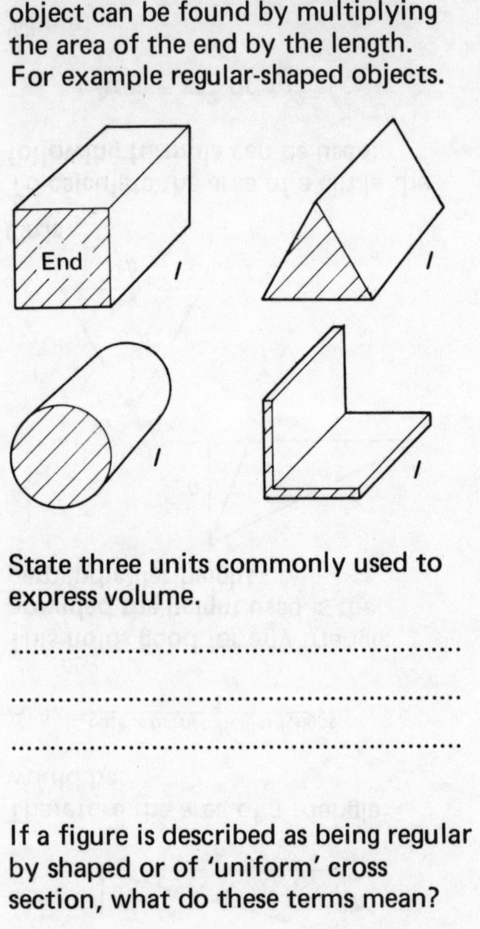


State three units commonly used to express volume.

..............................................

..............................................

..............................................

If a figure is described as being regular by shaped or of 'uniform' cross section, what do these terms mean?

..............................................

..............................................

..............................................

..............................................

..............................................

*Examples*

1. Determine the volume of the rectangular prism shown below.

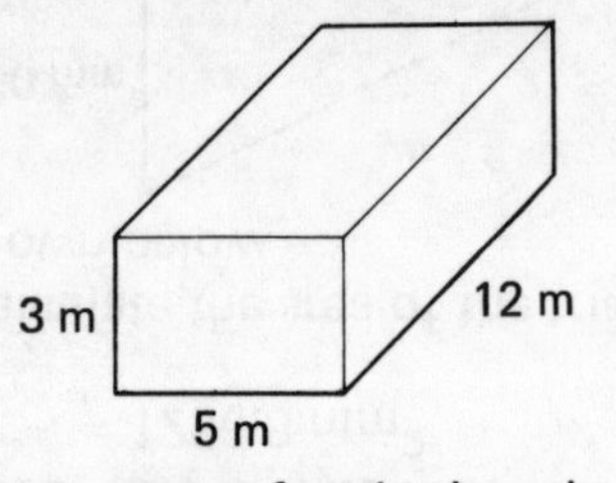


Volume = area of end x length
= 3 x 5 x 12
= 180 $m^3$

2. If the cross-sectional area of a metal bar of uniform section is 0.0025 $m^2$ and its length is 4 m, the volume of metal would be.

(a) 0.005 $m^3$ (b) 0.01 $m^3$

(c) 125 $mm^3$ (d) 150 $mm^3$

Answer ( )

..............................................

3. If a cube has sides measuring 5 mm x 5 mm, its volume would be.

(a) 25 $mm^3$ (b) 50 $mm^3$

(c) 125 $mm^3$ (d) 150 $mm^3$

Answer ( )

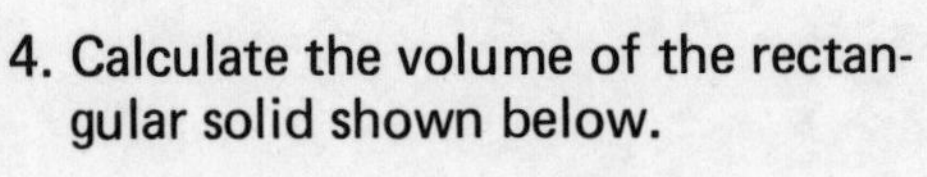

4. Calculate the volume of the rectangular solid shown below.

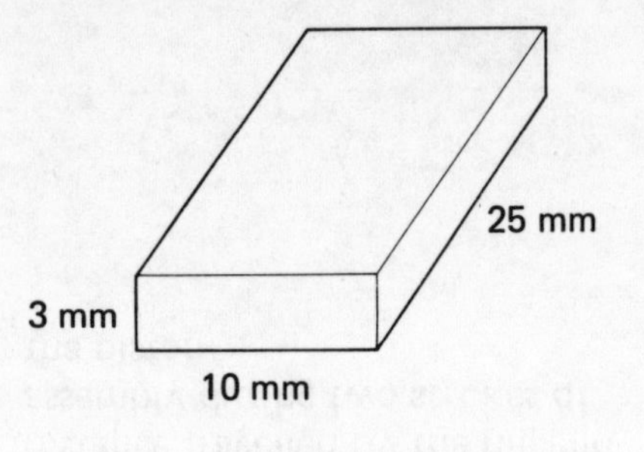


5. Calculate the volume of the section of angle iron shown below.

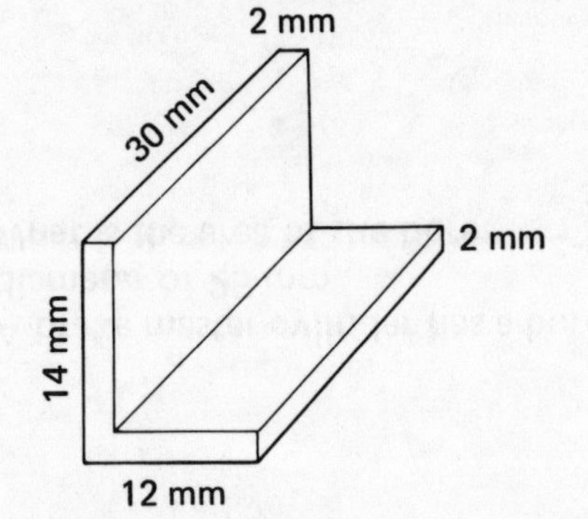


6. When the brakes are applied on a vehicle, the master-cylinder piston moves 20 mm along the cylinder. If the master-cylinder diameter is 25 mm, calculate the volume of fluid displaced.

7. If a 4-cylinder engine has a capacity of 2 litres and the bore diameter is 75 mm, calculate the length of stroke.

# CAPACITY

The capacity of a container or tank is the cubic content or volume that it will hold. When stating the capacity of a tank in connection with a quantity of liquid, the units used are ...................... Capacity is determined by calculating the volume and converting the cubic measurement into litres.

I litre = 1000 $cm^3$

or I litre = 1 $dm^3$

or I litre = 0.001 $m^3$

The volume of a tank is 40 $dm^3$, its capacity in litres is:

(a) 4 (b) 40 (c) 400 (d) 40000

Answer ( )

Calculate the capacity of the fuel tank shown below (ignore capacity of filler neck and ignore rounded corners of tank).

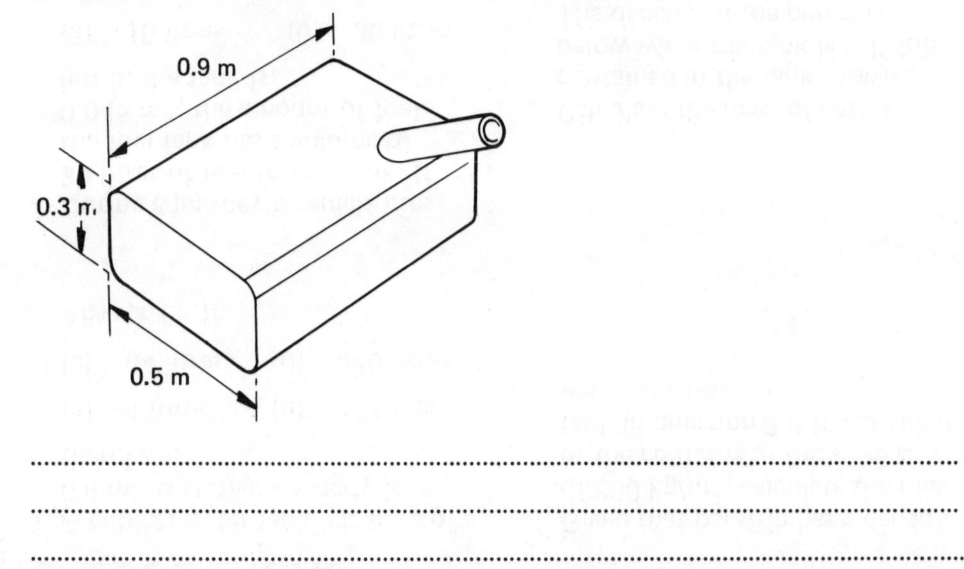


........................................................................................................................

........................................................................................................................

........................................................................................................................

# MASS

The mass of a quantity of liquid or of a solid object depends on the *amount of matter* it contains.

For the purpose of calculation 1 litre of water has a mass of ......................

# DENSITY

Density is the 'mass per unit volume' of a substance. For example the density of water is ............................ If therefore the volume and density of a liquid are known, the total mass can be calculated.

For example, tank has a volume of 0.05 $m^3$; state the capacity of the tank and calculate the mass of water in the tank when it is filled completely.

### Relative Density

The relative density of a substance is the 'ratio' of the mass of a certain volume of that substance to the mass of an equal volume of water.

Relative density =

If a quantity of petrol has a density of 720 $kg/m^3$, determine the relative density of the petrol.

Relative density = ――――――――――――――――――――

........................................................................................................................

........................................................................................................................

# CALCULATIONS

1. A cubical water tank has sides of 0.4 m, its storage capacity is therefore;

   (a) 4 litres (b) 12 litres

   (c) 64 litres (d) 640 litres

   Answer ( )

2. During a journey a vehicle uses 30 litres of fuel from a tank. If the fuel tank has a volume of 0.045 $m^3$, the amount of fuel left in the tank is:

   (a) 15 litres (b) 30 litres

   (c) 45 litres (d) 90 litres

   Answer ( )

3. A cylindrical oil storage tank is 0.75 m in diameter and 1.2 m long. How many litres of oil will the tank hold when it is full?

4. Given that paraffin has a density of 800 kg/$m^3$, calculate the mass of the contents of the storage tank in question 3 if it was filled with paraffin.

5. Calculate the mass of petrol contained in the tank shown below when the tank is half full. The density of the petrol is 720 kg/$m^3$. Ignore filler neck and rounded corners.

6. A diesel fuel tank contains 200 litres of fuel. What is the mass of the fuel if its relative density is 0.85?

7. A cylindrical petrol storage tank is 2 m in diameter and 3 m long. How many tonnes of fuel does the tank contain when full if the density of petrol is 720 kg/$m^3$. (1 tonne = 1000 kg)

8. What mass of paraffin is contained in the tank shown below when the tank is a quarter full, if the relative density of paraffin is 0.8?

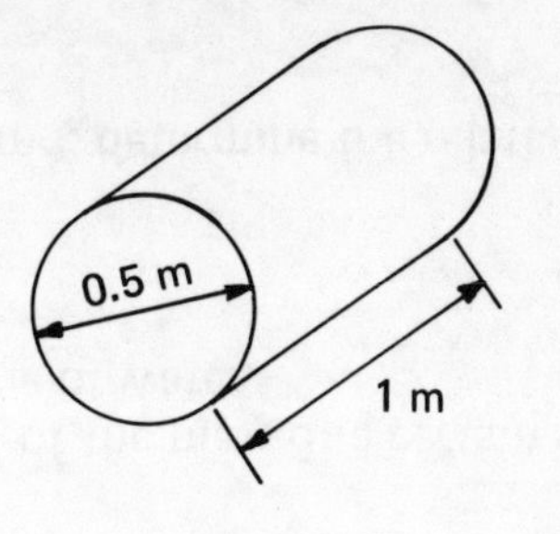


9. If a car petrol tank contains 36 litres of fuel when it is three-quarters full, the tank capacity is:

   (a) 36 litres (b) 48 litres

   (c) 60 litres (d) 72 litres

   Answer ( )

# TRANSPOSITION OF FORMULAE

Transposition of formulae means changing the formula round in order to make a new subject.

$$A = B - C$$

This is a formula in which $A$ is the subject. When this formula is rearranged as follows:

$$A + C = B$$

$B$ becomes the subject.

It is necessary to transpose a formula when the 'unknown quantity' is not the subject. For example,

If a rectangle 100 mm long has an area of 5000 mm$^2$, what is its breadth?

This may be called the given formula: $A = l \times b$

Transposed this becomes: $\frac{A}{l} = b$

$\therefore$ Breadth $= \frac{5000}{100} = 50$

$\therefore$ Breadth = 50 mm

Change the subject in the following formulae.

| No. | Formula | Subject | Result |
|---|---|---|---|
| 1 | $V = lbh$ | $b$ | |
| 2 | $c = \pi d$ | $d$ | |
| 3 | $A = \frac{bh}{2}$ | $h$ | |
| 4 | $P = 2\pi NT$ | $T$ | |
| 5 | $CR = \frac{V_s + V_c}{V_c}$ | $V_s$ | |
| 6 | $A = \pi r^2$ | $r^2$ | |
| 7 | $V = \frac{4}{3}\pi r^3$ | $r$ | |

**Problems**

1. To find voltage ($V$) in an electrical circuit we use the formula $V = I \times R$

   The formula to calculate resistance ($R$) would be:

   (a) $R = \frac{V}{I}$ (b) $R = V \times I$

   (c) $R = \frac{I}{V}$ (d) $R = V - I$

   Answer ( )

2. If $A = \frac{B + C}{2}$ transposing to make $B$ the subject will give:

   (a) $B = A - C \times 2$

   (b) $B = \frac{A}{2} \times C$

   (c) $B = (A \times 2) - C$

   (d) $B = \frac{A \times 2}{C}$

   Answer ( )

3. The volume of a hemispherical combustion chamber is given by the formula

   $V = \frac{2}{3}\pi r^3$. The subject $r^3$ is:

   (a) $r^3 = \frac{2V}{3}\pi$ (b) $r^3 = \frac{V - \pi}{2 + 3}$

   (c) $r^3 = \frac{3V}{2\pi}$ (d) $r^3 = \frac{2V}{3\pi}$

   Answer ( )

4. A merchanic applies a force of 60 N at the end of a spanner when he is tightening a bolt. If the torque exerted on the bolt is 18 N m, calculate the length of the spanner.

   (torque = force x radius)

   ..............................................................
   ..............................................................
   ..............................................................
   ..............................................................
   ..............................................................
   ..............................................................
   ..............................................................
   ..............................................................

5. Calculate the length of an engine cylinder which has a volume of 198 cm$^3$ and a diameter of 6 cm.

   (Cyl. vol. = $\pi r^2$ x length)

   ..............................................................
   ..............................................................
   ..............................................................
   ..............................................................
   ..............................................................
   ..............................................................
   ..............................................................
   ..............................................................

# EVALUATION OF FORMULAE

If the values for the symbols in a formula are known, the calculation can be completed by substituting numbers for the symbols in the formula. For example the length $l$ of a rectangle is 5 m and the breadth $b$ is 2 m. Calculate the area $A$

State basic formula: $A = l \times b$
Substitute values: $A = 5 \times 2$
Answer: $A = 10\ m^2$

Evaluate the following formulae

| No. | Formulae | Given | Calculation |
|---|---|---|---|
| 1 | $V = I \times R$ | $I = 0.8, R = 15$ | |
| 2 | $u = \frac{P}{W}$ | $P = 24, W = 96$ | |
| 3 | $A = \pi r^2$ | $\pi = \frac{22}{7}, r = 14$ | |
| 4 | $P = 2\pi NT$ | $\pi = \frac{22}{7}, N = 50, T = 110$ | |
| 5 | $V = blh$ | $b = 4, l = 10, h = 25$ | |
| 6 | $C = \pi d$ | $\pi = \frac{22}{7}, d = 28$ | |
| 7 | $B = GH + y$ | $G = 12, H = 8, y = 4$ | |
| 8 | $V = u + ft$ | $u = 20, f = 30, t = 5$ | |

1. The compression ratio (CR) of an engine is given by the formula

$$CR = \frac{V_s + V_c}{V_c}$$

If $V_s = 250\ cm^2$ and $V_c = 40\ cm^3$ CR is:

(a) 250:1
(b) 6.25:1
(c) 7.25:1
(d) 10:1

Answer ( )

2. In an electrical circuit $V = IR$, where $V$ is the pressure in volts $I$ is the current in amperes and $R$ is the resistance in ohms. If $I = 1.5$ A and $R = 8$ ohms

The voltage would be:

(a) 9.5 V (c) 24 V
(b) 12 V (d) 10 V

Answer ( )

3. If $H = \frac{2y - 5t}{V}$ calculate $H$ when $y = 15$ $t = 4$ and $V = 2.5$.

The value of $v$ will be:

(a) 4
(b) 8
(c) 60
(d) 5

Answer ( )

4. The volume of an engine cylinder is given by the formula $V = \pi r^3 h$

If $\pi = \frac{22}{7}$, $r = 30$ min and $h = 65$ mm, calculate the volume of the cylinder

..................................................
..................................................
..................................................
..................................................
..................................................
..................................................
..................................................

5. The torque transmitted by a friction clutch is given by the formula

$$\text{torque} = F \frac{r + r}{2} n$$

If the frictional force $F = 680$ N, $r_1 = 75$ mm, $r_2 = 112$ mm and the number of pairs of frictional faces ($n$) is 2, calculate the torque transmitted by the clutch.

..................................................
..................................................
..................................................
..................................................
..................................................
..................................................

# BRACKETED QUANTITIES

Brackets can be used to group quantities and separate signs within an expression. When evaluating an expression containing brackets it is usually best to deal with the bracketed quantities first.

*Examples*

(a) $4(a - b)$ can be expressed as
$4a - 4b$

(b) $5 + (3 - 2 + 4)$ can be expressed as
$5 + 3 - 2 + 4 = 10$

(c) $5 - (3-2+4)$ can be expressed as
$5 - 3 + 2 - 4 = 0$

It can be seen from example (c) above that when a bracket is preceded by a minus sign, all the signs previously within the bracket are changed.

**Problems**

Evaluate the following when

$a = 10 \quad b = 5$ and $c = 6$

1. $(ab)(bc)$

   $(10 \times 5)(5 \times 6)$

   $50 \times 30 = 1500$

2. $4(a + b - c)$

3. $10 + (a - b + c)$

4. $180 - (a + b - c)$

5. $\dfrac{a + (c - b) - (a - c)}{7}$

6. $\dfrac{(ab) + b}{(ac) - b}$

# SIMPLE EQUATIONS

An equation is a mathematical statement in which two sets of quantities are balanced or 'equated' For example

$3a = 12$

For the simple equation above to balance $a$ must be ..............................

When solving simple equation, the known quantities are brought together on one side of the equals sign, with the unknown quantitiy on the other.

To do this certain rules apply:

1. When a quantity changes sides it changes sign.
2. Whatever is done to one side is done to the other.

**Problems**

Solve the following:

1. $5x - 2 =$

   $5x \quad =$

   $5x \quad =$

   $x \quad =$

   $x \quad =$

2. $a + 10 = 45$

3. $3x + 5 = 50$

4. $\frac{2t}{6} = 60$

5. $5a + 8 = 2a + 29$

6. $6x - 12 = 2x + 38 - 10$

C1:1

# ALGEBRAIC SYMBOLS

Algebraic symbols are, in most cases, letters of the alphabet which are used to simplify a mathematical statement. By the use of symbols we can construct a formula, which is a rule or fact common to a number of problems. For example, if a motorist travels 120 km in 3 hours his average speed is $\frac{120}{3}$ km/h or 40 km/h, Similarly, if a motorist travels $S$ km in $t$ hours his average speed is $\frac{s}{t}$ km/h. Call the average speed $v$ km/h, then $v \frac{s}{t}$.

The formula used to calculate the area of a rectangle, where $a$ = ...................., $l$ = ......................, $b$ = ......................, is $a = l \times b$ or $a = 1b$

**Addition and subtraction of symbols**

$a + a + a = 3x\ a$ or $3a$

$a + a - b = 2a - b$

$a + a + a + b + b = 3a + 2b$

It can be seen that *like* quantities or terms are collected together.

Simplify the following:

$x + x - b - b + c + c =$

$2a + a + 3b + b =$

$x + x + 2y + 4y =$

$8a - 3a + 2b =$

$t + 2t + b + 2c + c =$

**Multiplication and division of symbols**

When multiplying symbols, $a \times b$ is written as ......................, or $2a \times b$ is written as ......................

Simplify the following.

$a \times a \times a \times b \times b =$

$4y \times 3y \times 8y =$

$8c \times 4d =$

$2a^2 \times 5a^3 =$

$2a^2 \times 5b^3 =$

When dividing symbols, 'like' symbols can be 'cancelled' to simplify the expression. For example

$$\frac{a \times a \times \not{a}}{\not{a} \times b} = \frac{a \times a}{b}$$

$$\frac{a \times a}{b} = \frac{a^2}{b}$$

Simplify the following:

1. $\frac{t \times t \times t \times y \times y}{y \times t \times y} =$

2. $\frac{4a \times 4b \times 3c}{a \times a \times c \times b} =$

3. $\frac{4a \times 2b}{a \times b} =$

C1:17, 18

# ANGLES

The two lines shown below meet at point O to form an angle; the angle AOB.

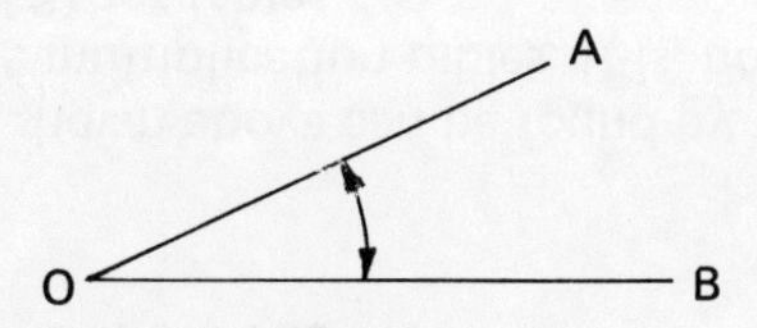


Angles are measured in degrees, minutes and seconds. As the line AO swings anti-clockwise about point O the angle AOB increases.

**Types of angle**

Name the angles shown below.

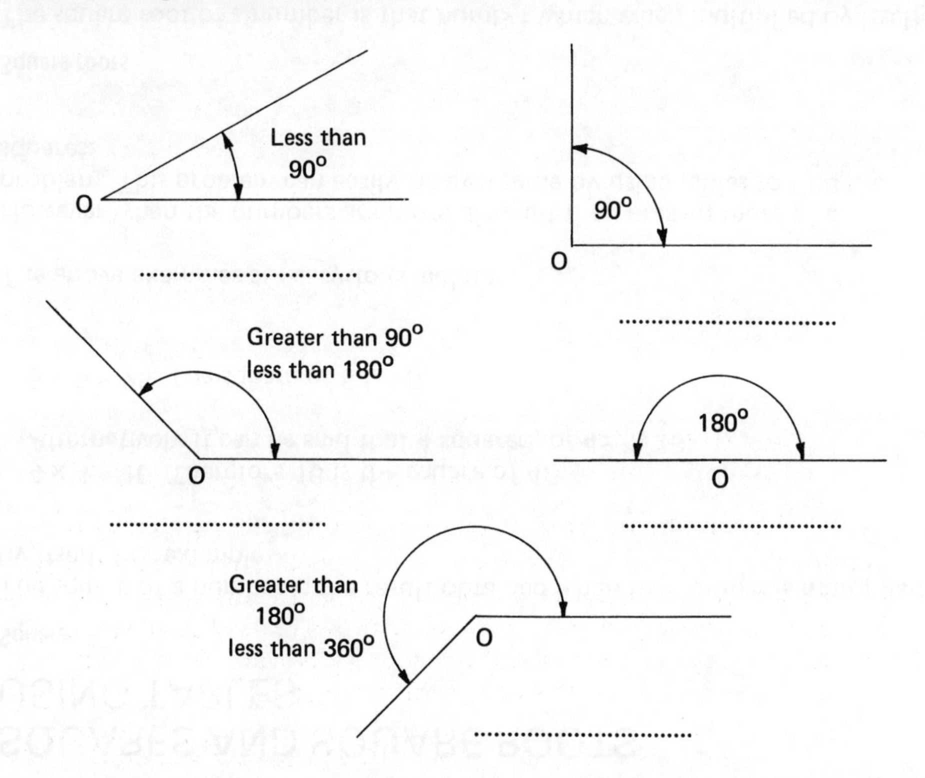


................................

The number of degrees in a circle is ..........................................

1 degree = .................................. minutes. 1 minute = .............. seconds.

Angles can be set out or measured by using a protractor; use a protractor to measure the 'acute', 'obtuse' and 'reflex' angles shown lower left.

Acute .................... Obtuse .................... Reflex ......................

**Types of triangle**

Triangles can be grouped or classified according to the relative lengths of the sides, or by the formation of the angles within the triangle.

The sum of the angles forming a triangle is ..........................................

Describe, with the aid of sketches, *isosceles, equilateral* and *right angle* triangles.

*Isosceles,* ..........................................

..........................................

*Equilateral,* ..........................................

..........................................

*Right angle,*..........................................

..........................................

# SQUARES AND SQUARE ROOTS USING TABLES

## Squares

The square of a number is the result obtained when the number is multiplied by itself. For example

$4 \times 4 = 16$. Therefore 16 is the square of 4.
Alternatively it can be said that 4 squared, or $4^2$, is 16.

$5 \times 5 = 25$. The square of 5 is 25.

The above examples are easy to calculate.

However when the numbers are more difficult they present more of a problem. This problem can easily be overcome by using tables to find the squares.

**Using tables answer the following**

| | | | | | |
|---|---|---|---|---|---|
| $3^2$ | = | .................... | $574.6^2$ | = | .................... |
| $7^2$ | = | .................... | $6.327^2$ | = | .................... |
| $11^2$ | = | .................... | $4.378^2$ | = | .................... |
| $13^2$ | = | .................... | $2.4^2$ | = | .................... |
| $118^2$ | = | .................... | $1.562^2$ | = | .................... |
| $5.6^2$ | = | .................... | $500^2$ | = | .................... |
| $12.9^2$ | = | .................... | $1.006^2$ | = | .................... |
| $14.81^2$ | = | .................... | $289.1^2$ | = | .................... |
| $2.38^2$ | = | .................... | $2001^2$ | = | .................... |
| $358.4^2$ | = | .................... | $999^2$ | = | .................... |

## Square roots

The square root of a number is that number which when multiplied by itself produces the given number. For example.

$6 \times 6 = 36$, the square root of 36 is 6
The symbol of the square root of a number is $\sqrt{}$
For example $\sqrt{64} = 8$ and $\sqrt{100} = 10$

Some square roots as shown above can be found by inspection and by having a knowledge of simple multiplication tables. It is, however, generally necessary to use square-root tables.

**Using tables answer the following**

| | | | | | |
|---|---|---|---|---|---|
| $\sqrt{9}$ | = | .................... | $\sqrt{8972}$ | = | .................... |
| $\sqrt{27}$ | = | .................... | $\sqrt{336}$ | = | .................... |
| $\sqrt{200}$ | = | .................... | $\sqrt{2.380}$ | = | .................... |
| $\sqrt{68}$ | = | .................... | $\sqrt{981.7}$ | = | .................... |
| $\sqrt{2300}$ | = | .................... | $\sqrt{3.07}$ | = | .................... |
| $\sqrt{15}$ | = | .................... | $\sqrt{400}$ | = | .................... |
| $\sqrt{2.5}$ | = | .................... | $\sqrt{50^2 + 12^2}$ | = | .................... |
| $\sqrt{13.8}$ | = | .................... | $\sqrt{2^2 + 15^2}$ | = | .................... |
| $\sqrt{9.68}$ | = | .................... | $\sqrt{11^2 + 10^2}$ | = | .................... |
| $\sqrt{46.44}$ | = | .................... | $\sqrt{31^2 + 11^2}$ | = | .................... |

# PROBLEMS ASSOCIATED WITH RIGHT-ANGLED TRIANGLES

In a right-angled triangle the longest side, which is that opposite the 90° angle, is called the 'hypotenuse'.

The square on the hypotenuse is equal to the sum of the squares on the other two sides; this is known as the Theorem of Pythagoras.

*Example*

1.

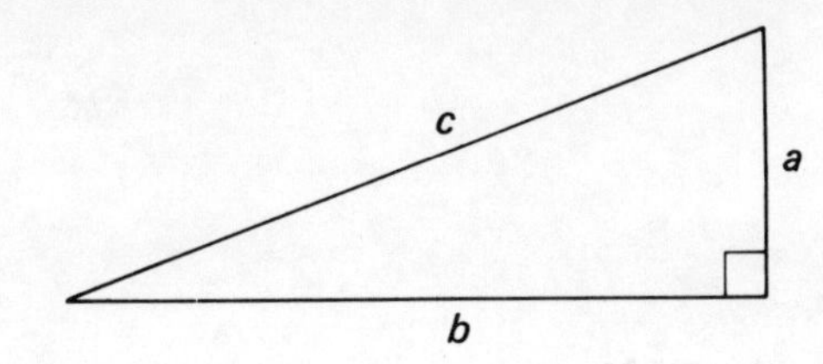


$c^2 = a^2 + b^2$

hence $c = \sqrt{a^2 + b^2}$

Calculate the length of the hypotenuse of a right-angled triangle having sides 3 m long and 4 m long.

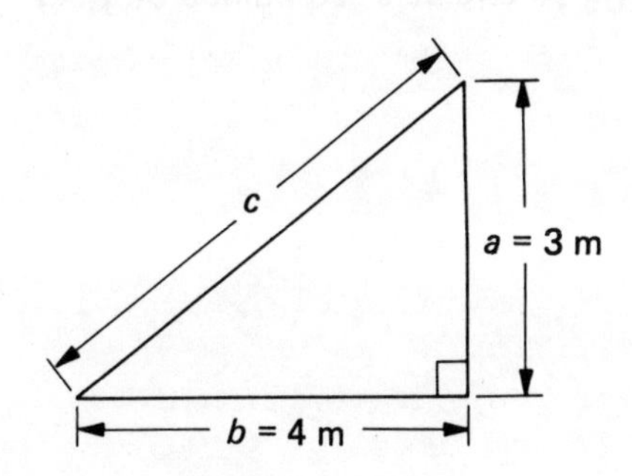


$c^2 = a^2 + b^2$

$c^2 = 3^2 + 4^2$

$c^2 = 9 + 16$

$c^2 = 25$

$c = \sqrt{25} = 5$ m

..........................................................................................

..........................................................................................

..........................................................................................

..........................................................................................

..........................................................................................

Problems

1.

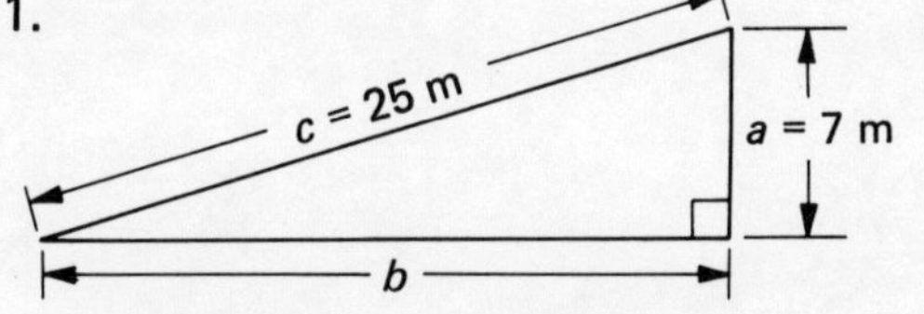


Find the length of side '*b*'

$c^2 = a^2 + b^2$

$c^2 - a^2 = b^2$

$25^2 - 7^2 = b^2$

$625 - 49 = b^2$

$b = \sqrt{576}$

$b = 24$ m

2. Find the length of the hypotenuse of a right-angled triangle having sides of 8 m and 15 m.

3.

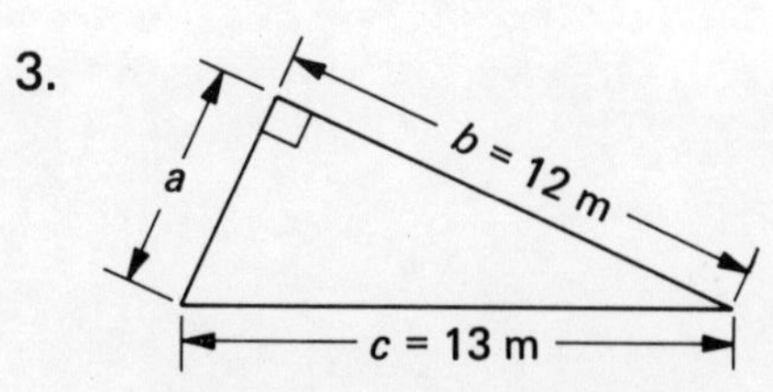


Find the length of side '*a*'.

4.

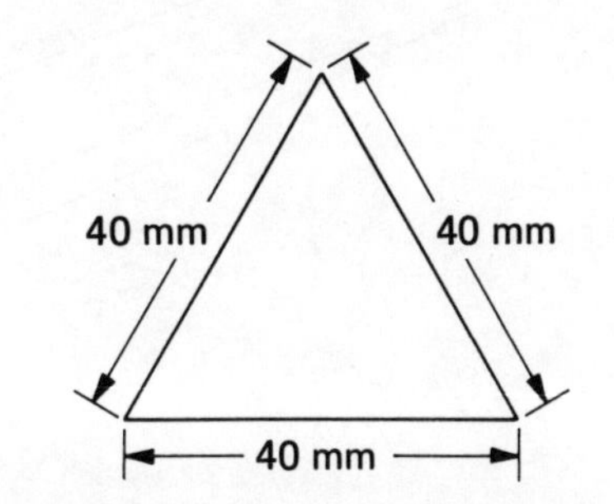


Calculate the perpendicular height of the triangle shown above.

C1:19

5. Calculate to the nearest mm, the longest straight line that can be scribed on a rectangular piece of metal measuring

   80 mm x 60 mm

7. A round bar of 52 mm diameter is to have a flat 18 mm wide filed on it, what is the distance (measured perpendicular to the flat) to the centre of the bar?

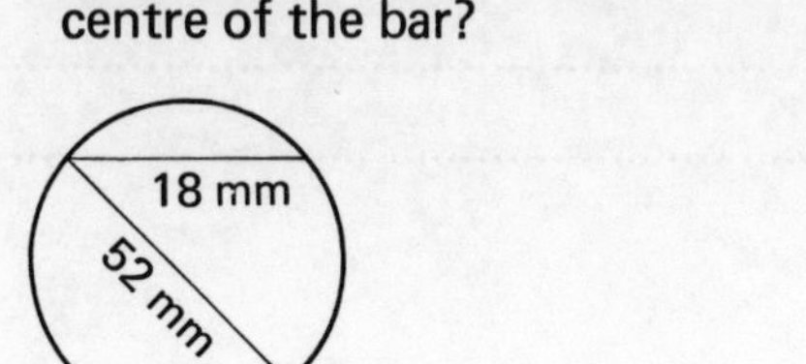
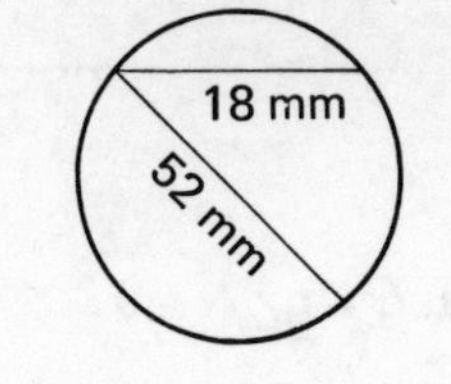


9. What would be the length of the hypotenuse for the right-angled triangle shown on the right?

   (a) 24 m (b) 15 m

   (c) 20 m (d) 20 m

   Answer ( )

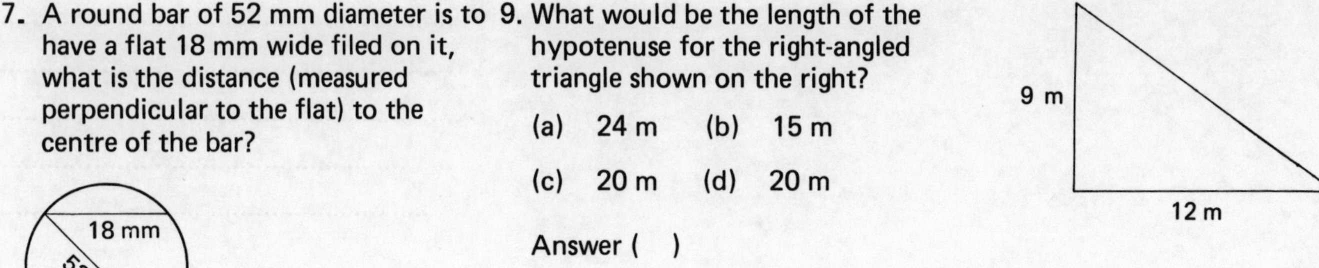


6. If an engine has a stroke of 50 mm and a connecting rod length of 65 mm, how far will the piston travel from t.d.c. when the crank and connecting rod are at 90°?

8. A length of angle iron leaning against a wall, touches the wall at a height of 5.5 m. If the angle iron is 6 m long, how far would it stand away from the wall at the bottom?

10. The diagram above illustrates the conditions necessary for true rolling when a vehicle is cornering. Determine the track measurement of the rear wheels ($t$) for the vehicle shown if the wheelbase is 2.5 m. (Answer to 1 decimal place).

C2.

# Measurement And Marking Out

C2: 1

# MEASUREMENT

(i) Identify the measuring instruments shown below and (ii) state a typical motor vehicle measuring application for each item. In some cases two instruments are used in conjunction with one another.

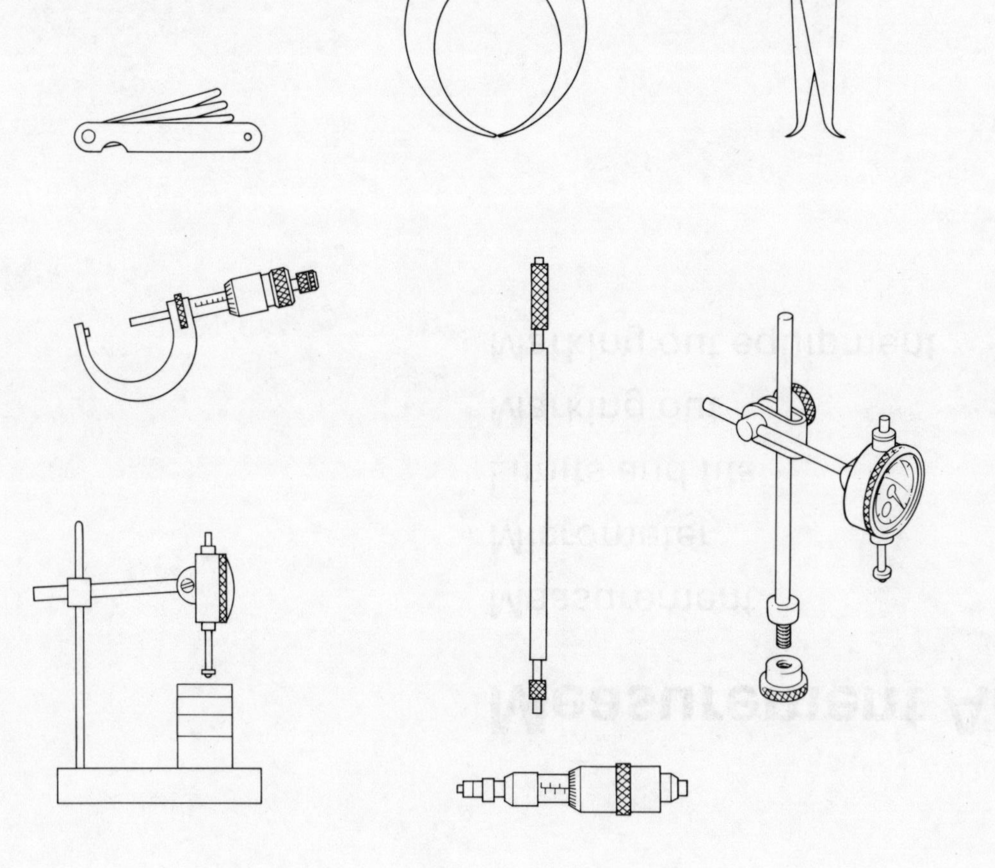

The scientific unit of measurement for length is the metre. A simple measuring instrument is the rule. This is used for most general purposes. If an accuracy to a limit of 0.01 mm is required then a vernier or micrometer caliper may be used.

Using a rule measure the lengths of the lines below. State answer in units required.

____ ..................mm

__________ ..................mm

____________________ ..................mm

________________________ ..................m

Draw accurately lines to the requirements below

5 mm

17 mm

32 mm

0.04 m

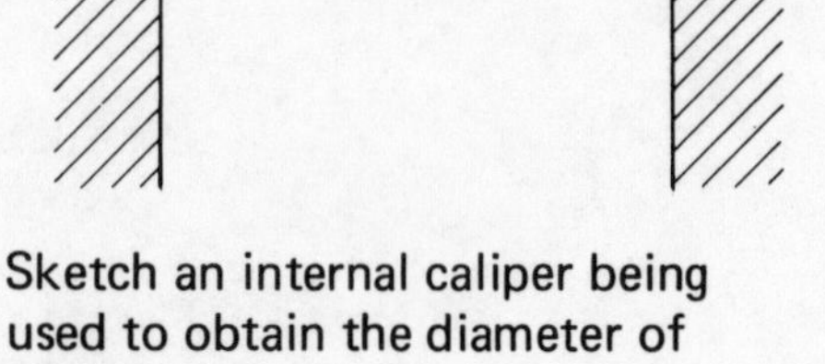

Sketch an external caliper being used to obtain the diameter of the shaft.

Sketch an internal caliper being used to obtain the diameter of the bore.

# MICROMETER

The micrometer caliper is used to measure the diameter of shafts to an accuracy of 0.01 mm (1/100 mm).

State the principle on which it operates to achieve this accuracy.

..................................................................................................................

..................................................................................................................

..................................................................................................................

..................................................................................................................

..................................................................................................................

..................................................................................................................

..................................................................................................................

..................................................................................................................

..................................................................................................................

..................................................................................................................

Micrometers are made in size ranges of 0–25 mm, 25–50 mm, 50–75 mm etc. A big end bearing journal of 45.50 mm diameter would be measured by using 25–50 mm micrometer.

Examine a micrometer and make a sketch of one positioned measuring the bar below. Name the important parts.

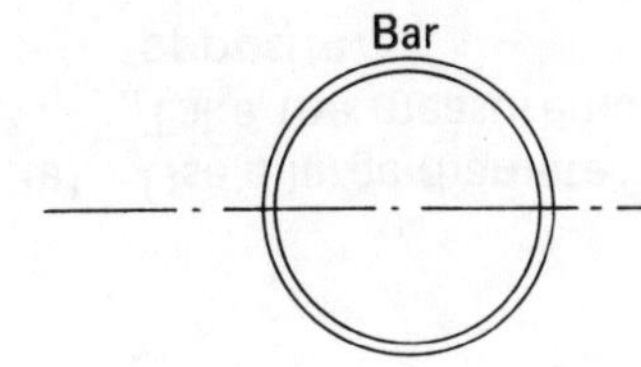


Reading the micrometer scale.

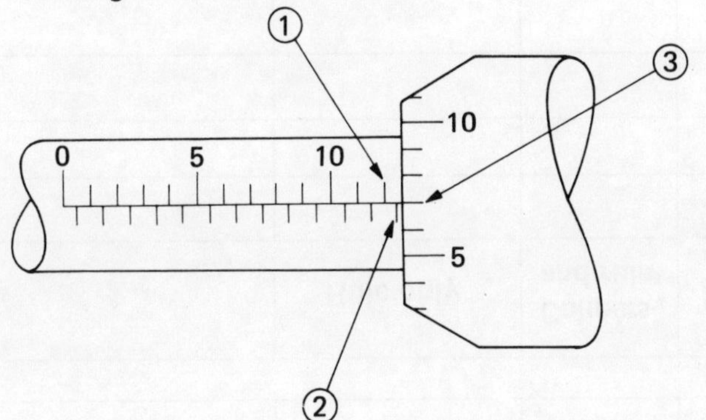


Reading at 1 = 12.00 mm
Reading at 2 = 0.50 mm
Reading at 3 = 0.07 mm

Micrometer reading = 12.57 mm

State the readings of the scales of the metric micrometers below.

0–25 mm

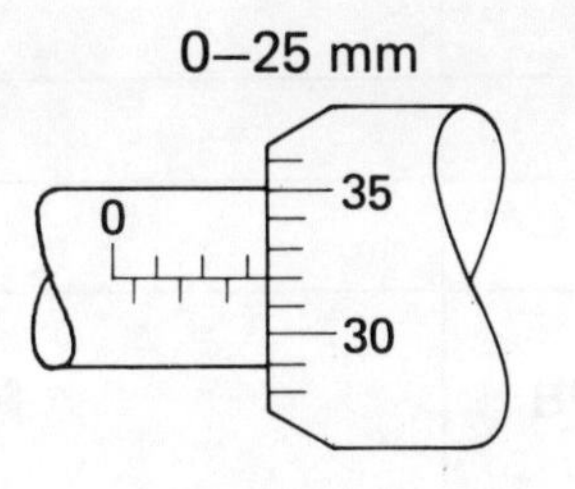


..............................

0–25 mm

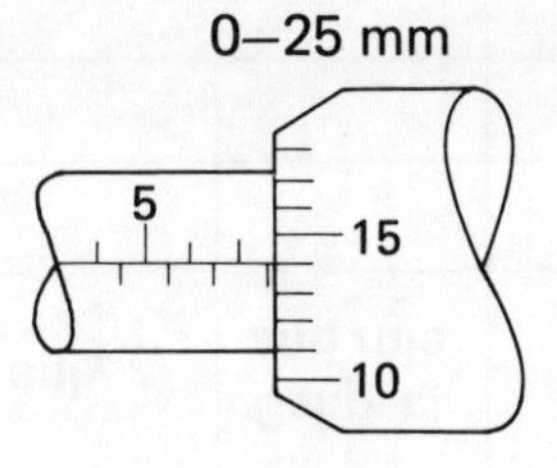


..............................

25–50 mm

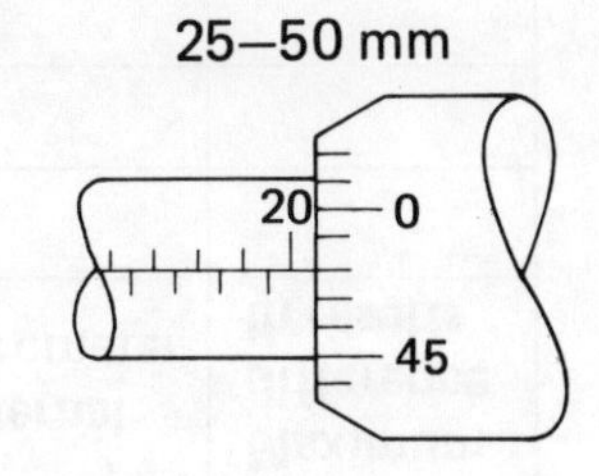


..............................

25–50 mm

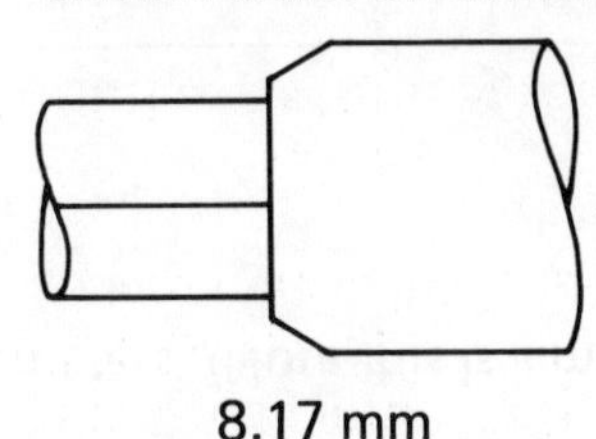


..............................

50–75 mm

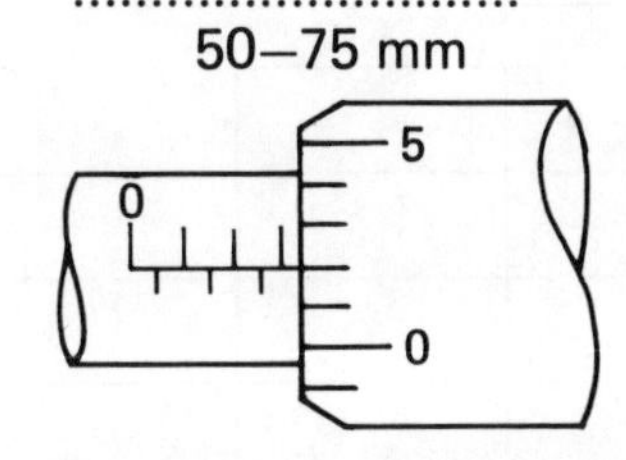


..............................

50–75 mm

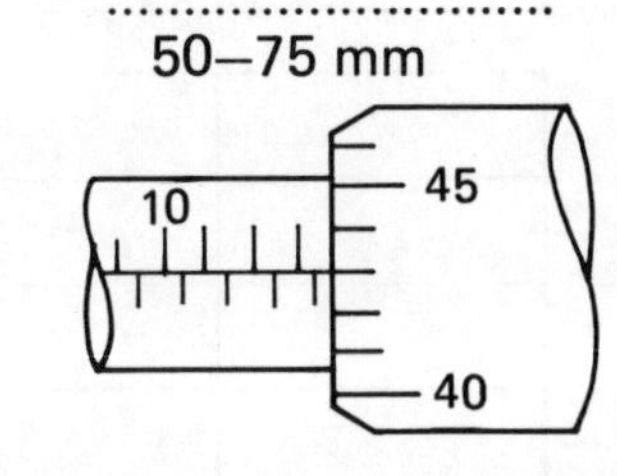


..............................

Sketch scales on the micrometers to give the readings indicated.

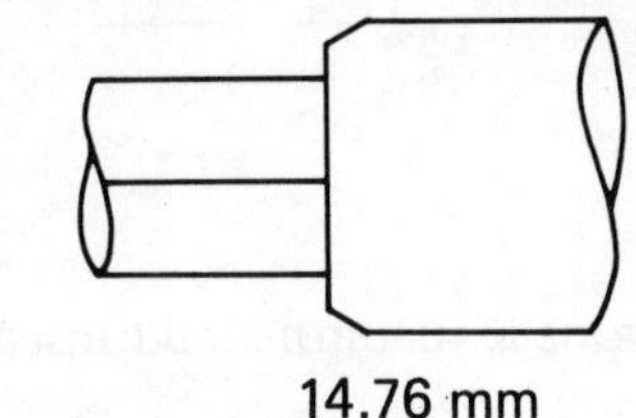

8.17 mm

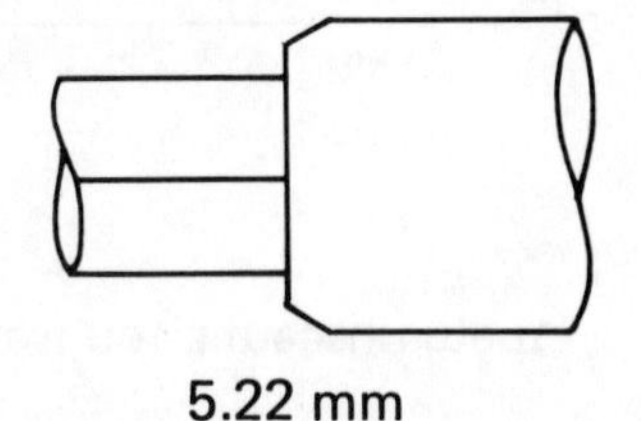

14.76 mm

5.22 mm

C2: 13

**Investigation**

To compare the relative degree of accuracy between calipers with rule and micrometers. (Note this is a measuring-instrument accuracy test not a measurement for wear test.)

(a) Use a large-diameter piston. Take the measurements as shown opposite.

| Piston diameters | | Rule only | Calipers and rule | Micrometer | Maximum difference in results |
|---|---|---|---|---|---|
| Top land | Across thrust face axis | | | | |
| | Across gudgeon pin axis | | | | |
| Bottom of skirt | Across thrust face axis | | | | |
| | Across gudgeon pin axis | | | | |

(b) Using four different cylinder blocks, take diameter measurements of one cylinder bore only. Take measurements at the top of the cylinders.

| Cylinder-bore diameters | | Rule only | Calipers and rule | Internal micrometer | Maximum difference in results |
|---|---|---|---|---|---|
| Engine make | | | | | |
| .................... | | | | | |
| and capacity | | | | | |
| .................... | | | | | |

(c) Using two different crankshafts take diameter measurements from one big end and one main bearing only.

| Crankshaft diameters | | Rule only | Calipers and rule | Micrometer | Maximum difference in results |
|---|---|---|---|---|---|
| Engine make | Big-end bearing | | | | |
| .................... | Main bearing | | | | |
| Engine make | Big-end bearing | | | | |
| .................... | Main bearing | | | | |

C2: 3

**Investigation**

To determine the amount of wear components have received in service:

(a) Use a micrometer to determine the wear of a heavily loaded motor-vehicle component, for example shackle pins, stub axle-pins.

| Component | Standard diameter | Worn diameter | Amount of wear |
|---|---|---|---|
| | | | |
| | | | |
| | | | |

(b) Using a micrometer measure one big end and one main bearing of a worn engine crankshaft to determine maximum wear, taper and ovality.

Crankshaft: Engine make................................ Model ............................

To determine maximum wear of crankshaft journals

| Journal | Original diameter | Maximum wear diameter | (Difference in readings) maximum wear |
|---|---|---|---|
| Big end | | | |
| Main bearing | | | |

To determine ovality

| Journal | Maximum wear diameter | Minimum wear diameter | (Difference in readings) ovality |
|---|---|---|---|
| Big end | | | |
| Main bearing | | | |

To determine taper

| Journal | Diameter towards front of shaft | Diameter towards rear of shaft | (Difference in readings) taper |
|---|---|---|---|
| Big end | | | |
| Main bearing | | | |

C2:4, 5

# LIMITS AND FITS

Mass-produced components must be made to within certain specific limits of accuracy. This allowance on size means that engineering dimensions are given certain limits.

When two components are mated together a fit is obtained.

Below are shown two important types of fit. Name the type and state why they are so called. Label the diagrams.

1 ..............................................

..............................................

..............................................

..............................................

..............................................

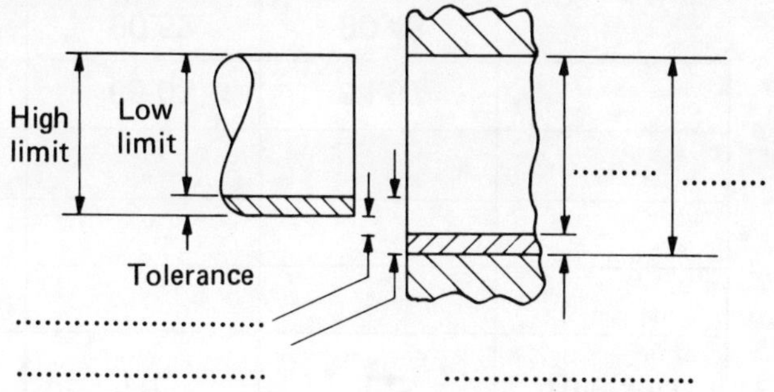

High limit

Low limit

Tolerance

......... .........

.......................... ..........................

..........................

2..............................................

..............................................

..............................................

..............................................

..............................................

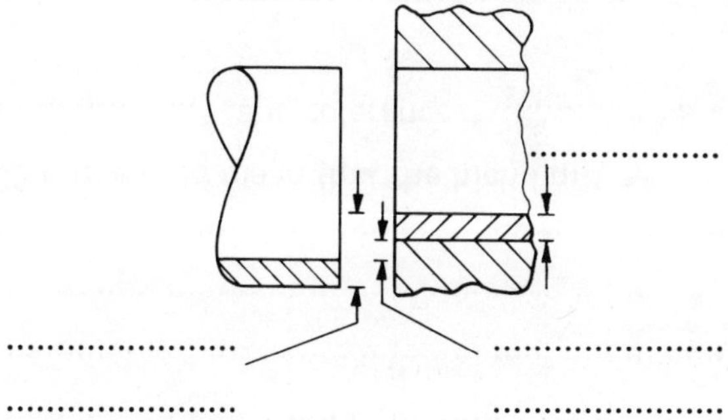

..................

...................... ......................

...................... ......................

Name typical motor-vehicle components that have:

| interference fits | clearance fits |
|---|---|
| 1. .................................................. | 1. .................................................. |
| 2. .................................................. | 2. .................................................. |
| 3. .................................................. | 3. .................................................. |

C2: 6–9

Measure the diameters of any two motor-vehicle components that make an interference fit.

Component measured ................................................................

| Shaft diameter | Hole diameter | Total interference |
|---|---|---|
| | | |

State two typical components where a specified clearance fit may be measured using feeler gauges.

1. .............................................. 2. ..............................................

Give THREE examples of components fitted to a motor vehicle which are known to have an interference fit and list the workshop procedures for fitting such components.

..........................................................................................

..........................................................................................

..........................................................................................

..........................................................................................

..........................................................................................

..........................................................................................

..........................................................................................

..........................................................................................

..........................................................................................

..........................................................................................

..........................................................................................

..........................................................................................

..........................................................................................

..........................................................................................

..........................................................................................

A machining size may be given as $50.00^{+0.02}_{-0.02}$ mm.

This means that the size has:

a high limit of..............................mm and a low limit of ....................mm.

The lower limit is ..........................................................................................

..........................................................................................

..........................................................................................

Tolerance is ..........................................................................................

..........................................................................................

A machining size of 50.00 + 0.06 mm would mean that the high limit = ......................low limit = ..........................and tolerance = ......................

Complete the following table

| Nominal size and indication of limit | HL | LL | Tolerance |
|---|---|---|---|
| $75.00 \pm 0.03$ mm | | | |
| $30.50 \pm 0.06$ mm | | | |
| $50.00^{+0.04}_{-0.02}$ mm | | | |
| 65.00.............mm | 65.03 | 64.97 | |
| 90.50.............mm | 90.52 | 90.48 | |
| 70.50.............mm | | 70.46 | 0.08 |
| $55.00^{+0.08}$ mm | | | |
| $110.00^{+0.10}$ mm | | | |
| mm | 74.06 | 74.00 | |
| mm | 25.54 | 25.50 | |
| mm | | 32.60 | 0.07 |

C2 

# MARKING OUT

When a simple component is to be made lines are reproduced on the material's surface from an engineering drawing. This is known as marking out. Datum lines or straight surface edges are necessary in order to ensure that the other lines are parallel. Centre lines are important when components are required to have slanting sides, curves or holes.

..............................................................................................................................

..............................................................................................................................

..............................................................................................................................

..............................................................................................................................

Sketch and name the following marking out tools:

(a) Tool for scribing circles;

(b) Tool for drawing lines parallel to a datum edge.

Name ..........................................

Name ..........................................

Indicate two edges suitable for use as datum lines.

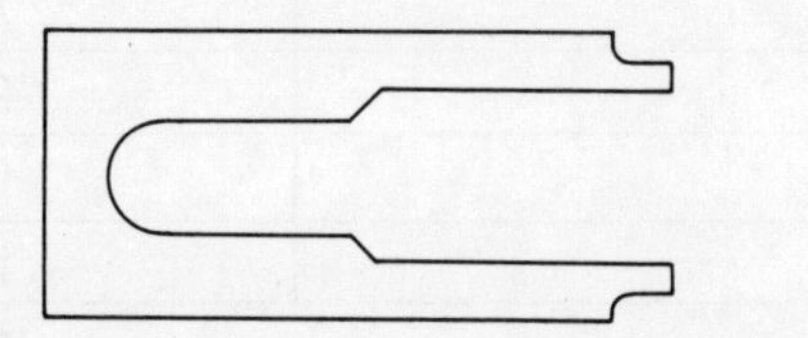

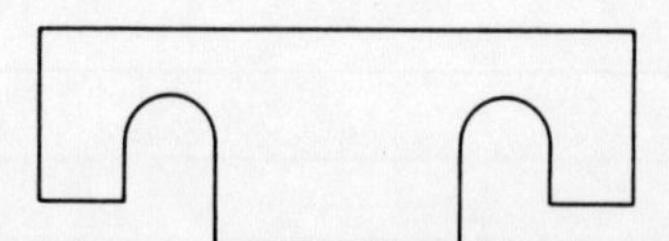

Sketch suitable centre lines required to mark out the components below:

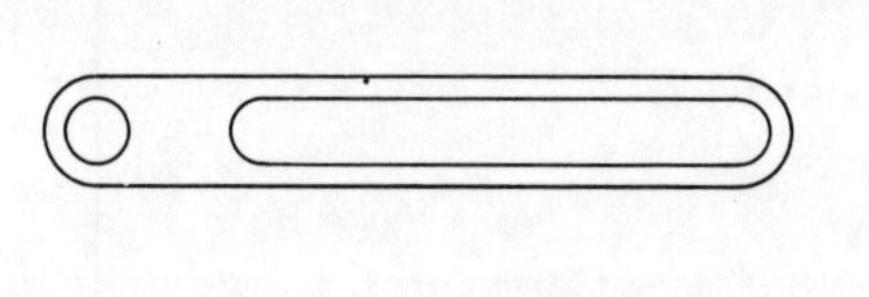

..............................................................................

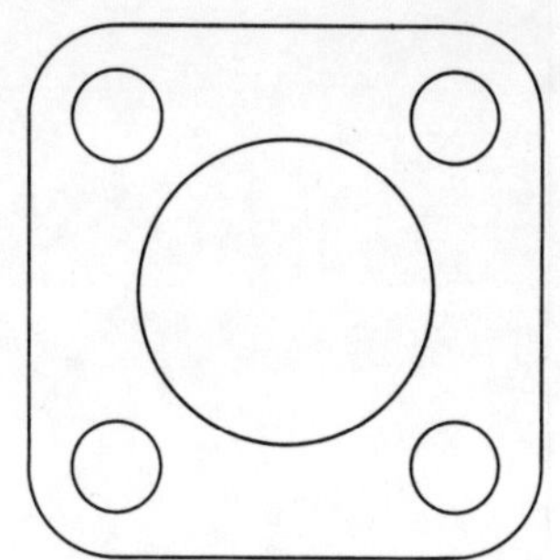

..............................................................................

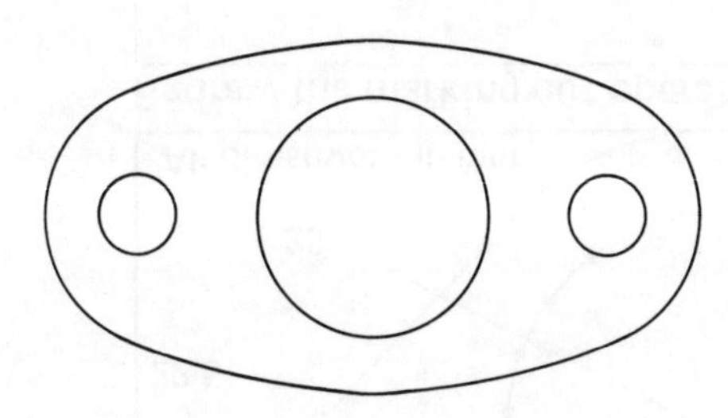

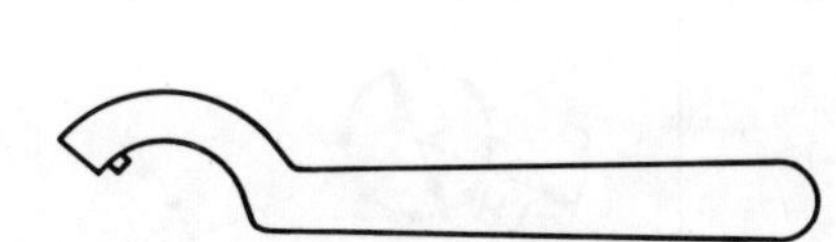

..............................................................................

..............................................................................

Identify the above four components from the following:

carburettor flange, C spanner, alternator adjusting bracket, exhaust flange.

# C2: MARKING OUT EQUIPMENT

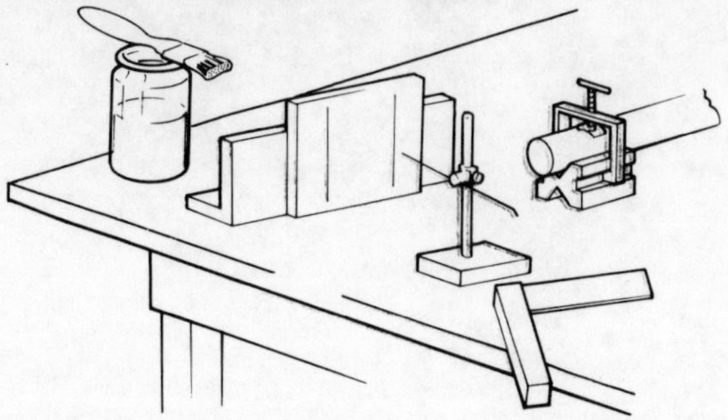

The tool used for making straight lines on a component is called ....................

State a purpose of the following with regard to marking out.

Set square..........................................................................................................

..........................................................................................................................

Vee blocks and clamps .....................................................................................

..........................................................................................................................

Surface plate.....................................................................................................

..........................................................................................................................

Angle plate and surface gauge .........................................................................

..........................................................................................................................

To enable the marking out on material such as mild steel to be seen clearly, the surface may be coated with some colouring.

Name two such coatings.

1. ................................................ 2. ................................................

The circles shown on the sketch opposite are centre-punched

What is the reason for this?

..........................................................................................................................

..........................................................................................................................

The component below has been marked out prior to cutting out and making.

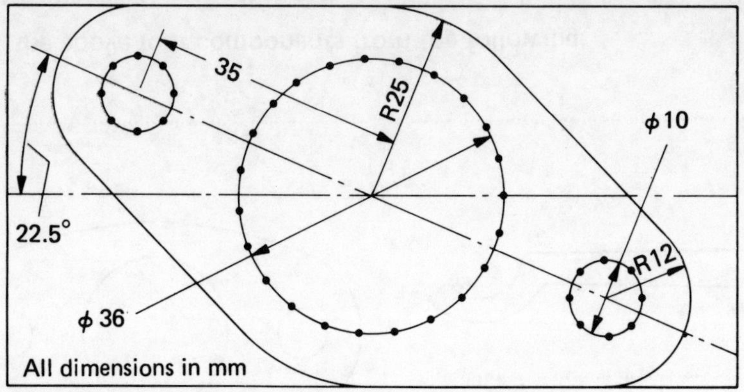

35
R25
$\phi$10
22.5°
R12
$\phi$ 36
All dimensions in mm

Redraw the marking out operations in this space.

List the stages of marking out

| | |
|---|---|
| 1. | |
| 2. | |
| 3. | |
| 4. | |
| 5. | |
| 6. | |
| 7. | |
| 8. | |

C3.

# Heat, Temperature, Pressure

# HEAT AND TEMPERATURE

Heat is a form of energy. ..........................................................................

..........................................................................

..........................................................................

The S.I. unit for measuring heat is the ..........................................

Heat will flow in one direction only ..........................................

..........................................................................

**Investigation**

Heat a motor vehicle component (for example in a gas flame) until it is very hot. Then place the component in a container holding sufficient water to submerge the component.

Note the temperature of the water before and after submersion.
Explain what happens to the flow of heat.

| Temp. of water | Before | °C |
|---|---|---|
| | After | °C |

..........................................

..........................................

..........................................

..........................................

Sketch the component being submerged.

..........................................

..........................................

Temperature does not measure heat; it is ..........................................

..........................................................................

**Investigation**

Fill two beakers with water and heat as shown in sketch.

Identical beakers

Small volume of water

Large volume of water

Identical quantities of heat

Note the temperature rise in both beakers at half-minute intervals until the water in the small beaker boils.

| Time (min) | 0 | 0.5 | 1.0 | 1.5 | 2.0 | 2.5 |
|---|---|---|---|---|---|---|
| Temperature (°C) small volume | 20 | | | | | |
| Temperature (°C) large volume | 20 | | | | | |

These results show the basic difference between heat and temperature.

..........................................................................

..........................................................................

..........................................................................

# TEMPERATURE

The instrument commonly used to measure temperature is called a................

The common temperature scale is the ............................scale.

This may also be known (although not recommended in science) as the

...................................scale.

This scale has.............divisions and two fixed points.

Indicate these on the sketch opposite.

..................................................

..................................................

..................................................

..................................................

..................................................

Name TWO liquids suitable for use in thermometers.

1. ..................................................

2. ..................................................

Why is water not suitable for a thermometer?

.....................................................................................

.....................................................................................

Explain how the mercury thermometer measures temperature

.....................................................................................

.....................................................................................

.....................................................................................

.....................................................................................

.....................................................................................

Upper fixed point

Lower fixed point

Celsius

The temperature scale used to measure absolute temperature is called the

..........................scale. Although the divisions are the same as the

..........................scale its zero point is at a temperature so cold that all molecular or atomic vibration ceases, that is there is no heat.

This occurs at a temperature of..........................°C.

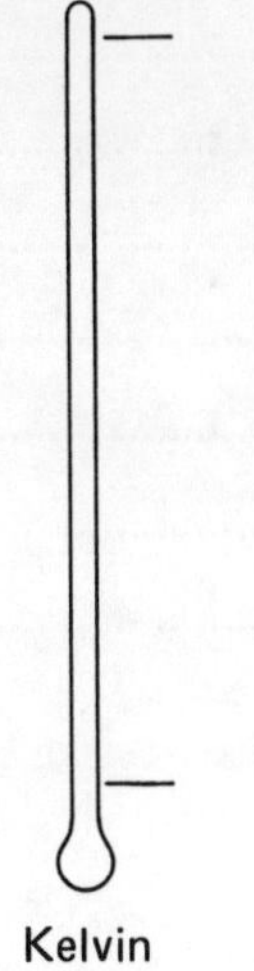

Kelvin

Absolute zero —

Indicate the fixed points on this scale and write in the absolute zero temperatures on both scales.

To convert from Celsius to Kelvin add ..............

Note:

The symbol for Celsius is ................................

While the symbol for Kelvin is ..........................

Both symbols are recognised in the SI system.

*Examples:*

1. Convert 27°C to Kelvins

2. Convert 833 K to degrees Celsius

3. The temperature of gas in an engine cylinder at the commencement and end of compression was 30 and 580°C. Express these temperatures in Kelvins.

4. The temperature of air in a tyre during running increased from 290 K to 327 K. State these temperatures in °C and calculate the temperature increase in °C and in K.

# EXPANSION

When metals are heated they expand and as they cool they contract. Many uses are made of this principle in a motor vehicle and in repair work.

Name two instances on a vehicle where clearance is allowed for expansion due to heat.

1. ..........................................................................................................

2. ..........................................................................................................

Describe what principle is used when a flywheel ring gear is fitted.

..........................................................................................................

..........................................................................................................

..........................................................................................................

### Type of expansion

When expansion is considered in terms of length only it is called .................. expansion. This type of expansion is most important when the component is long and thin.

A common example in a car engine is ..............................................................

It follows that if an expansion has taken place in length it must also expand in width. This is most important when dealing with items made from flat plate or sheets. The measurement of an expansion of an area is called ..........................................expansion.

A motor vehicle example would be ..............................................................

The expansion of a cube (or other three-dimensional object ) must be in three (or all) directions at once. This is known as ..................................................expansion.

It can easily be shown using a metal ball passing through a ring. A motor vehicle example would be a ......................................

### Investigation

Using various metal bars such as aluminium, steel, copper, brass, cast iron or invar show how these expand at different rates.

Sketch the equipment used.

List of order of expansion

| Order | Material |
|---|---|
| 1. | |
| 2. | |
| 3. | |
| 4. | |
| 5. | |

..........................................................

..........................................................

..........................................................

..........................................................

..........................................................

..........................................................

..........................................................

The basis of a flasher unit and an automatic choke can involve a

..........................................................................................................

Heat a demonstration type and note the effect.

..........................................................................................................

..........................................................................................................

# CHANGE OF STATE

Certain materials, depending upon their temperature may be in one of three states. These are:

1. .................................. 2. .................................. 3. ..................................

....................................................................................................

....................................................................................................

....................................................................................................

....................................................................................................

....................................................................................................

The most common example of a change of state is water.

The graph below shows these changes of state.

Identify each heating state.

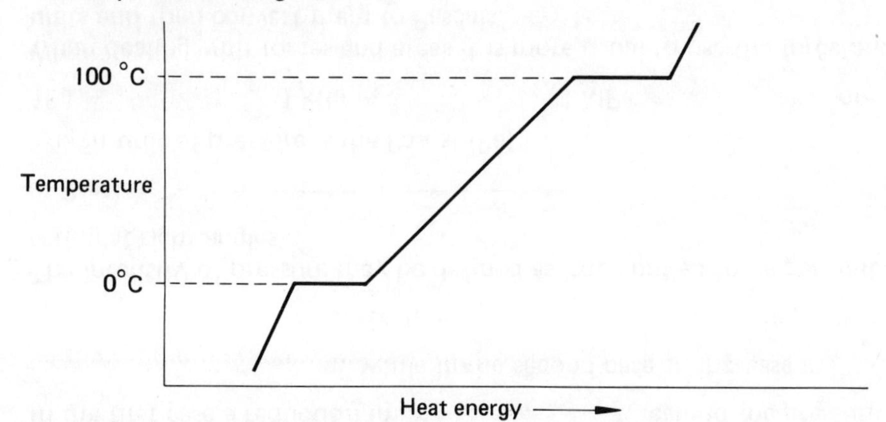


Explain the heating process during a change of state:

....................................................................................................

....................................................................................................

....................................................................................................

....................................................................................................

**Investigation**

Using either ice or wax watch the change of state period from a solid to a liquid or vice versa when heating or cooling.

Show sketches of the apparatus used. Tabulate the time and temperature required for the change of state to occur and comment on the results obtained.

| Time (min) | | | | | | | | | | |
|---|---|---|---|---|---|---|---|---|---|---|
| Temp. (°C) | | | | | | | | | | |

....................................................................................................

....................................................................................................

....................................................................................................

....................................................................................................

....................................................................................................

....................................................................................................

....................................................................................................

....................................................................................................

....................................................................................................

....................................................................................................

# PRESSURE

An excellent example of pressure and change in pressure is in an engine cylinder.
The mixture is drawn into the cylinder and the piston arises. The pressure is

.................................................. The mixture is then ignited and the

pressure is further ........................................

In the first case a reduction in ..............................caused the pressure to

........................................while in the second case an increase in

.................................. caused the .................................... in pressure.

The intensity of pressure may be defined as 'the applied force per unit area acting at right angles'.

or Pressure = ______________________

The SI unit of pressure is the Pascal (Pa)

1Pa = , 1 kPa = 1 MPa = or

When dealing with forces and areas it is more usual to use the force/area units and then convert them to Pascals.

*Examples*

1. Calculate the pressure acting on a piston when a total force of 16 kN is applied to the piston crown whose cross-sectional area is 0.004 $m^2$.

..........................................................
..........................................................
..........................................................
..........................................................
..........................................................
..........................................................
..........................................................

2. Calculate the pressure in a brake cylinder when a force of 450 N is applied to the piston whose cross-sectional area is 150 $mm^2$

..........................................................
..........................................................
..........................................................
..........................................................
..........................................................
..........................................................
..........................................................

## Investigation

An experiment to show the change in pressure of a quantity of air when its temperature is raised can be performed using the type of equipment shown.

Pressure gauge — Tyre valve — Stout steel cylinder

Stand apparatus in hot water or in water being heated.

Record below your observations: ..............................................................

..........................................................................................................
..........................................................................................................
..........................................................................................................
..........................................................................................................

3. Calculate the pressure acting on a radiator cap when the spring force is 24 N and the cap area resisting force is 6 $cm^2$ (0.0006 $m^2$).

..........................................................
..........................................................
..........................................................
..........................................................
..........................................................
..........................................................
..........................................................

4. Calculate the force acting on a piston when the average pressure is 900 kPa and the cross-sectional area of the piston is 0.008 $m^2$.

..........................................................
..........................................................
..........................................................
..........................................................
..........................................................
..........................................................
..........................................................

C4.

# Force and Moments

C4: 1,2,3

## MASS

All substances consist of matter or molecules packed together to form a material, be it made of steel, wood, glass, plastic etc.

Mass is defined as ..........................................................................................

The SI unit of mass is the ..............................................................................

## FORCE

Force cannot be seen or touched but its effects can be observed, that is if a force applied to a stationery object causes that object to move it would move in the ..........................................................................................
The effect that a force has on an object will depend upon:

F F F

1. ............................ 2. ............................ 3. ............................

............................ ............................ ............................

If a force is applied to a moving object the object will either:

1. ............................ 2. ............................ 3. ............................

Sir Isaac Newton defined force and gave certain basic statements regarding the action of force. These can be expressed in simple terms:

..........................................................................................

..........................................................................................

..........................................................................................

..........................................................................................

..........................................................................................

The SI unit of force is the ..............................................................

## ACCELERATION

Velocity is the distance travelled in a unit time, for example the number of metres travelled in one second (m/s).
When an object moves and steadily increases its velocity, for example when a car drives away from rest, the object is said to have ......................................

Acceleration is ..........................................................................................

The SI unit of acceleration being ......................................................................

The relationship between force, mass and acceleration is found directly from the effects that a force produces.

..........................................................................................

..........................................................................................

..........................................................................................

..........................................................................................

## GRAVITATIONAL ACCELERATION

C4: 4

The Earth's gravity attempts to pull everything on the Earth towards the centre of the Earth. The force of gravity being proportional to

..............................................

Any component or mass that is dropped will accelerate due to the force of gravity. This acceleration of falling objects when measured in a vacuum is found to be

..............................................

If a car fell over a cliff it would accelerate at approximately

......................

Now since 1 N is required to accelerate 1 kg at 1 $m/s^2$ then ................ N

are required to accelerate 1 kg at ..............................

Therefore the effect of the Earth's gravity causes

..........................................................................................

C4: 5,6

## Problems

1. A mass of 10 kg would create a force of ..............................................

2. A load of 981 N would form a mass of ..............................................

3. A car when placed on a weighbridge registered 950 kg. What downward acting force would this produce?

..............................................

..............................................

..............................................

4. An engine having a mass of 50 kg is suspended by a sling. What is its potential force?

..............................................

..............................................

5. A balance weight of 90 g is lost from a wheel. What is the wheels static out of balance force?

..............................................

..............................................

..............................................

6. When the driver of a vehicle sits in the car the downward acting force of the vehicle increases by 800 N. What is the weight or mass of the driver?

..............................................

..............................................

7. A car positioned at the top of a hill has a potential force of 10 kN. The vehicle's mass must therefore be:

..............................................

..............................................

..............................................

8. The downward acting force of a fully loaded car was 15 kN. When unloaded it was 9.114 kN. What mass was removed from the car?

..............................................

..............................................

..............................................

One of the effects of force is that to every action there is an equal and opposite reaction. Name some vehicle applications that obviously show this effect.

1 ..............................................

2 ..............................................

3 ..............................................

4 ..............................................

5 ..............................................

6 ..............................................

C4: 7,8

# TORQUE

When a spanner is placed on a bolt and an effort is made to turn the bolt, the applied force is said to have created a turning movement or a torque.

Define what is meant by torque ..............................................

..............................................

..............................................

To calculate torque the following formula is used:

Torque =

Where the force is usually expressed in................and the radius in ...........

The SI unit for torque is ..............................................

Complete the following exercise:

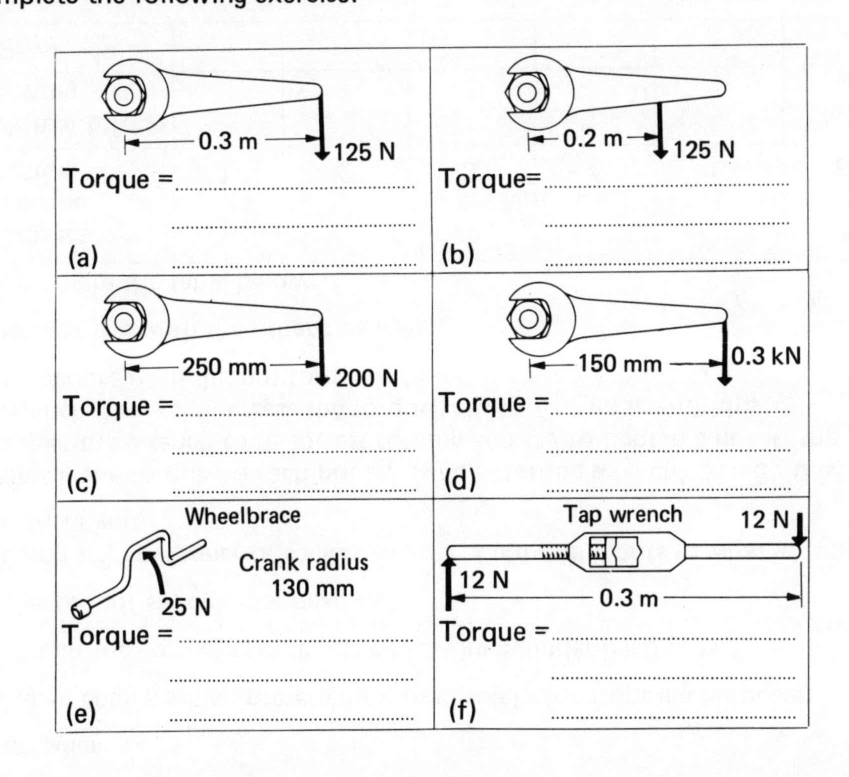

Explain how a nut should be correctly tightened.

..................................................................................................

..................................................................................................

..................................................................................................

..................................................................................................

..................................................................................................

State typical units found on torque wrenches.

..................................................................................................

Show a sketch of a typical torque wrench; for example the one used in the investigation opposite.

When tightening bearing assemblies such as rear axle pinion assemblies the bearings require a very light pre-loading.

Show a sketch of a pinion pre-load gauge.

Explain how the pre-load gauge is used to measure the torque needed to cause bearings to rotate.

..................................................................................................

..................................................................................................

..................................................................................................

..................................................................................................

..................................................................................................

**Investigation**

**Using an engine which preferably is used solely for stripping purposes:**

1. **Obtain the correct torque setting for the cylinder-head nuts.**
2. **Slacken off six cylinder head nuts.**
3. **Using a ring spanner or socket and bar, tighten the nuts to what you feel is sufficient.**
4. **Check the torque on each nut by using a 'torque wrench'. (To do this, adjust the wrench to its lowest reading and try to tighten a nut. If the wrench 'breaks', increase the torque setting. Continue with this procedure until the nut torque is found.)**
5. **Repeat this with the other five nuts.**
6. **Complete the table below.**

| Correct Torque setting | Nut 1 | 2 | 3 | 4 | 5 | 6 |
|---|---|---|---|---|---|---|
| Actual torque setting | | | | | | |
| Error $\pm$ | | | | | | |

Complete the table below in respect of a vehicle of your choice.

| Nut-tightening torque data | |
|---|---|
| Vehicle make ................................ Model ................................ | |
| Cylinder head nuts or bolts | |
| Connecting rod big end nuts or bolts | |
| Main bearing nuts or bolts | |
| Flywheel nuts or bolts | |
| | |
| | |

C4: 9,11

**Investigation**

1. Use a small metal block with three clearance holes drilled through it to take three small bolts of different diameters. Fit the bolts through the block and screw nuts on the other ends. Clamp the block in the vice with the nuts uppermost.

2. Tighten the nuts with a torque spanner and determine the torque necessary to shear each bolt.

3. Taking into consideration the effective length of the torque spanner, calculate the force applied at the end of the torque spanner to shear each bolt.

Complete this table

| Diameter of bolt | Effective length of torque spanner | Shearing torque | Force applied to shear bolt |
|---|---|---|---|
| | | | |
| | | | |
| | | | |

**Calculations**

..........................................................................................................

..........................................................................................................

..........................................................................................................

..........................................................................................................

..........................................................................................................

Comments

..........................................................................................................

..........................................................................................................

..........................................................................................................

C4: 10

# APPLIED FORCE NOT AT 90°

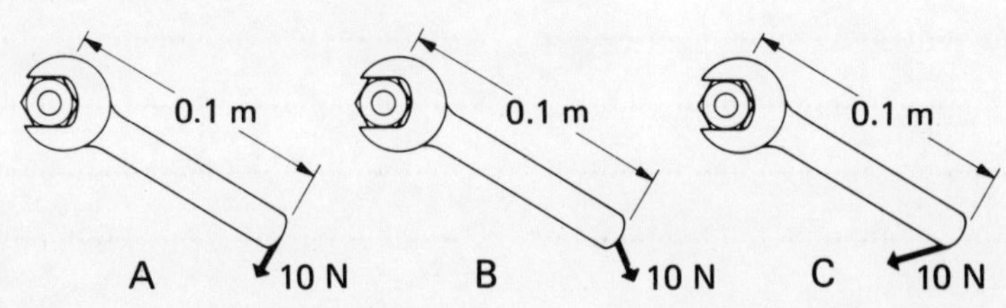


Which of the forces shown above will have the greatest turning effect? .........

**Experiment**

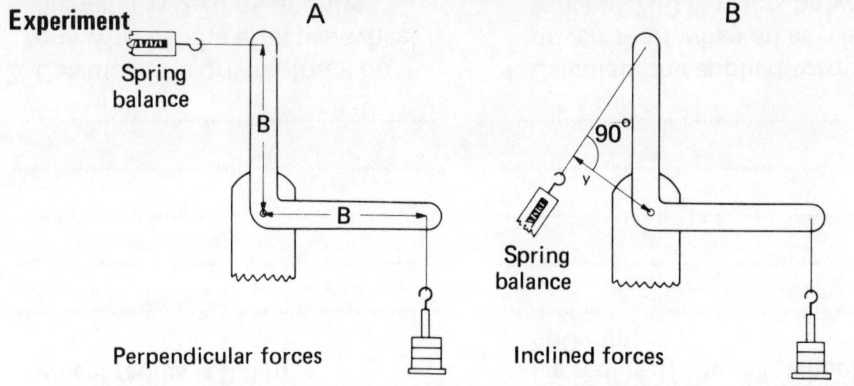


1. Using a 90° lever with a known load acting downwards, hold the lever in the position shown at (A) using a spring balance. Record the spring balance reading. Distance *B*..........................SB reading.........................

2. With the same downward load hold the lever in the same position, with the spring balance as shown at (B). Measure the distance '*y* and record this together with the spring balance reading.

Distance *y* ..........................SB reading.........................

What is the difference between the two spring-balance readings?

..........................................................................................................

Why is this? ..........................................................................................

..........................................................................................................

..........................................................................................................

# EFFECTS OF GEARING ON TORQUE

A vehicle's gear-box provides a gear reduction. This has the effect of

........................................ the speed of the output shaft relative to the input

shaft while at the same time it............................the output torque by a similar ratio (assuming there are no losses due to friction).

Below is shown a simple gear-box layout. Name the shafts.

Driver
From engine
15T
31 T
Driven
37T
14T

........................ ........................

........................ ........................ ........................

For both sets of gears the gear ratio is:

Gear Ratio = ____________________

Gear ratio of first set is: ................ Gear ratio of second set is:..............

In both cases the output speed will.........................and this causes the output

torque to be ..............................

The formula to determine torque output is:

Torque output =

**Problems** (assume no friction losses)

1. Calculate the output torque of a set of gears when the driving torque is 75 Nm. The driven gear has 35 teeth and the driver gear has 21 teeth.

........................................................
........................................................
........................................................
........................................................

2. Calculate the output torque of a set of gears when the input torque is 81 Nm. The driving gear has 54 teeth and the driven gear 42 teeth.

........................................................
........................................................
........................................................
........................................................

The driving force that propels a vehicle along the road depends upon the torque and the diameter of the wheels.

State the forces indicated by the arrows.

Radius

The driving force of the vehicle = ........................................................

**Problems**

1. Calculate the driving force on one wheel if the torque applied to that wheel is 210 N and the effective wheel radius is 0.3 m.

........................................................
........................................................
........................................................
........................................................
........................................................

2. Calculate the driving force on one wheel if the effective wheel diameter is 0.76 m, and the torque applied to that wheel is 570 Nm.

........................................................
........................................................
........................................................
........................................................
........................................................

3. Calculate the driving force on each wheel when the rear axle torque is 500 Nm and the effective radius of the rear wheels is 450 mm.

........................................................
........................................................
........................................................
........................................................
........................................................

4. Calculate the applied torque on a driven shaft when an accelerating force of 700 N reacts between the tyre and road. Effective wheel diameter = 800 mm.

........................................................
........................................................
........................................................
........................................................
........................................................

# PRINCIPLE OF MOMENTS

Using a simple beam (for example a metre rule) which can be pivoted on a stand as shown below, apply forces of different value to either side of the pivot. Position the forces by the use of 'cord loops' to obtain a state of balance, as shown in the diagram.

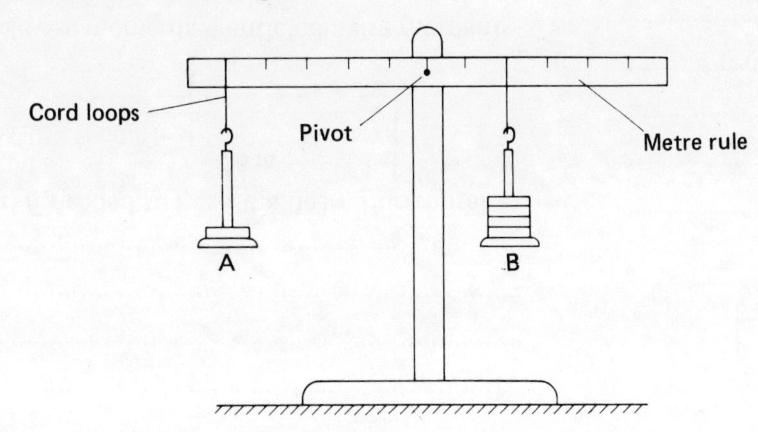


Add the information as required below:

force $A$ = ..................................    force $B$ = ..................................

distance from pivot = ...................    distance from pivot = ...................

Each force will produce a moment about the pivot.

that is a moment = ..........................................................................................

force $B$ will produce a clockwise moment =

force $A$ will produce an .......................... =

The product of both these moments is ......................................

It can be seen therefore that to obtain a state of balance (equilibrium),

........................................................ must equal ..........................................

.......................................................................................................................

This is the *principle of moments.*

There are considered to be three types of levers, all using the principle of moments in their operation.
The lever may be considered to be the simplest form of machine.

Type 1 has a force at one end while the resisting load is at the other.
The fulcrum being somewhere along the lever.

(1)

F

Mass

Fulcrum

Type 2 ..........................................................
..........................................................................
..........................................................................
..........................................................................

(2)

Mass

Fulcrum

F

Type 3 ..........................................................
..........................................................................
..........................................................................
..........................................................................
..........................................................................
..........................................................................
..........................................................................

(3)

Show by simple sketches one motor vehicle or garage application of each of the types of levers shown above.

C4: 14

**Problems**

1. Determine $F$ needed to balance the beam.

12 N — 0.2 m — 0.3 m — $F$ N

clockwise moments = anticlockwise moments

.............................................................

.............................................................

.............................................................

.............................................................

2. Determine $F$ needed to balance the beam

$F$ N — 0.5 m — 0.2 m — 10 N — 0.2 m — 25 N

clockwise moments = anticlockwise moments

.............................................................

.............................................................

.............................................................

.............................................................

3. Find $F$ needed to keep the beam horizontal

0.6 m — 10N; 0.2 m — $F$ N

clockwise moments = anticlockwise moments

.............................................................

.............................................................

.............................................................

4. Determine the force $F$

(a) Handbrake lever (b) Brake pedal

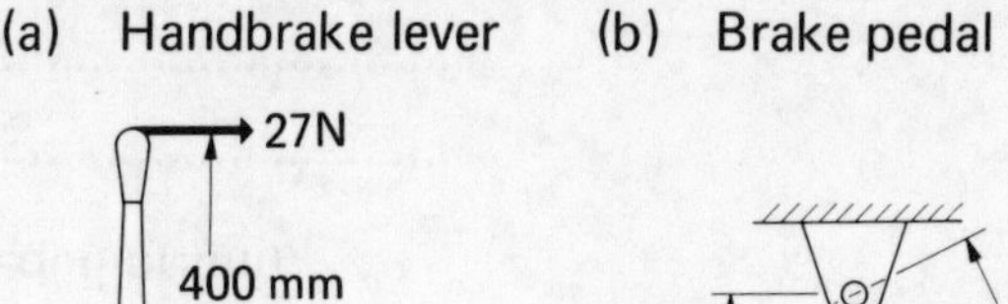


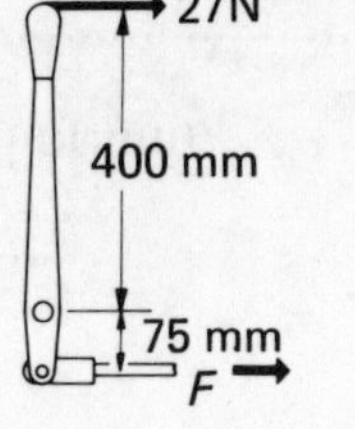

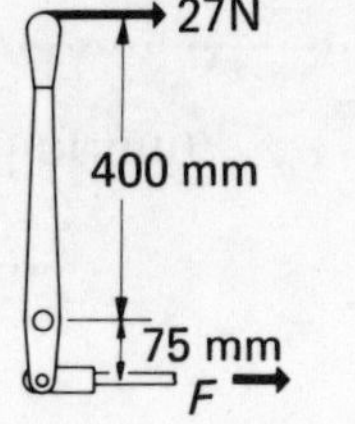

.............................. ..............................

.............................. ..............................

.............................. ..............................

.............................. ..............................

.............................. ..............................

5. Determine $F$ needed to maintain equilibrium.

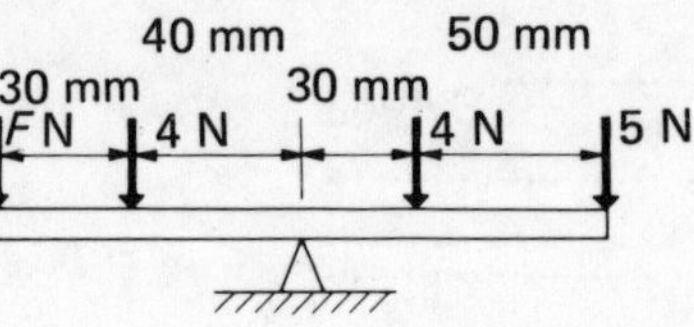

.............................................................

.............................................................

.............................................................

.............................................................

.............................................................

.............................................................

.............................................................

.............................................................

6.

W — 2.5 m — 1.5 kN; 1.5m; Jacking point

The jacking point shown is at the centre of balance. Determine the weight $W$ on the front wheels.

.............................................................

.............................................................

.............................................................

.............................................................

C4: 15

## CENTRE OF GRAVITY

In the last example the jacking point is shown at the centre of balance.

Explain what is meant by the centre of gravity and indicate its position on the car.

.............................................................

.............................................................

.............................................................

.............................................................

.............................................................

.............................................................

.............................................................

.............................................................

.............................................................

# C5.

# Energy, Work, Power

# ENERGY

Energy is obtained in many forms. It cannot be created or destroyed. It can only be converted from one form to another.
List the four basic forms of energy found in a car.

1. .......................... 2. .......................... 3. .......................... 4. ..................

The engine converts the potential energy contained in the fuel, to mechanical energy which is used to propel the vehicle.

How does this energy conversion take place?

..........................................................................................................

..........................................................................................................

..........................................................................................................

..........................................................................................................

..........................................................................................................

The battery-charging system uses the four basic forms of energy. Explain how the energy is converted from one form to another.

..........................................................................................................

..........................................................................................................

..........................................................................................................

..........................................................................................................

..........................................................................................................

..........................................................................................................

..........................................................................................................

When solving simple mechanical and heating problems:

Energy can be defined as ..........................................................................

The SI unit of energy is the .......................................................................

# WORK

The two factors which govern the amount of work done are

..........................................................................................................

Work done is defined as ............................................................................

..........................................................................................................

..........................................................................................................

Force is expressed in ..................................

Distance is expressed in ..............................

These two valves would produce ........................................

But the unit used to measure work is the ............................

and one ........................ = one ........................................

Consider the situation below.

Force required to push vehicle 320 N

20 m

The work done by the man in moving the vehicle will be: 320 x 20 = 6400 Nm

This is .....................................................................................................

**Problems**

1. A hydraulic lift exerts a force of 7000 N to raise a vehicle to a height of 2 m. Calculate the work done.

...................................................

...................................................

...................................................

...................................................

2. If the force required to tow a vehicle is 800 N how much work is done if the vehicle is towed for one kilometre?

...................................................

...................................................

...................................................

...................................................

*(continued on next page)*

3. Find the work done when an engine having a mass of 200 kg is lifted a vertical distance of 1.5 m.

..............................................

..............................................

..............................................

..............................................

..............................................

..............................................

4. Calculate the work done to drive a car 250 m if there is a rolling resistance of 50 N and a constant gradient resistance of 150 N.

..............................................

..............................................

..............................................

..............................................

..............................................

5. The work done in dragging a metal box a distance of 6 m along a workshop floor is 726 Nm. Calculate the force required to pull the box.

..............................................

..............................................

..............................................

..............................................

..............................................

6. The work done in raising the front end of a vehicle was 320 Nm. If the force exerted by the lifting jack is 3200 N to what height was the vehicle raised?

..............................................

..............................................

..............................................

..............................................

..............................................

7. The work done in propelling a car 300 m was 72 kJ. What was the car's total resistance to motion?

..............................................

..............................................

..............................................

..............................................

..............................................

8. The work done by a press to push a bearing on to a shaft was 200 J. If the applied force was 10 kN how far was the bearing pushed on to the shaft?

..............................................

..............................................

..............................................

..............................................

..............................................

C5: 7

## Work done by a torque

When using a spanner to tighten a bolt, the force applied at the end of the spanner will, in one revolution of the bolt, move through a distance which is, in fact, the circumference of a circle whose radius is the 'effective length' of the spanner.

The work done per rev. = ..............................................................

Circumference = $2\pi r$ where $r$ = radius

Therefore work done per = ..................................

but force x radius = ..................................

∴ work done per rev. = ..............................x $2\pi$

If more than 1 rev. was involved then this would be multiplied by $N$ (number of revs.)

∴ work done by a torque = ..............................................................

Note: $\pi$ may be expressed as 3.142 or $\frac{22}{7}$

*Example*

When tightening a bolt a mechanic applies a force of 8 N at the end of a spanner 150 mm long.

Calculate the work done during 6 turns of the bolt.

Work done = $2\pi NT$

= 2 x 3.142 x 6 x 1.2

= 45.25 N m

or 45.25 J

No. of revs $N$ = 6

radius = 150 mm = 0.15 m

torque = force x radius

torque = 8 x 0.15 = 1.2 N m

**Problems**

1. A man using a starting handle rotates an engine twice. If the torque required to do this is 35 N m what is the work done by the man?

2. The force applied at the end of a spanner 100 mm long is 28 N. Calculate the work done during three revolutions of the spanner.

3. The force applied at the end of a vice handle of 0.3 m radius during a quarter of a turn is 80 N. Calculate the work done.

4. When propelling a vehicle, the torque in each halfshaft is 1200 N m. If the effective tyre radius is 0.25 m, calculate the work done in propelling the vehicle 25 m.

5. To rotate a car engine at 80 rev/min a starter motor must apply a force at the flywheel ring gear of 112 N. If the flywheel radius is 200 mm, calculate the work done to crank the engine through 7 revolutions.

7. The retarding force due to a brake shoe binding as shown opposite is 120 N. How much energy (work done) is absorbed in overcoming this during 50 revolutions?

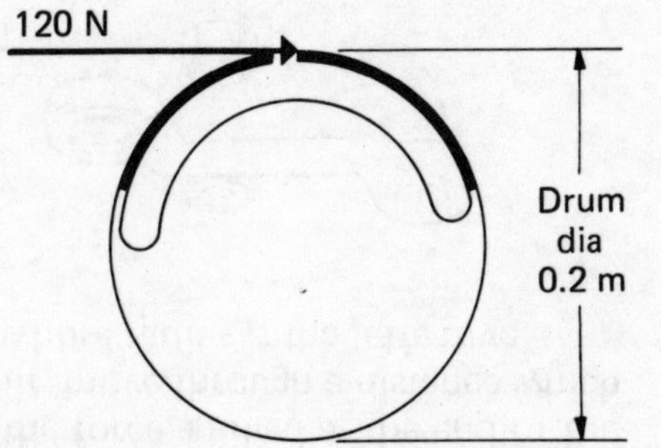

6. The work done to move a vehicle 300 m is 75 kJ. If the wheel diameter is 0.8 m calculate the torque applied to the wheels and the number of revolutions turned by the wheels.

120 N

Drum dia 0.2 m

# POWER

Power is the amount of work done over a specific time period.

Power is defined as ............................................................................................

.............................................................................................................................

The SI unit of power is the ..........................................

One .......................... = one ............................. = one ............................

The formula used to calculate power is:

Power = ________________________

Where work done = ........................ (or) ......................................

*Examples*

A man pushes with a force of 400 N to move a vehicle 15 m in 40 s. What power does this represent?

$$\text{Power} = \frac{\text{Work done}}{\text{Time taken}} = \frac{\text{Force x Distance}}{\text{Seconds}} = \frac{400 \times 15}{40} = 150 \text{ W}$$

Calculate the power of an engine developing a torque of 105 N m at 3000 rev/min.

$$\text{Power} = \frac{\text{Work done}}{\text{Time taken}} = \frac{2\pi NT}{\text{Seconds}} = 2 \times \frac{22}{7} \times \frac{3000 \times 105}{60} = 33000 \text{ W} = 33 \text{ kW}$$

**Problems**

1. A crane exerts a force of 900 N to lift an engine to a height of 1.5 m in 4 s. What power does this represent?

$$\text{Power} = \frac{\text{work done}}{\text{time taken}} = \frac{\text{Force x Distance}}{\text{Seconds}}$$

.............................................................

.............................................................

.............................................................

.............................................................

2. An engine running at 2000 rev/min develops a torque of 80 Nm. Calculate the power of the engine at this speed.

$$\text{Power} = \frac{\text{work done}}{\text{Time taken}} = \frac{2\pi NT}{\text{Seconds}}$$

.............................................................

.............................................................

.............................................................

.............................................................

3. A tractive force of 800 N propels a vehicle for 100 m in 10 s. Calculate the power developed.

.............................................................

.............................................................

.............................................................

.............................................................

.............................................................

4. A hoist exerts a force of 7200 N to raise a vehicle at the rate of 0.25 m/s. What power does this represent?

.............................................................

.............................................................

.............................................................

.............................................................

.............................................................

5. The torque in a propeller shaft is 100 Nm at a speed of 1500 rev/min. Calculate the power at the propeller shaft.

.............................................................

.............................................................

.............................................................

.............................................................

.............................................................

.............................................................

.............................................................

6. An engine supplies a power of 66 kW at a speed of 3500 rev/min. Calculate the engine torque.

.............................................................

.............................................................

.............................................................

.............................................................

.............................................................

.............................................................

.............................................................

When using the Imperial or British System, power is expressed as horsepower (h.p.)

One h.p. being equal to 746 W

Therefore if we wish to convert from one system to the other, we can use this as a basis for conversion.

*Convert*

(a) 3 h.p. to watt ..........................................................................

(b) 800 watt to h.p. ......................................................................

(c) 30 h.p. to watt ........................................................................

# C6.

# Machines

Simple machines 239

C6: 1-4

# SIMPLE MACHINES

A machine is a device by which it is possible to overcome a large resistance or load, by the application of only a small effort.

The lever is possibly the simplest form of machine (see Section C4.14)

A simple machine used for lifting is the screw jack shown opposite.

Name six other simple forms of machine.

1. ................................................ 2. ................................................

3. ................................................ 4. ................................................

5. ................................................ 6. ................................................

The ratio of the resisting force to the force applying the effort is known as the force ratio.

Force ratio = ______________

With the screw jack shown, the movement of the input, in one turn of the screw will depend upon

..............................................................................................................................

The movement of the output will depend upon

..............................................................................................................................

These input and output movements give a ratio known as the movement ratio.

Movement ratio = ______________________________

For the machine to be 100% efficient, the work input must equal the work output. With the jack shown, as with most machines, some of the effort is used to overcome ........................between the moving parts of the machine. Therefore some of the work is lost. The work input and output can be used to calculate efficiency. For example:

$$\% \text{ Efficiency} = \frac{\text{work done on load}}{\text{work done by effort}} \times \frac{100}{1}$$

or because they are in the same ratio:

% Efficiency =

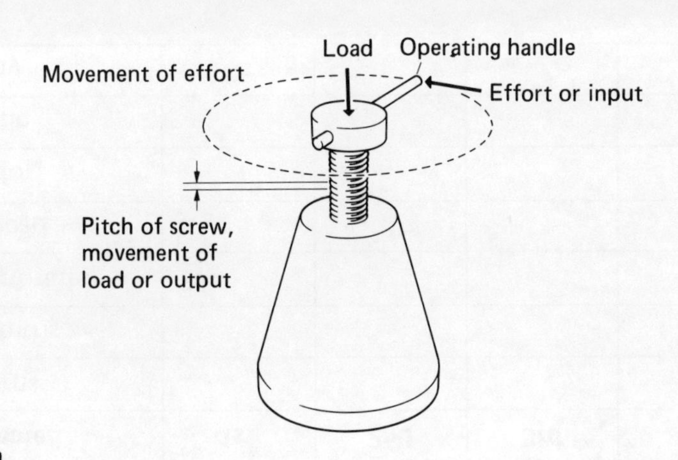


**Investigation**

Using a screw jack similar to the one above determine its jacking force ratio, movement ratio and efficiency.

Load = ................................. Effort = .....................................

Force ratio = ..............................=....................=.............................

Effective length of handle = $r$ = ..................................

Distance moved by effort in one revolution = $2\pi r$

= =

Distance moved by load = ................ = ............................

Movement ratio = ............................ = ........................... = .......................

Jack efficiency = ......................................................................................................

= ....................................................... = ...........................

With this type of machine a .................effort can lift a ................load but the movement required by the effort is very .......................for the .............. distance moved by the load.

Why is the efficiency so low? ...............................................................................

......................................................................................................................

## Problems

A screw jack has a pitch of 10 mm and an operating arm 250 mm long. If when raising a vehicle the jack exerts a force of 8000 N by the application of only 150 N at the end of the operating lever, calculate.

(a) force ratio, (b) movement ratio, (c) efficiency.

..............................................................................

..............................................................................

..............................................................................

..............................................................................

..............................................................................

2. A lifting-jack handle moves 150 mm while the load rises 6 mm. What load will be lifted by an effort of 40 N if the efficiency of the jack is 100%?

..............................................................................

..............................................................................

..............................................................................

..............................................................................

..............................................................................

3. In a lifting machine the load moves 12 mm, while the effort moves 1500 mm. If an effort of 9 N overcomes a resistance of 600 N, calculate

(a) force ratio, (b) movement ratio, (c) efficiency.

..............................................................................

..............................................................................

..............................................................................

..............................................................................

..............................................................................

## Investigation

Determine the movement ratio, force ratio and efficiency of a motor vehicle gearbox.

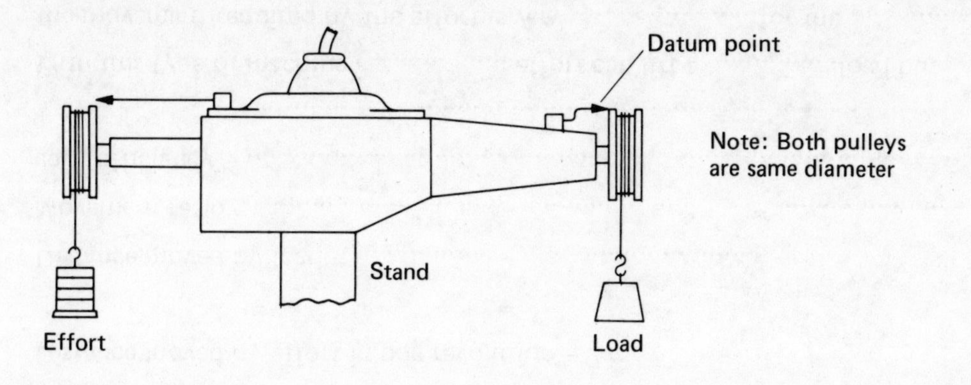


Use a gearbox adapted as shown and complete the table below.

$$\text{Movement ratio} = \frac{\text{revs of input}}{\text{revs of output}}, \ \text{Force ratio} = \frac{\text{Load}}{\text{Effort}}, \ \text{Efficiency} = \frac{\text{FR}}{\text{MR}}$$

| Gear selected | 1st | 2nd | 3rd | 4th |
|---|---|---|---|---|
| Input turns | | | | |
| Output turns | | | | |
| **Movement ratio** | | | | |
| Output load | | | | |
| Input effort | | | | |
| **Force ratio** | | | | |
| **Efficiency** | | | | |

C7.

# Materials

# CHARACTERISTICS (OR PROPERTIES) OF METALS

The selection of materials for a particular application is determined by their characteristics.
A material may possess one or more of these characteristics.
Define each characteristic and give an example of a motor-vehicle component which demonstrates this characteristic.

| Characteristics | Description | Typical MV component |
|---|---|---|
| Hardness | | |
| Strength | | |
| Brittleness | | |
| Toughness | | |
| Ductility | | |
| Malleability | | |
| Elasticity | | |
| Plasticity | | |

**Material selection with regard to its properties**

*Low-carbon steel or mild steel*

List the properties that make low carbon steel a very suitable material for car bodies

........................................................................................................................

........................................................................................................................

........................................................................................................................

........................................................................................................................

........................................................................................................................

........................................................................................................................

*Cast iron*

List the properties that make cast iron a particularly suitable material from which to make such parts as engine cylinder heads and blocks, cylinder liners, piston rings, brake drums and clutch pressure-plates?

........................................................................................................................

........................................................................................................................

........................................................................................................................

........................................................................................................................

........................................................................................................................

........................................................................................................................

**Investigation**

Using simple tests determine how properties vary in different materials.

1. *Hardness*

Use small metal plates of similar thickness. Place a ball bearing between plates and squeeze in a press or between the jaws of a vice.

Repeat on all materials. (Apply equal pressure each time.)

| **Material** | | | | |
|---|---|---|---|---|
| **Diameter of indentation (mm)** | | | | |

Rank the materials in order of their relative hardness (hardest first).

| **Material** | | | | |
|---|---|---|---|---|

2. *Ductility*

Suspend long lengths of thin wire of different materials and gradually load each wire until it breaks.

| **Material** | **Original length (mm)** | **Total length after breakage** | **Extension (mm)** |
|---|---|---|---|
| | | | |
| | | | |
| | | | |

The most ductile material was the wire that ..........................the most,

this material was ...........................

3. *Brittleness*

Grip bars of different metals but a similar diameter and length securely in a vice. Place a long tube over each bar in turn and bend to and fro.

State most brittle material first.

| **Material** | | | | |
|---|---|---|---|---|

How did you determine which was the most brittle metal?

.......................................................................................................................

4. *Toughness*

Using similar bars to (3) held upright in a vice, strike each a similar blow with a hammer.

State the toughest material first.

| **Material** | | | | |
|---|---|---|---|---|

The toughest material was the one that .......................................................

5. *Elasticity and strength*

Use long thin bars of equal length and diameter. Grip each bar in turn horizontally in a vice.

Suspend a hanger on the end of each bar and load until the bar bends.

*Note* (1) The amount of deflection each bar makes before bending.

(2) The mass on the hanger when each bar bends.

(3) Remove hanger to see if the bars return to their original positions.

| **Material** | | | | |
|---|---|---|---|---|
| Maximum deflection before bending (mm) | | | | |
| Maximum load before bending | | | | |

The material that has the greatest elasticity will: ..........................................

.......................................................................................................................

The material having the greatest strength will: ...............................................

.......................................................................................................................

6. *Plasticity*

Use thin sheets of metal and indent the centre with a ball-pein hammer or cupping machine until the metal fractures.

| **Material** | | | | |
|---|---|---|---|---|
| Depth of indentation before fracture (mm) | | | | |

State the material having the best plasticity first and list others in relative order.

| **Material** | | | | |
|---|---|---|---|---|

# FERROUS AND NON-FERROUS METALS

Most of the main mechanical and structural components of a car are made from metal.

Metals may be split into two main groups:

Ferrous and non-ferrous metals

A ferrous metal is: ..........................................................................

..........................................................................

A non-ferrous metal is: ..........................................................................

..........................................................................

..........................................................................

Name typical motor-vehicle components made from the materials below:

| Ferrous metal | Components | Non-ferrous metals | Components |
|---|---|---|---|
| Low carbon (mild) steel | | Aluminium alloy | |
| | | | |
| High-carbon steel | | Copper | |
| | | | |
| Cast iron | | Copper-based alloys, brass and bronze | |
| | | | |
| Alloy steels | | Lead-based alloys | |
| | | | |
| | | Zinc-based alloys (diecasting) | |
| | | | |

Ferrous metals are defined by the amount of carbon contained in the metal.

..........................................................................

..........................................................................

..........................................................................

..........................................................................

State which metal will have the percentage carbon content shown opposite.

Cast iron
Mild steel
High-carbon steel
Wrought iron
Medium-carbon steel

| Material | % Carbon |
|---|---|
| | 0.01 |
| | 0.25 |
| | 0.50 |
| | 1.20 |
| | 3.00 |

Steel that is produced in the medium- and high-carbon steel range is particularly suitable for heat treatment to improve its characteristics (or properties).

..........................................................................

..........................................................................

..........................................................................

..........................................................................

..........................................................................

..........................................................................

..........................................................................

..........................................................................

..........................................................................

..........................................................................

..........................................................................

## C7: 6 EFFECTS OF HARDENING AND TEMPERING

Heat treatment affects the mechanical properties of steel.

Indicate the changes that occur during heat treatment and state how these affect the mechanical properties of the steels mentioned in the next column.

1. Examine fractured bars that have had various treatments and show how the grain structure varies in each case.

(a) *Untreated high carbon steel*

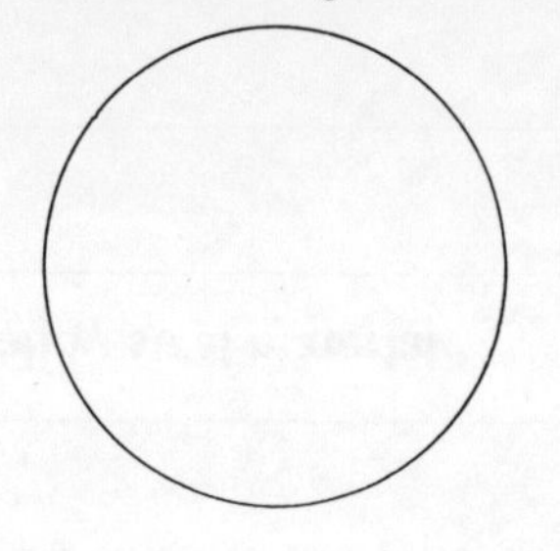

(b) *Hardened high carbon steel*

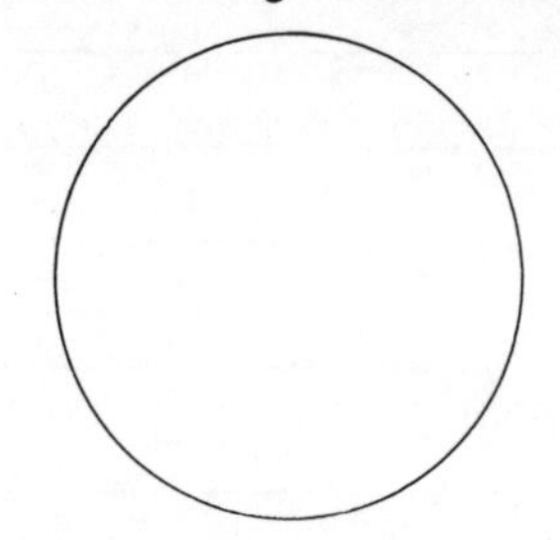

(c) *Hardened and tempered high carbon steel*

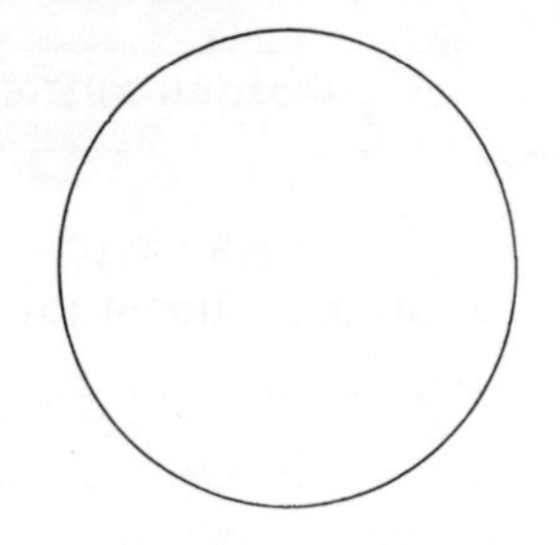

## C7: 5 CASE HARDENING

The outer case of a low carbon steel component may be hardened by submerging the component at high temperature in a carbon-rich material for a certain period of time.

The component can then be suitably heat treated.

What is the purpose of case hardening?

..........................................................

..........................................................

Name three motor-vehicle components that may be case hardened.

*Case-hardened low carbon steel*

Examine such a fractured specimen and draw a representation of the grain structure.

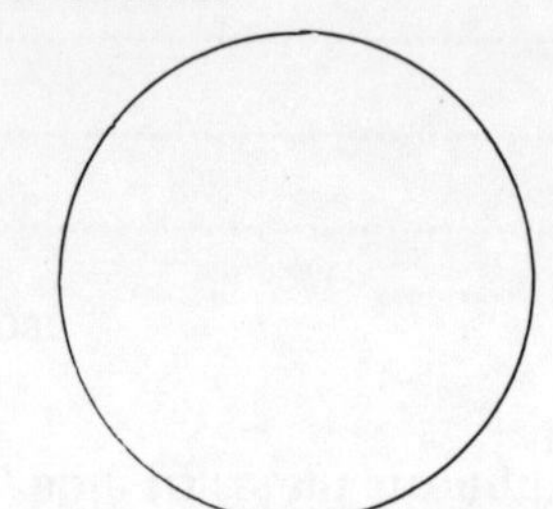

## C7: 7 ALLOY STEELS

Alloy steels are used for most of the highly stressed components used in the modern car.

What is meant by an alloy steel.

..........................................................

..........................................................

..........................................................

..........................................................

..........................................................

..........................................................

Most of the tools in a mechanic's tool box are made from alloy steel, for example spanners, pliers, hammers, screwdrivers, chisels, hacksaw blades.

Examine a selection of spanners. From what alloy steel are they made.

| Spanner | Type of alloy steel |
|---|---|
| | |
| | |

C7: 8

Why are alloying elements such as those listed below added to steel?

..............................................................................................

..............................................................................................

Complete the table giving the reasons why each (or a combination) of the elements shown is used to improve the properties of a steel.

| Material | Properties improved |
|---|---|
| Nickel | |
| Chromium | |
| Nickel and chromium | |
| Chromium and vanadium | |
| Chromium and molybdenum | |
| Tungsten | |
| Manganese | |

List some typical steel motor-vehicle components and state the type of alloy steel from which they may be made.

| Typical motor vehicle components | Typical alloy steel material |
|---|---|
| | |
| | |
| | |
| | |
| | |

C7: 9

# NON-FERROUS METALS

Most of the pure non-ferrous metals are not used separately but are alloyed with other materials when used to produce motor-vehicle components.

The reason for this is ..............................................................................

..............................................................................................

..............................................................................................

State the main properties of the non-ferrous metals shown below.

| Material | Colour | Main properties |
|---|---|---|
| Aluminium | | |
| Copper | | |
| Tin | | |
| Lead | | |
| Zinc | | |

*Aluminium and its alloys*

Pure aluminium is not commonly used in a vehicle because it is too ductile and malleable. But, when small amounts of other materials are added, alloys can be produced that are much stronger, harder, able to retain strength at high temperatures and are corrosion resistant.

Aluminium alloys can be divided into two groups:

..............................................................................................

..............................................................................................

..............................................................................................

..............................................................................................

..............................................................................................

..............................................................................................

..............................................................................................

C7: 9,10

Give reasons why the following non-ferrous metals are considered very suitable materials for the following components:

| Component | Material | Reason for choice |
|---|---|---|
| Pistons Some cylinder heads | Aluminium | |
| Radiator core (or stack) | Copper | |
| Electrical cables | Copper | |
| Fuel pumps, carburettors | Zinc based aluminium alloy | |
| Small plain bearings | Bronze | |
| Radiator header tanks | Brass | |
| Bearings | Aluminium, tin, copper, lead | |

The main alloys of copper are brass and bronze.

Brass is an alloy of copper and ..........................................................

Bronze is an alloy of copper and ..........................................................

C7: 11

# SURFACE PROTECTION

Surfaces are given various types of protective coatings. Sometimes these coatings are also decorative, for example body paintwork.

What are the basic reasons for providing 'surface' protection?

..........................................................................................................................

..........................................................................................................................

..........................................................................................................................

One method of protecting materials is by coating the material with a thin layer of non-corrosive material. Some examples of this are shown below. State any motor-vehicle component protected by the processes named.

| Protection process | Motor-vehicle component |
|---|---|
| Galvanising | |
| Tin-plating | |
| Anodising | |
| Cadmium-plating | |
| Chromium-plating | |

Spare parts which may be stored for a long time are protected with various substances. Examine some such components.

State how or what material is used to protect their surfaces.

| Component | Type of protection |
|---|---|
| | |
| | |
| | |
| | |
| | |

The vehicle body may be protected by various painting processes. With each process different types of paint materials are applied to the surface.

What is the object of:

(a) The first surface primer-coat; ..............................................

..............................................

..............................................

..............................................

(b) Various layers of undercoat; ..............................................

..............................................

..............................................

..............................................

..............................................

(c) Final high-gloss coat? ..............................................

..............................................

..............................................

The underside of a vehicle is usually given extra protection. Name and very briefly describe three types of protection that may be used:

1. ..............................................
2. ..............................................
3. ..............................................

Vehicle bodies when left unprotected are particularly vulnerable to corrosion.

..............................................

..............................................

..............................................

..............................................

..............................................

List the main causes of corrosion.

1. ..............................................
2. ..............................................
3. ..............................................
4. ..............................................
5. ..............................................

**Investigation**

Use small pieces of unpainted and painted sheet steel.

Suspend both painted and unpainted sheets in breakers of different liquids.

Observe effects after a suitable period.

| Liquid | Condition of steel after immersion | |
|---|---|---|
| | **Painted** | **Unpainted** |
| Salted water | | |
| Brake fluid | | |
| Thinners | | |
| Antifreeze | | |
| Battery acid | | |
| Paraffin | | |
| Petrol | | |
| Grease | | |

Note: For this investigation to be successful, continuous observations will be required over a period of at least one month — longer if possible.

C7: 15,16

# PLASTICS

Plastics are a large group of man-made materials. They may be formed into any required shape under the application of heat and pressure.
There are two groups of plastics.

1. Thermosetting

..........................................................................................

..........................................................................................

..........................................................................................

..........................................................................................

..........................................................................................

..........................................................................................

2. Thermoplastic

..........................................................................................

..........................................................................................

..........................................................................................

..........................................................................................

..........................................................................................

..........................................................................................

State whether the following materials are thermoplastic or thermosetting;

| Material | Type | Material | Type |
|---|---|---|---|
| Celluloid | | Bakelite | |
| Formica | | Polythene | |
| Polystyrene | | PVC | |
| PTFE (Teflon) | | Nylon | |
| Terylene | | Epoxy resins | |

Listed are three common plastics used on vehicles.
Complete the table as required.

| Material | Properties | Vehicle applications |
|---|---|---|
| Nylon | | |
| PTFE | | |
| PVC | | |

Some body panels and one-piece car bodies are manufactured by using thermosetting plastics (polyester resins) to reinforce glass fibre.
State advantages of this type of body over an 'all-steel' body.

1. ..........................................................................................
2. ..........................................................................................
3. ..........................................................................................
4. ..........................................................................................

C7:17

# CERAMICS

A ceramic material is one that has been produced through a heating process and forms a pot-like substance that is very hard and brittle.

One of the few ceramic substances used on a vehicle is for

..........................................................................................

..........................................................................................

..........................................................................................

C8.

# Electricity

C8: 1,2,8

# ELECTRICAL TERMS AND MEASURING INSTRUMENTS

For an electric current to flow there must be a complete electrical circuit. Basically this consists of a pressure source, for example a battery; a resistance through which the current will do useful work, for example a light bulb; and supply lines to make the circuit complete.

Define the following electrical terms:

1. Ampere ..........................................................................................

..........................................................................................

..........................................................................................

2. Volt ..........................................................................................

..........................................................................................

..........................................................................................

3. Ohm ..........................................................................................

..........................................................................................

..........................................................................................

4. Power ..........................................................................................

..........................................................................................

..........................................................................................

The electron theory explains that all matter is made up of positive and negative charges of electricity. The negatively charged particles are called electrons and in some materials these are free to move. When a force causes these electrons to move a current of electricity is the result.

Materials that allow an easy flow of electrons are called ..............................

Materials that resist the flow of electrons are called ..................................

The conventionally accepted direction of electron flow is said to be from

.................................................... to ....................................................

The conventionally accepted direction of current flow is said to be from

.................................................... to ....................................................

The unit of current flow is called the ..........................................................

The unit of electrical pressure is called the ..................................................

The unit of electrical resistance is called the..................................................

The unit of electrical power is called the ......................................................

**Investigation**

Connect the following components to build an electrical circuit:

battery, ammeter, switch, light bulb.

Using conventional symbols draw the circuit diagram. Indicate using arrows the conventionally accepted direction of current flow.

State the amount of current flowing in the circuit shown ..............................

The bulb wattage was ..........................................................................

## MEASURING INSTRUMENTS

An ......................... measures the amount of current flow. This instrument when used, must always be connected into the circuit in ...........................

When checking the voltage (or potential difference) across components in a circuit a ................... is used. This must be connected across the terminals of the components being tested, that is in ..............................................

To check the resistance of an electrical component, for example coil, the meter used is called an......................... In what way does this meter differ from the other two? ..........................................................................

..........................................................................................

..........................................................................................

Check the resistance of the following:

coil ...................., field winding ...................., small light bulbs ................,

# ELECTRICAL SIGNS AND SYMBOLS

Each component on the list below can be represented by one of the symbols shown on this page. Write the appropriate name beneath each symbol.

Voltmeter
Switches
Battery of many cells
Sparking plug
Light bulbs
Starter motor
Generator
Transistor
Coil
Control box
Positive
Fuel pump
Crossed wires not connected
Horn
Resistor fixed
Fuse
Diode
Negative
Contact-breaker points
Variable resistor
Gauge
Single cell
Crossed wires connected
Ammeter Capacitor Alternator

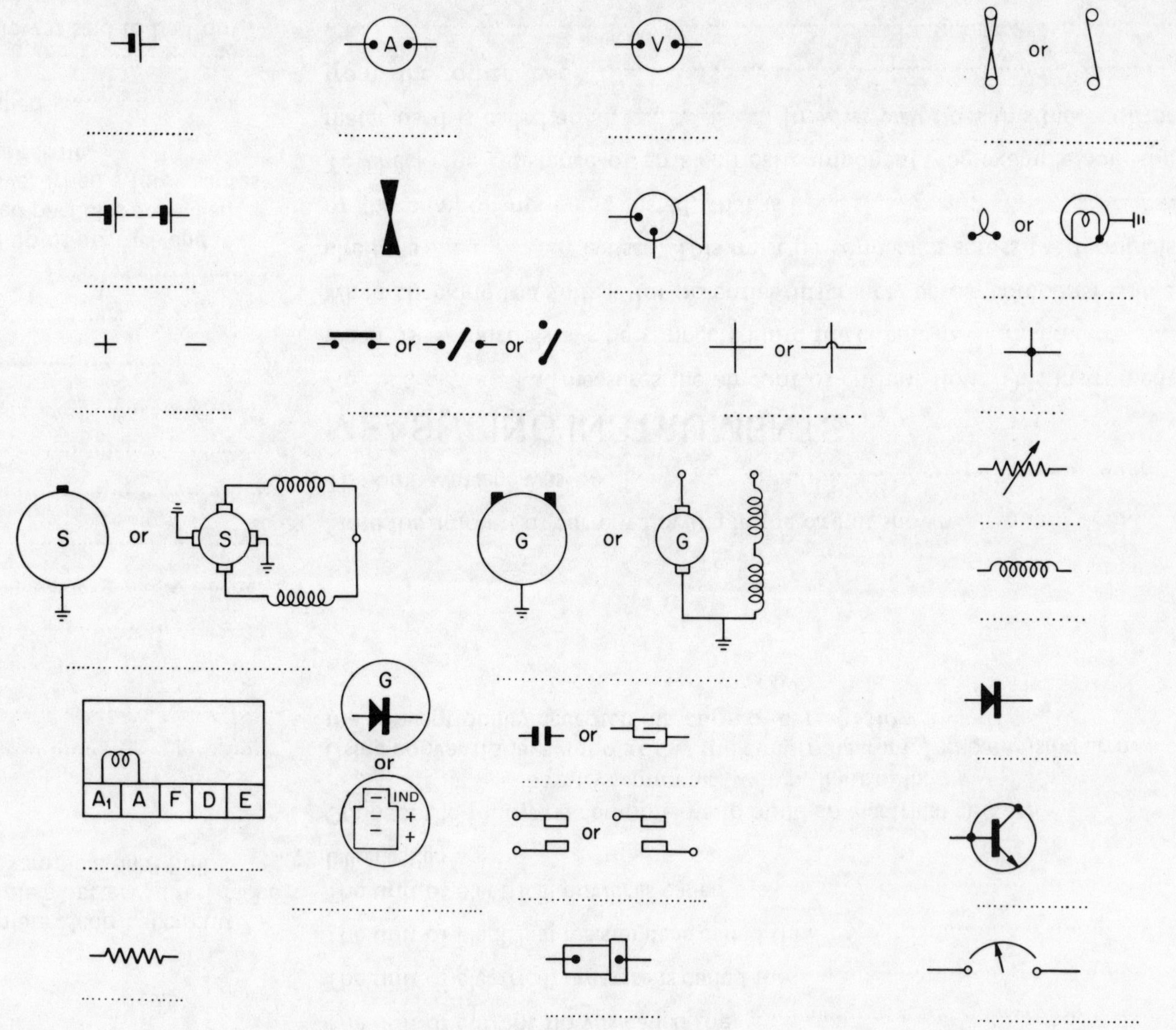

A V or

................ ................ ................ ..........................

or

................ ................ ..........................

\+ − or or or

................ ................ .......................... ..........................

S or S G or G

..........................

G

or

IND

\+

\+

A1 A F D E

or

or

................................ ................................ ................

................ ................

C8: 4,5,8

# SERIES AND PARALLEL CIRCUITS

**Investigation**

Built two electrical circuits as shown

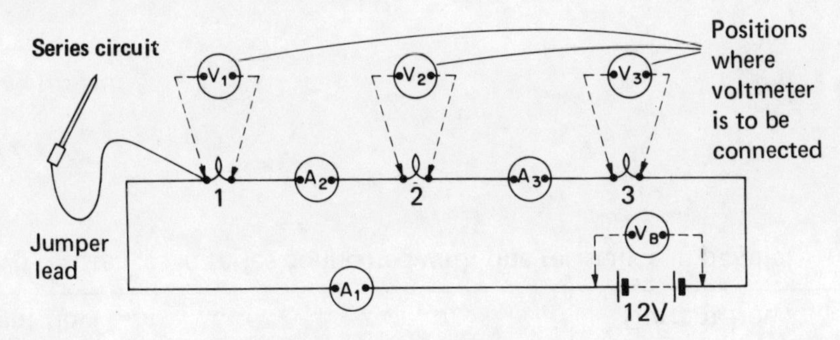


Connect all bulbs in circuit and note readings.

**Voltage**

| $V_1$ | $V_2$ | $V_3$ | Total | $V_B$ |
|---|---|---|---|---|
| | | | | |

**Current flow**

| $A_1$ | $A_2$ | $A_3$ |
|---|---|---|
| | | |

Why are the bulbs dim? ..........................................................................

Remove bulb 1, what happens? ..........................................................................

Why does this occur? ..........................................................................

Place prod of jumper lead to bulb 2, take readings:

**Voltage**

| $V_2$ | $V_3$ | Total | $V_B$ |
|---|---|---|---|
| | | | |

**Current flow**

| $A_1$ | $A_3$ |
|---|---|
| | |

What differences have now occurred and why?

..........................................................................

Remove bulb 2, connect prod of jumper lead to bulb 3, take readings

**Voltage**

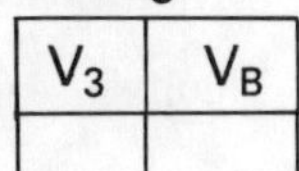

| $V_3$ | $V_B$ |
|---|---|
| | |

**Current flow**

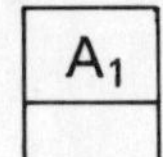

| $A_1$ |
|---|
| |

*Parallel circuit*

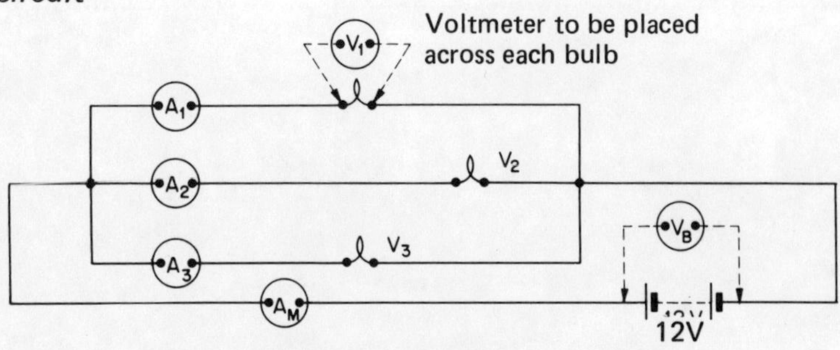


Connect all bulbs in circuit and note readings

**Voltage**

| $V_1$ | $V_2$ | $V_3$ | $V_B$ |
|---|---|---|---|
| | | | |

**Current flow**

| $A_1$ | $A_2$ | $A_3$ | Total | $A_M$ |
|---|---|---|---|---|
| | | | | |

When three bulbs are connected, compared with the series circuit what differences occur with regard to the following. Give reasons.

Voltage ..........................................................................

..........................................................................

Current flow ..........................................................................

..........................................................................

Light intensity ..........................................................................

..........................................................................

Note current flow when removing bulbs.

| | $A_1$ | $A_2$ | $A_3$ | Total | $A_M$ |
|---|---|---|---|---|---|
| One bulb removed | | | | | |
| Two bulbs removed | | | | | |

Why didn't the same thing occur as in the series circuit?

..........................................................................

# BUILDING VARIOUS ELECTRICAL CIRCUITS

**Investigation**

Equipment:

various types of resistances; switches; cables; ammeter; voltmeter; battery

Assemble the circuits described below, include in each circuit an ammeter, switch and battery.

You may be provided with **either:**

(a) motor-vehicle components (b) a peg board (c) a construction kit

Sketch the circuit diagrams and state the total current flow in each case

In a series circuit the bulbs or resistances are connected:

..............................................................

..............................................................

..............................................................

..............................................................

In a parallel circuit the bulbs or resistances are connected:

..............................................................

..............................................................

1. Two resistances connected in parallel

Current flow..............................................

2. Four resistances connected in series

Current flow..............................................

3. Six resistances connected in parallel

Current flow..............................................

4. Two resistances in series connected with one resistance in parallel

Current flow ..............................................

5. Two resistances in parallel connected to one resistance in series. Repeat this layout using three *additional* resistances and connect *both layouts* in parallel with one another

Current flow ..............................................

# EFFECTS OF AN ELECTRICAL CURRENT

The flow of current in an electrical circuit produces three main effects:

..........................................................................................................

**Investigation**

To show the heating effect of an electric current when used to advantage.

Connect vehicle bulbs of various sizes individually into a simple circuit as shown. Complete the table.

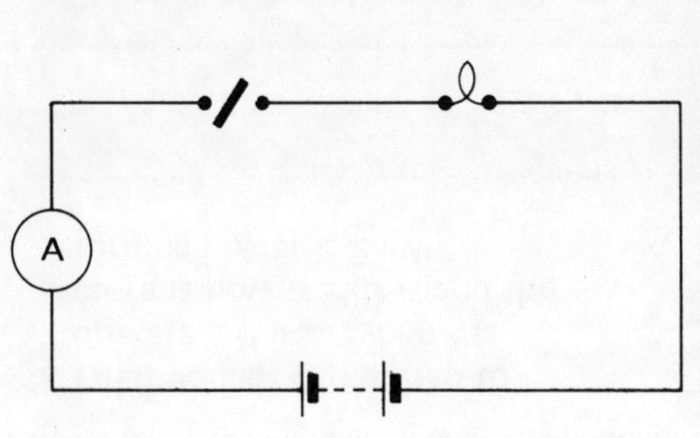


| Type of bulb | Wattage | Current flow | Light intensity grade 1 to 5 |
|---|---|---|---|
| | | | |
| | | | |
| | | | |
| | | | |
| | | | |

More ............................is created as the light intensity increases.

Wattage is the value given to the power output. This value .................as the light intensity increases.

The thicker the bulb filament wire, the ......................... the light intensity.

Name three components that use the heating effect of an electric current to advantage.

1. ................................. 2. ................................. 3. .................................

See Applied studies – engine electrical system for investigation on magnetic effect.

Name THREE components that use the magnetic effect of an electric current to advantage.

1. ................................. 2. ................................. 3. .................................

What motor-vehicle component uses a chemical effect?

..........................................................................................................

**Investigation**

To show the chemical effect of an electric current use a simple cell similar to that shown below. The cables should be capable of connecting to a low-voltage direct-current supply and a circuit containing a light bulb of low voltage. A centre scale ammeter should be used to indicate amount and direction of current flow.

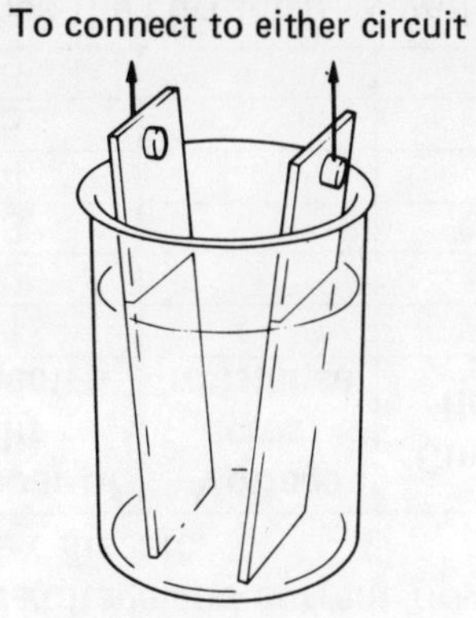


Cell contains two strips of ordinary lead, separated electrically from each other and partly immersed in sulphuric acid diluted with distilled water.
(Approx. S.G. 1.250)

| Operation | Current flow | |
|---|---|---|
| | Amount | Direction |
| a. | | |
| b. | | |
| c. | | |

(a) Connect simple cell to bulb circuit.

Does the circuit operate? ..........................................................................

What is the reason? ..........................................................................

..........................................................................

(b) Connect simple cell to low-voltage direct-current supply for about five minutes. What is now happening?

..........................................................................

Why do the plates bubble? ..........................................................................

..........................................................................

(c) Reconnect to bulb circuit. The time taken before the bulb goes out is:

..........................................................................

Why is the time the bulb remained alight different to the charging time?

..........................................................................

C8: 8,9

# ELECTRICAL POWER

Power is the rate of doing work.

The unit of power is the ..........................................................................

When a pressure of 1 V causes a current of 1 A to flow in a circuit the power produced in the circuit is 1 W.

Hence Watts =

**Problems**

1. A 12-V lamp consumes 3 A. What is the power rating of the lamp?
2. A starter motor requires 1800 W at a pressure of 10 V to turn the engine. What current is required to produce the power.

..........................................................................

..........................................................................

..........................................................................

3. What voltage is required to operate a starter when the current flow is 220 A and the turning power is 2 kW.
4. What current would flow in a side lamp circuit using five 12-V,6-W lamps.

..........................................................................

..........................................................................

..........................................................................

5. Sketch a circuit diagram to show two 12-V, 60-W lamps connected in parallel to a 12-V Battery. Include in the circuit the instruments that would be required to measure the total power output of the lamps and indicate the expected readings on the meters.

..........................................

..........................................

..........................................

..........................................

..........................................

C8: 10

# RELATIONSHIP OF VOLTAGE, CURRENT AND RESISTANCE

The voltage current flow and resistance of a circuit are all related to one another. A change in one may cause the other two to vary. In the solving of problems it is usual to consider that one of the units remains constant. For example, if the voltage is doubled the current flow will double provided the resistance does not change; or the current flow will double if the resistance is halved provided the voltage is kept constant.

These variations in strict ratios all obey ..........................................................

**Investigation**

Show that the ratio voltage/current is near constant when the potential difference (applied voltage) is varied.

Equipment: 12-V battery; ammeter; voltmeter; resistance, cables and test prods.

Connect voltmeter and ammeter in a circuit as shown, using one bulb only. Connect prods to one cell only of battery, note voltage and current flow. Repeat connecting test prods to two cells, three cells, etc.

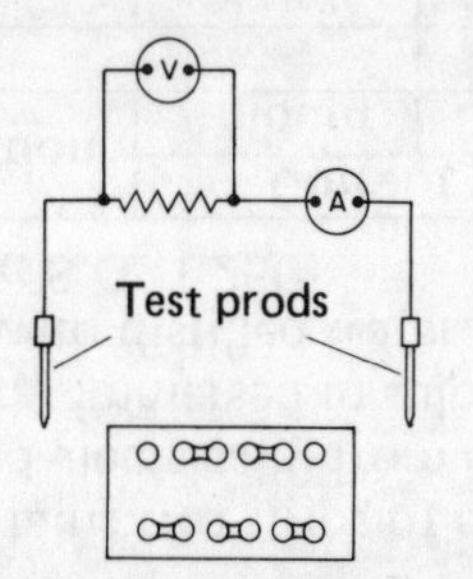


| Number of cells connected | Voltage across resistance | Current flow |
|---|---|---|
| 1. | | |
| 2. | | |
| 3. | | |
| 4. | | |
| 5. | | |
| 6. | | |

If the voltage is doubled using the same resistance the current flow will ........

C8: 11

# ELECTRICAL RESISTANCE

The electrical resistance does not always remain constant as is assumed above. With most metals as the temperature increases the electrical resistance

..........................................................................

Certain alloys ..............................................are unaffected by temperature and are used in measuring instruments.

# C9.

# Drawing

Engineering drawing is a means of communication. It is a simpler, more accurate and less ambiguous form of communication than the spoken or written word. By 'reading' and understanding a drawing the engineer can make or assemble and dismantle components.

Many different forms of drawing are used by engineers. These vary from simple freehand sketches to a variety of other types of drawing. List below different types of engineering drawings.

..........................................................................

..........................................................................

..........................................................................

..........................................................................

..........................................................................

..........................................................................

..........................................................................

To enable all engineers to understand and use the same rules when drawing, British Standard Specification (BSS) 308 is used.

List the equipment required to produce good clear drawings.

..........................................................................

..........................................................................

..........................................................................

..........................................................................

..........................................................................

..........................................................................

..........................................................................

..........................................................................

..........................................................................

# GENERAL RULES

**Types of lines**

The types of lines used in engineering drawing are shown below. Complete the description of the lines by giving examples of their applications in drawing.

Thick continuous

..........................................

Thin continuous

..........................................

..........................................

Thin short dashes

..........................................

Thin chain

..........................................

Thick chain

..........................................

Thin wavy

..........................................

..........................................

To produce the correct type of line to suit the application, not only requires some expertise but well-sharpened pencils of the correct grade. Give examples of the grades of pencils used for:

1. Visible outlines ..............................

2. Projection or centre lines ..........................

# DIMENSIONING (MAIN RULES)

The simple drawing below is dimensioned in accordance with recognised standards.

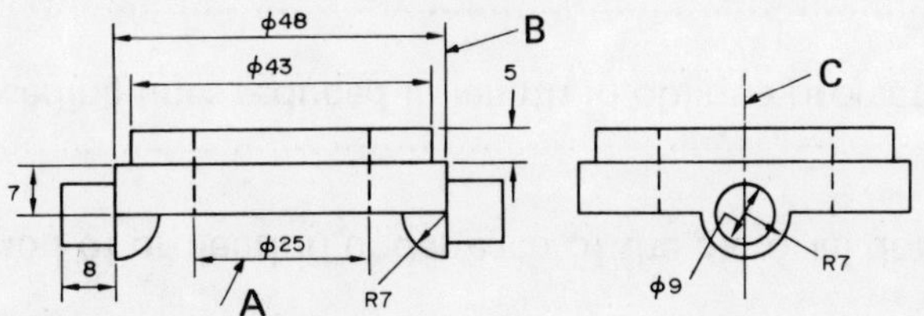


Line A is a ..........................................................................................

Line B is a ..........................................................................................

Line C is a ..........................................................................................

List the main rules for dimensioning a drawing.

..........................................................................................

..........................................................................................

..........................................................................................

..........................................................................................

..........................................................................................

..........................................................................................

..........................................................................................

..........................................................................................

..........................................................................................

..........................................................................................

..........................................................................................

..........................................................................................

The symbol    represents ..........................................................................................

State the units used for linear dimensions on drawings

..........................................................................................

# CONVENTIONAL REPRESENTATION

To avoid wasting time on engineering drawings common features are often simplified, that is they are shown by conventional symbols.

Complete the table by making sketches to show what the conventions represent.

| Subject | Convention |
| --- | --- |
| | |
| | |
| | |
| | |
| | |
| | |
| | |

C9: 1

# PICTORIAL PROJECTION

A pictorial view of an object gives a three-dimensional impression where its height width and depth are shown simultaneously.

Two methods of representing an object pictorially are by:

1. ................................................ projection

or

2. ................................................ projection

*Features of isometric projection*

1. The lines receding from the horizontal are drawn at ................................ to the horizontal.
2. Circles are drawn as ..........................................................................

*Features of oblique projection*

1. The lines receding from the horizontal are drawn at ................................ to the horizontal.
2. The front face is drawn as a ................................face.
3. The lines receding from the horizontal are drawn at ................................ full size.

Sketch two 2 cm cubes to illustrate isometric and oblique projection at the top of the page opposite.

Name the method of projection under each of the pictorial drawings shown opposite.

Why are the receding lines reduced in length in oblique projection?

.............................................................................................................

.............................................................................................................

.............................................................................................................

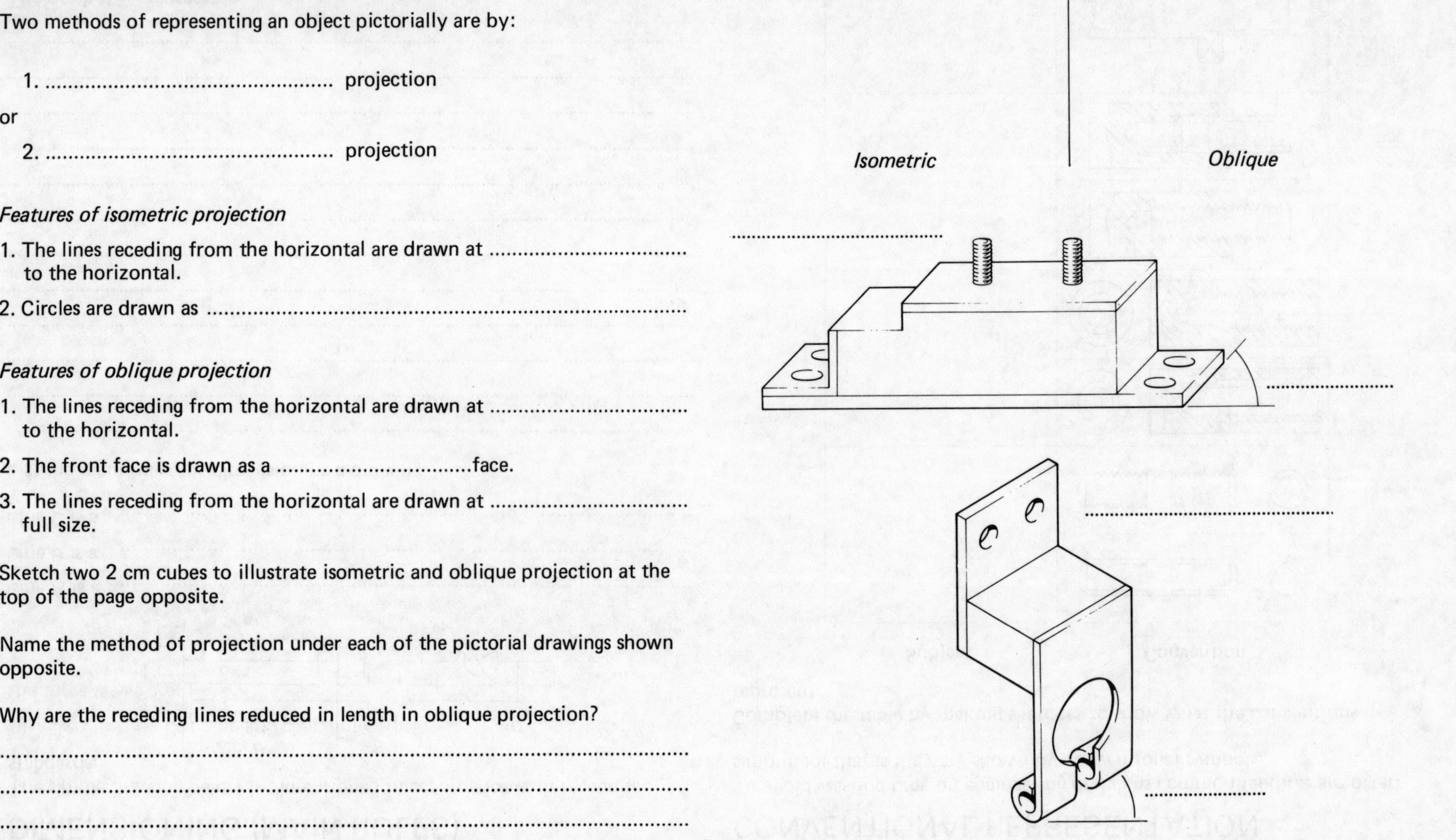

C9: 1,5

# ORTHOGRAPHIC PROJECTION

Orthographic projection is a method used to present the various faces of an object when viewed squarely. For relatively simple objects three views are sufficient to fully describe and give dimensions.

The three views are:

.......................................................................................................................

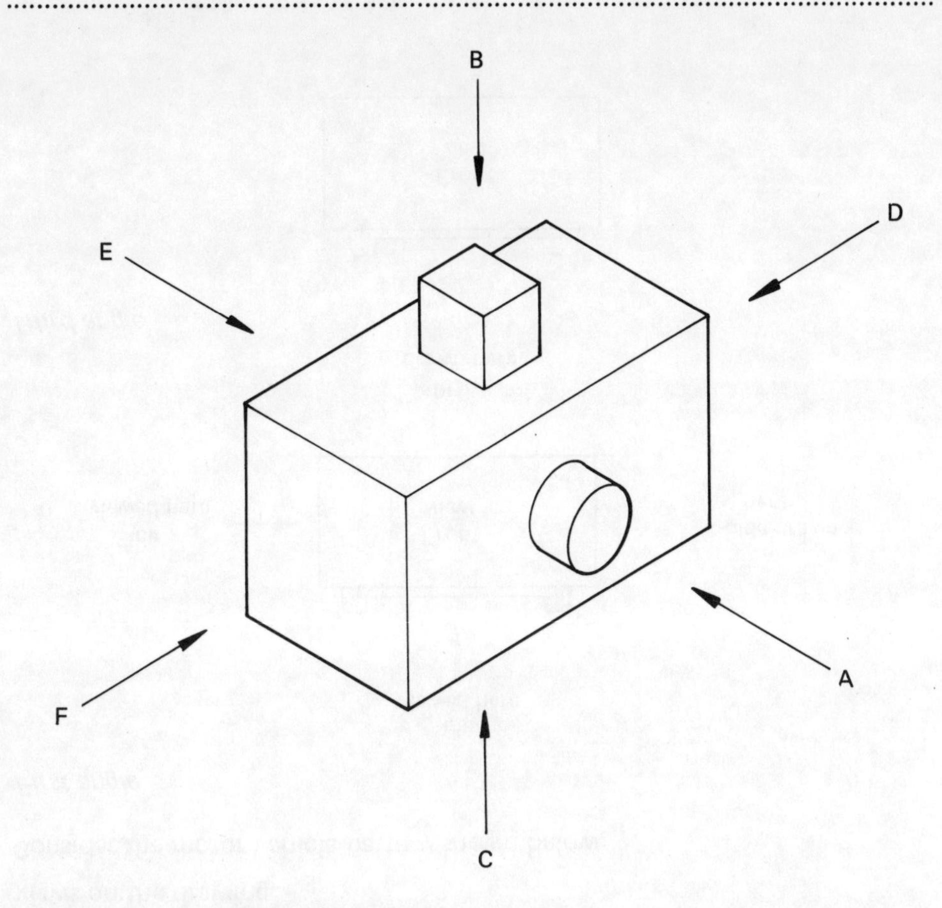


In which direction must the object above be viewed to produce the views shown opposite, taking 'A' as the FRONT VIEW. Put the appropriate letter under the view.

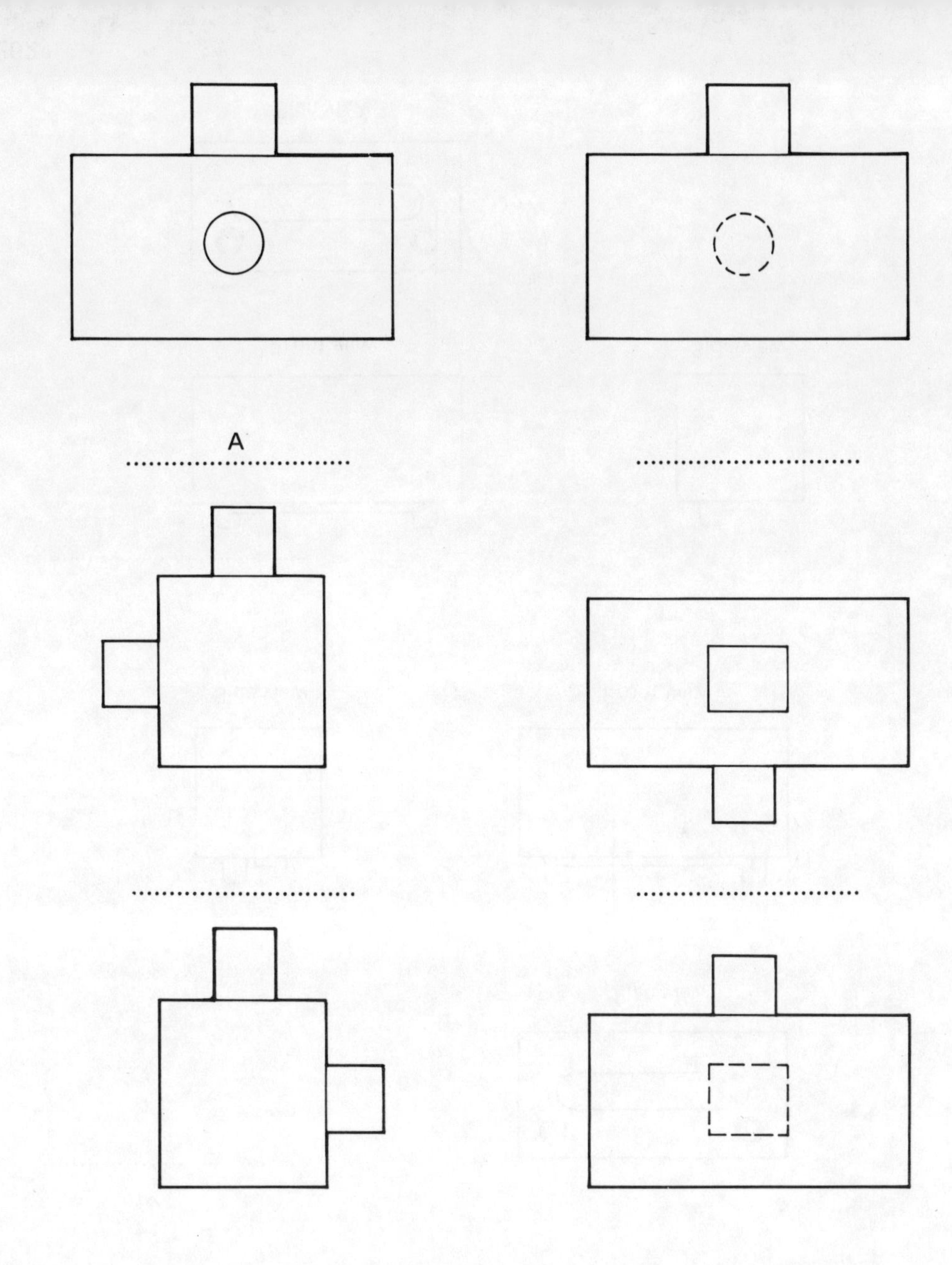

C9: 2 **First angle and third angle projection**

Two systems of orthographic projection are *first angle* and *third angle.* The difference between the two systems is the relative positioning of the three views on the drawing.

Consider the motor vehicle battery shown below

*First angle*

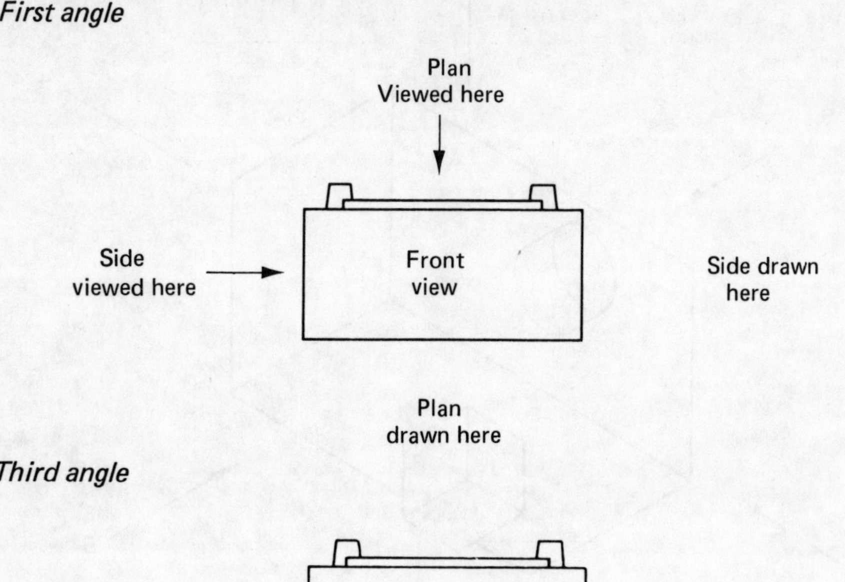


*Third angle*

Front
view

Label the 'third angle' drawing above to describe 'third angle' projection and show where the other two views would be shown. Will the actual drawings produced for first angle be different to the drawings for third angle projection? ........................................................................

........................................................................................

........................................................................................

Name the angle of projection used in each 'three view' drawing below.

................................

Plan view

Side view

Front view

................................

Front view

Side view

Plan view

C9: 3.5

The arrow on the pictorial drawings of the mounting brackets shown represents the front view. Study the views opposite and complete the table to indicate the correct front, side and plan views for the different brackets.

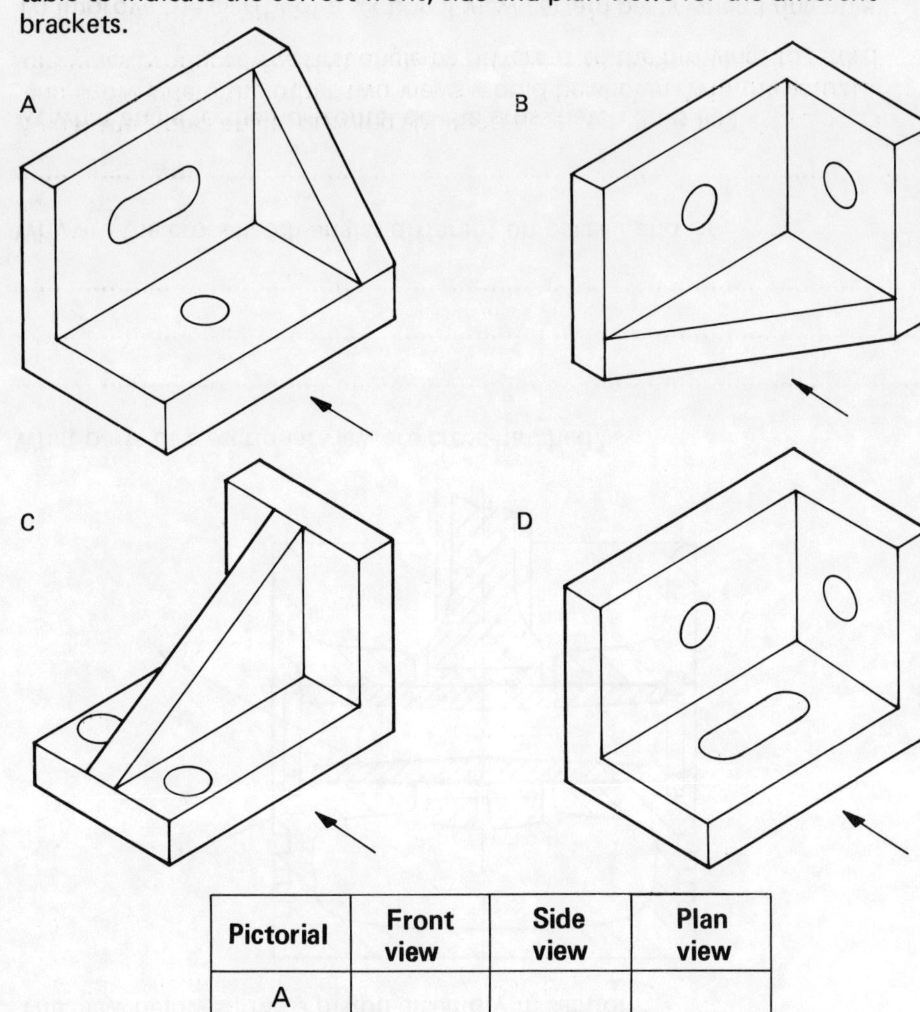


| Pictorial | Front view | Side view | Plan view |
|---|---|---|---|
| A | | | |
| B | | | |
| C | | | |
| D | | | |

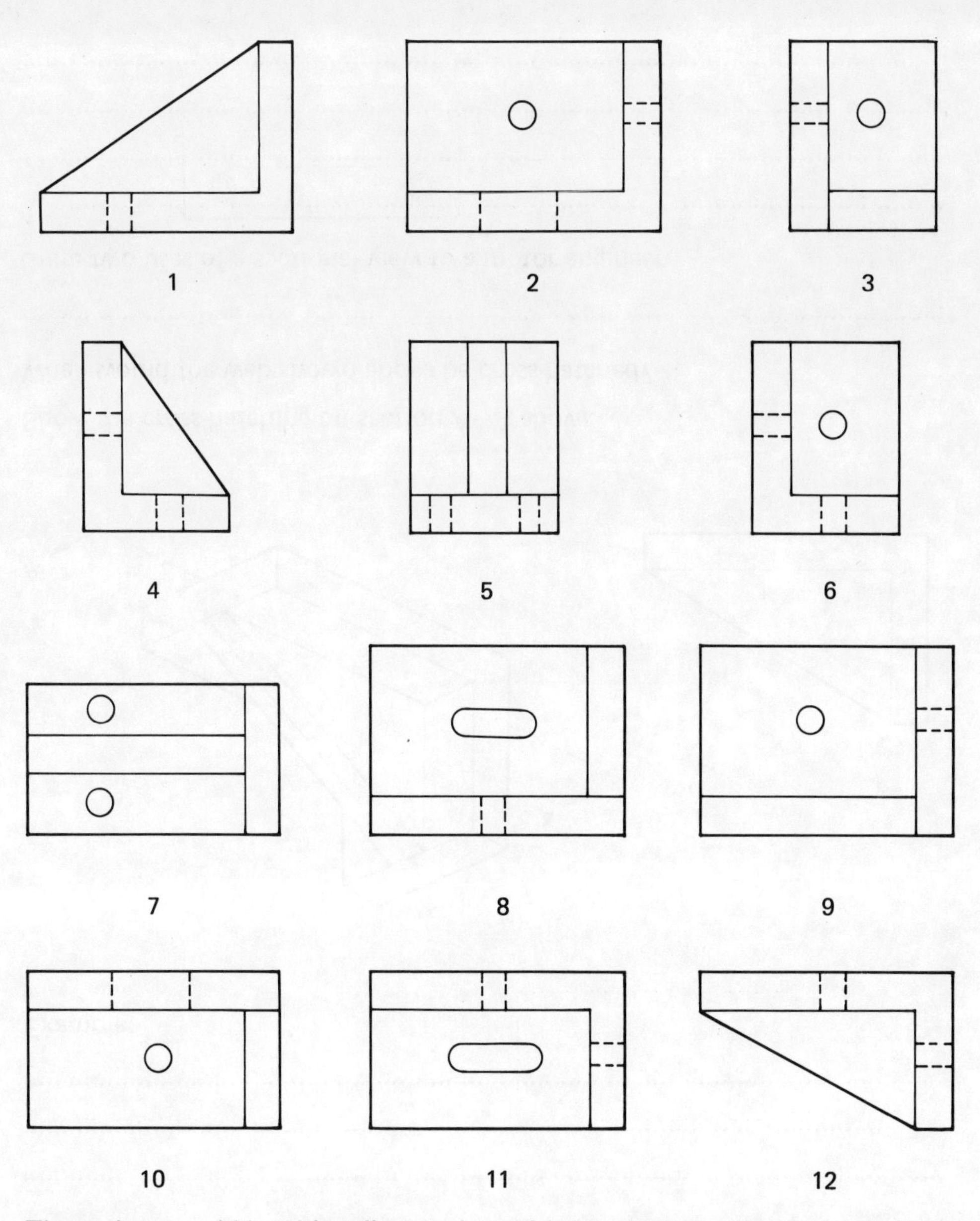


These views could be either first angle or third angle depending upon their relative positions on the actual three view drawing.

# SECTIONAL VIEWS

To get a true indication of the actual cross-sectional shape of an object it is often necessary to produce a 'sectional view' (see drawing below).

The view below shows a piston assembly in section.

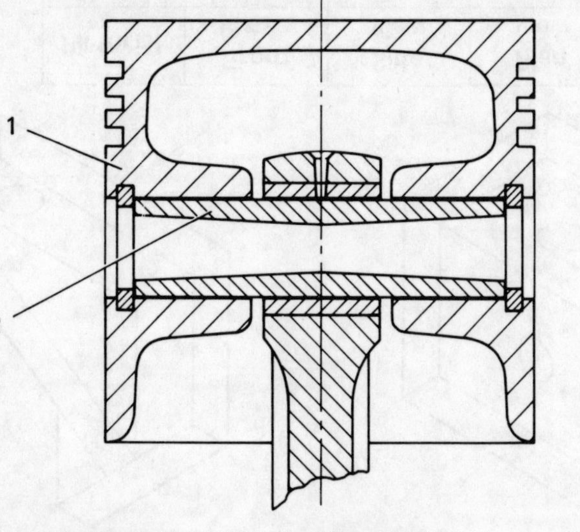


What parts of a sectional view are cross-hatched?

..............................................................................................................

..............................................................................................................

..............................................................................................................

Why are the cross-hatch angles different on parts 1 and 2?

..............................................................................................................

At what angle to the horizontal do the cross hatch lines lie?

..............................................................................................................

To improve the clarity of a sectional view certain parts when lying on a longtitudinal cutting plane, are not cross-hatched. These include such items as:

Solid shafts and rods.

..............................................................................................................

..............................................................................................................

..............................................................................................................

..............................................................................................................

Example:

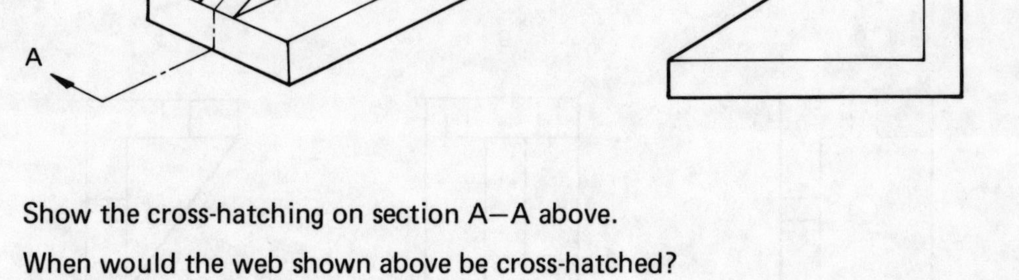


Show the cross-hatching on section A–A above.

When would the web shown above be cross-hatched?

..............................................................................................................

State two uses of a sectional view to a motor engineer.

1. ..........................................................................................................

2. ..........................................................................................................

..............................................................................................................

..............................................................................................................

# BLOCK AND LINE DIAGRAMS

Block and line diagrams are used to illustrate, in a simplified form, component construction, layout of relative components or layout of certain systems (for example hydraulic systems).

Name the type of diagram and the component or system illustrated below.

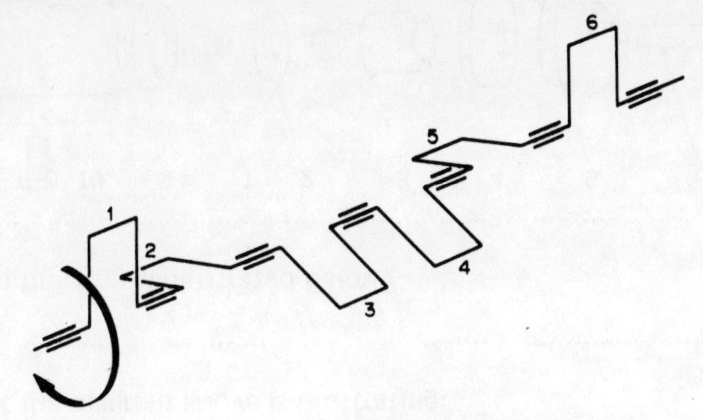


Diagram type ................................ Component ..................................

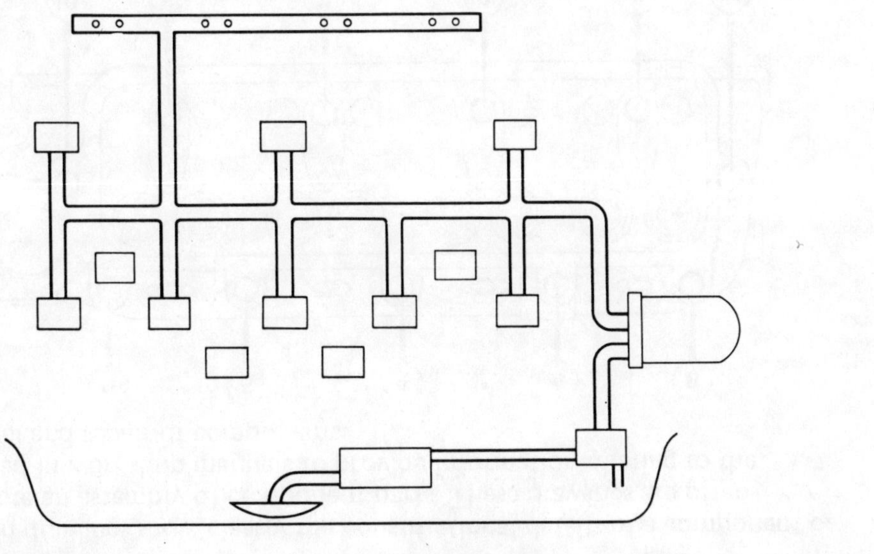

Diagram type ................................ Component ..................................

The simple line diagram above represents a ..................................................

Label the diagram.

Illustrate below the layout of a petrol engine fuel system by using a block diagram.

The drawings on the left below show a piston assembly and a valve. Make simple line diagrams on the right to illustrate the same.

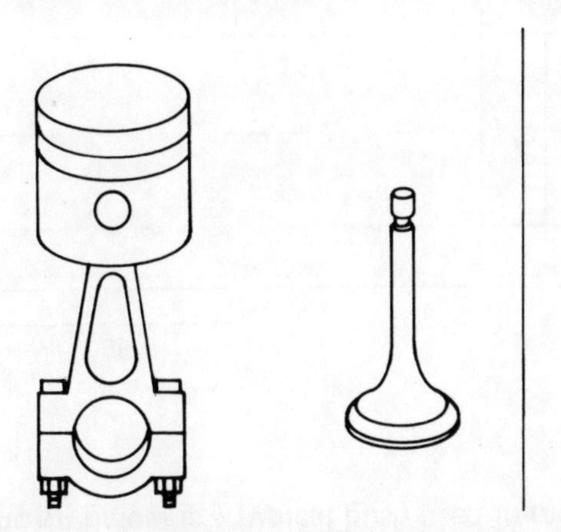

# CONSTRUCTIONAL DETAILS

Certain drawings show clearly the constructional details of a component or illustrate an assembly of component parts. These drawings are often featured in workshop manuals to provide information relating to the removal and repair of components.

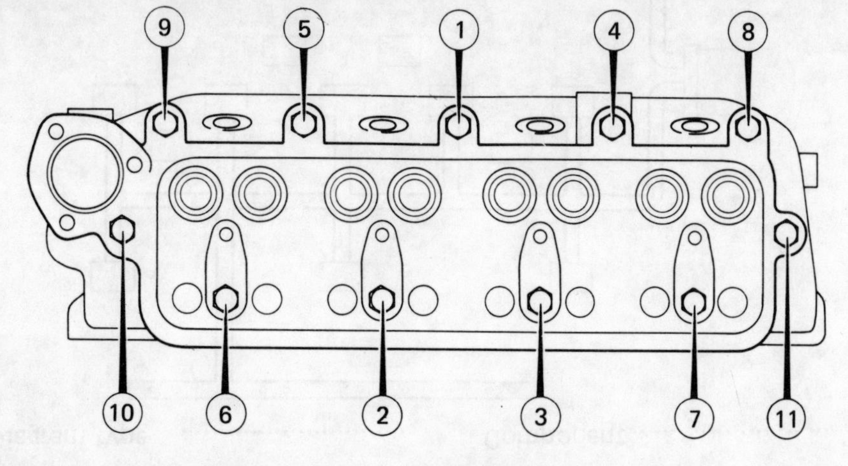


Explain what the diagram above is illustrating.

.................................................................................................

What form of drawing is illustrated below?

.................................................................................................

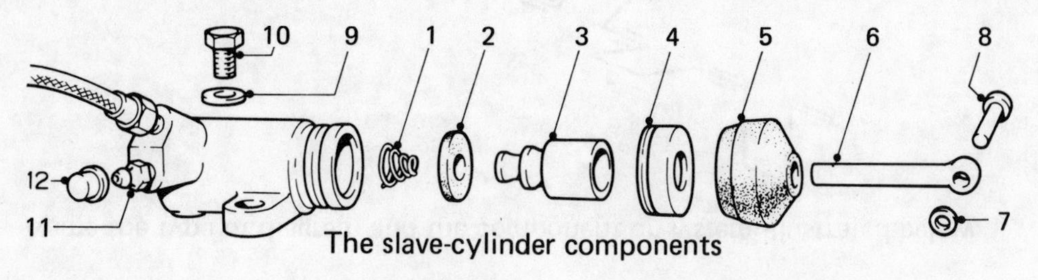


The slave-cylinder components

1. Spring
2. Piston seal
3. Piston
4. End cap—piston stop
5. Dust cover
6. Push-rod
7. Plain washer
8. Clevis pin
9. Spring washer
10. Screw—cylinder to housing
11. Bleed screw
12. Bleed screw cover

Shown below is a typical bush used in motor-vehicle construction.

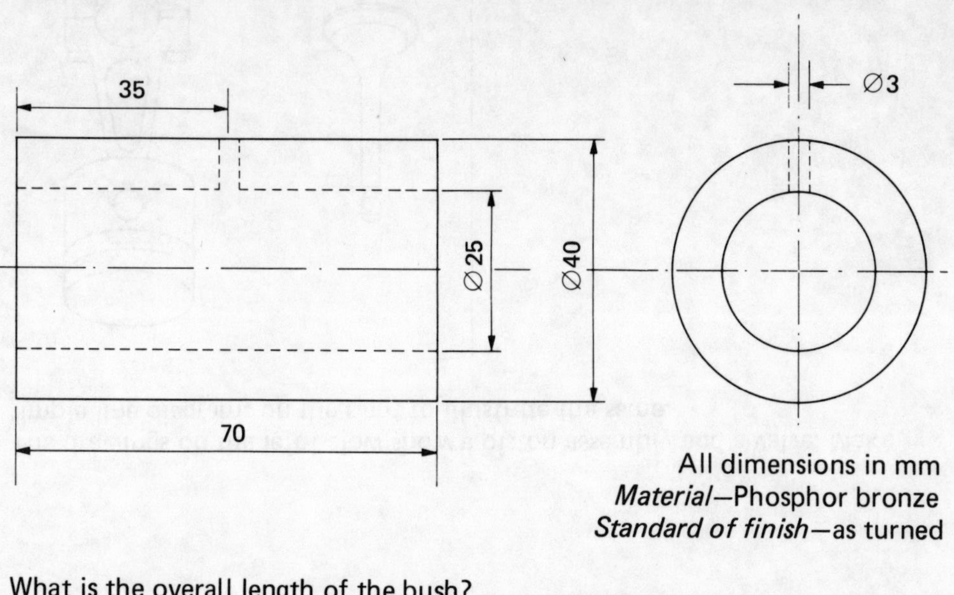


All dimensions in mm
*Material*—Phosphor bronze
*Standard of finish*—as turned

What is the overall length of the bush? ..............................................

State the inside diameter of the bush ..............................................

State the diameter of the oil-feed hole ..............................................

From what material is the bush made? ..............................................

What is the wall thickness of the bush? ..............................................

For what purpose might the drawing above be used?

.................................................................................................

For what purpose might the drawing of the slave cylinder be used?

1. .................................................................................................

2. .................................................................................................

3. .................................................................................................